THE CHUCK BERRY
INTERNATIONAL DIRECTORY

VOLUME 1

THE CHUCK BERRY INTERNATIONAL DIRECTORY

VOLUME 1

Morten Reff

MUSIC MENTOR BOOKS

York, England

British Library Cataloguing-in-Publication Data
A catalogue record for this book is available from the British Library.

ISBN-13: 978-0-9547068-6-9

Published worldwide by Music Mentor Books *(Proprietor: G.R. Groom-White)*
69 Station Road, Upper Poppleton, York YO26 6PZ, North Yorkshire, England.
Telephone/Fax: +44 (0)1904 330308   *Email:* music.mentor@lineone.net

Cover by It's Great To Be Rich, York.

Printed and bound in Great Britain by Printondemand-Worldwide, Peterborough.

ACKNOWLEDGMENTS

No one in this business has ever managed to accomplish what they set out to do without the help and support of 'friends and neighbours' – other music lovers. Therefore, my endless gratitude and a very special thank you must go to the following people, without whose help this publication would have been much the poorer:

Per Arvesen (Norway), the other true Berry collector I know in my country, who is also interested in many other aspects of black music including Bo Diddley, John Lee Hooker, Buddy Guy, etc. And he's the only one I know who actually collects Berry's output on cassette!

Howard DeWitt (USA), who was the first to appreciate the importance of a 'solid' (it was at that time) Chuck Berry discography compiled by yours truly, way back in the early '80s, which was published in his book, *Rock And Roll Music* (second edition) in 1984.

Rune Halland (Norway), whom I've known since 1971. We went to Gothenburg, Sweden on 16 May 1972 to see Jerry Lee Lewis and interviewed him afterwards backstage. What a show – and what an experience! In the early Seventies, Rune started the magazine, *Whole Lotta Rockin'*, which later became *R-O-C-K*. He's always sold records, and through his Cruisin' Records has supplied me with a lot of Berry recordings and Berry covers over the years.

Johan Hasselberg (Sweden), one of the 'younger' generation and a true Berry fan, if there ever was one! I met Johan in 1984 in connection with Howard DeWitt coming to Europe to promote his Chuck Berry book, and we've remained friends ever since.

Bjørn Knudsen (Norway), an Elvis fan who understands the value of other people's musical interests. He was extremely helpful in searching for Berry covers on the Internet and compiled a CD for me titled *Elvis Sings Johnny B. Goode*, containing 28 various live versions (we're talking bootlegs here) of the Berry classic, featuring James Burton on guitar! Had it not been for Bjørn, the list of cover versions in *Volumes 3* and *4* of this work would have been significantly less detailed and shorter by some 150 artists.

Malte Koch (Denmark), who phoned me in 1994, since when we've built a strong and remarkable friendship through Berry's music. Malte is a minister in Farum County, north of Copenhagen, and in a very short time (around five years) almost bankrupted himself buying Berry records.

I got to know Ari Niskanen (Finland) relatively recently through email correspondence and sent him a list of all the missing information I was looking for on Finnish cover versions. I was amazed by all the additions he sent me. Thanks a lot, Ari! I wish there was an 'Ari' in every country.

Jean-Pierre Ravelli (France) ran a Chuck Berry fan club in France from 1967 until 1976. I still remember visiting him for the first time in 1972 and seeing many Chuck Berry records I had never seen before. Jean-Pierre is one of Berry's closest friends and often spends his summer vacations at Berry Park. I can't praise his friendship enough, and how much it has meant to my work. Additionally, he has supplied me with pictures of Berry for three decades, many of them featured in this publication. Believe it or not, my late first wife, Solveig, and I travelled by train from Oslo to Paris in 1975 to catch two Chuck Berry shows at the Olympia, and then back again the next day. What an experience! We even got to meet Berry for a couple of minutes. (I honestly never thought he would ever make it to Norway. Well, he did – in 1977.)

Acknowledgments

Fred Rothwell (UK), author of the definitive annotated Berry sessionography, *Long Distance Information* (Music Mentor Books, 2001). I was in touch with Fred for several years while he was working on his book, and we've combined our knowledge and efforts for a long time. Without him, the book you hold in your hands might never have come to fruition. His encouragement, assistance and friendship have been invaluable.

Dietmar Rudolph (Germany), another true Berry fan and collector who has helped me greatly with various important aspects of Berry's music, as well as scanning many album covers. He also has a great Chuck Berry website.

Roy Rydland (Norway), whom I've known since 1980, largely as a result of an article I wrote in *R-O-C-K* magazine about Chuck Berry. Roy experienced the '50s first-hand and, among many other things, remembers buying Berry singles imported from England and USA. He was rock'n'roll then, and still is today. LaVern Baker and Brook Benton rank highly in his collection, and his EP record collection is extraordinary. It took over ten years for him to be persuaded to buy CDs.

George R. White (UK), author of Bo Diddley's biography and discography, and the man behind Music Mentor Books. Thanks a lot for showing interest in my work. The layout and professional look of this book are all thanks to you. Your help and skills have really been appreciated, more than you probably know.

Other people who also deserve a big thank you are:

Country music expert Agnar Bakke (Norway). His music room is filled with pictures of him posing with all the greatest country stars, and almost all are autographed! You wouldn't believe it unless you saw it.

Petter Bakke (Norway), a guy with whom I've travelled a lot of highways and experienced many musical events in the '80s, and '90s, especially when I was running my record company, Fox Records. We both made it to Berry Park in '91, but were informed by the gardener that Chuck Berry wasn't there and sadly never got past the front gates.

Eigil Berg (Norway), musician and leader of the Norwegian rock'n'roll band, the New Jordal Swingers. Besides backing Berry twice in Norway, his expertise as a musician has been a real inspiration when discussing Berry's music.

Little Richard expert John Garodkin (Denmark), who did his utmost when asked for help with cover records and various tour dates.

Tommy Holmström (Sweden), a musician (guitar and saxophone) and one of the greatest admirers of, and an authority on, Muddy Waters and his music. The road from Muddy to Chuck Berry is not long – at least, not for Tommy.

Bjørn Luka (Norway), garage band and Black Sabbath collector from whom I've borrowed a lot of interesting reference books while researching cover versions.

Christer Lundberg (Sweden), a true Berry fan and collector, and also a committed blues fanatic. He provided invaluable help in filling holes in the *Soundalikes* section in *Volume 4*. Like Tommy, I've known Christer for over twenty years now.

Jim Reeves expert Bjørn Tore Stølen (Norway), who spent days scanning many of my LP covers for this book.

Also a thank you to Dave Barnes of the British Archive of Country Music and Dave Penny (UK), who so willingly assisted with my hillbilly queries; Damian Johnstone (Australia), who contributed lots of info about Berry's Australian tours; Andrew Kay (UK) who gave me my first Berry US Chess EP, *After School Session* – free of charge; Christian Nauwelaers (Belgium) and especially Gareth Jones (Australia, now UK), who provided a huge amount of international chart information; Tor Arne Petzold (Norway), editor of *R-O-C-K* magazine for many years – a true fan of rockabilly and rock'n'roll in general; John Poole (UK), who spent many hours in the library researching details of UK TV shows; Wim van Cleef (Netherlands); and Ian Wallis, author of *American Rock'n'Roll: The UK Tours 1956-72* (Music Mentor Books, 2003), who took the time and trouble to check and help me with my listing of Chuck Berry's international tours, particularly the UK tours after 1972.

Gene Ackmann (USA), musician and personal friend of Johnnie Johnson; Hamish Cameron and Amy Robbins of Chief Entertainment Pty (Australia); Lez Karski of the Nervous Investors (UK, now Australia); Neil Mumme (Australia), Johnnie Johnson's promoter down under; St. Louis' own Billy Peek (USA); and Rick Ryckart of the Jones Boys (USA) for their invaluable help with my Johnnie Johnson research.

Hartmut Bauer (Germany), who died in August 2007, bless his rock'n'roll soul; Bo Berglind (Sweden), editor of *American Music Magazine*; Marc Bristol and Gaby Maag-Bristol (USA), editors of Seattle's *Blue Suede News* magazine; Trevor Cajiao (UK), editor of *Now Dig This*; Thierry Chanu (France); Peter Checksfield (UK); Dave Clarke (UK); country music expert Howard Cockburn (UK); author Lee Cotten (USA); Erling Daell (Denmark); Theo Dasbach (Netherlands, now USA), the driving force behind Clarksdale's Rock'n'Roll & Blues Heritage Museum; Thomas Einarsson (Sweden); author Colin Escott (Canada); rockabilly artist Narvel Felts (USA), who celebrated 50 years in the business in 2006; Micke Finell (Sweden); Björn Forsberg (Sweden); author and Buddy Holly expert, Bill Griggs (USA); Wolfgang Guhl (Germany), who also has a great website; broadcaster and John Lee Hooker expert, Gary 'Bluesman' Hearn (UK); Hans Jansen (Netherlands), who has sent me record sale lists for more than three decades; Tore Jensen (Norway), thanks for the pictures; musician and author Joe Keene (USA); Martin Malmqvist (Sweden); Ulrich Mayer (Germany); Andy McKaie (USA); Dieter Moll (Germany); Pierre Pennone (France); Jan Richter (Germany); Jan-Ola Sjöberg (Sweden); rock'n'roll and country expert Adriaan Sturm (USA); Rob Vader (Netherlands); blues expert Phil Wight (UK); and Willy B, Pål Didriksen, Thor-Rune Haugen, Tor Arne Hermansen, Stein-Ivar Hølmo, Helge Jørgensen, Egil Martinsen, Arne Metzner, Frank Narheim, Johnny Olsen, Sigbjørn Stabbursvik, Svein Sørlie, Jan Thoresen and Tormod Uleberg (Norway) – all of them music lovers and experts in various categories who have come to my assistance at different times.

Please forgive me if I've accidentally overlooked anyone. I am, of course, immensely grateful to *everyone* who has assisted me throughout four decades of intensive research, so here is a star for each and every one of you: ★

And, last but not least, to my dearest wife, Bente, who has hung in there with me while I've been reelin' and rockin' by the computer hour after hour, month after month and year after year. You really are *my little love light!*

Morten Reff
Drøbak, Norway
January 2008

Acknowledgments

CONTENTS

Volume 1

Contents

INTRODUCTION

To set the record straight once and for all, Chuck Berry was born at 6.59 in the morning on Wednesday, 18 October 1926 at 2520 Goode Avenue (now Annie Malone Drive) in St. Louis, Missouri. Don't believe anything else you read.

The *Chuck Berry International Directory* is the product of over forty years of record collecting, research, and meeting and communicating with Berry fans around the world.

Volume 1 contains US, UK and international discographies.

Volume 2 contains lists of bootlegs, radio concept albums, a guide to the rarest Berry releases, Berry on the radio, in movies and on TV, notable video and DVD releases, international tour itineraries, songs, chart hits and other achievements, influence on other artists, tributes, Chuck Berry in print, Berry's musical roots, fan clubs and websites, a comprehensive Johnnie Johnson discography, plus a discography of Eddy Clearwater, Berry copyist *par excellence*.

Volumes 3 and *4* consist of a massive listing of around 4,000 cover versions and some 800 soundalikes on record, in the movies and on TV that bear testimony to Berry's immense influence on Western popular music over the past half-century.

Throughout these volumes I have provided analyses and commentaries to guide the listener through the immense output of Berry and his followers, and have tried to indicate what material is essential or worthwhile – and what is not.

At various points, I make reference to Fred Rothwell's *Long Distance Information* (Music Mentor Books, 2001). This book is now universally accepted as the standard reference work on Chuck Berry's recording sessions – information I have not attempted to reproduce or replicate here. It may therefore be regarded as a companion volume to the *Chuck Berry International Directory*, and should be read in conjunction with it. (*Long Distance Information* is still available – see the back pages of this volume for more information.)

I hope you will find the *Chuck Berry International Directory* interesting and informative. If you should have any additions or corrections, I would really like to hear from you. Please don't hesitate to get in touch. Write to:

Morten Reff
Bråtabakken 6
N-1440 DRØBAK
Norway

or email me at: **mreff@online.no**

TECHNICAL NOTES

1   Several standard symbols are used throughout this volume:

   (a) **+** immediately after a song title indicates that the song is not a Chuck Berry composition.

   (b) The following are used to indicate formats:

○	= Single	◆	= DVD
▫	= EP	⊗	= Laserdisc
■	= LP	▣	= Videotape
◎	= CD		

2   Discographies are presented in the following order:

   Chuck Berry singles
   Chuck Berry EPs
   Chuck Berry LPs
   Chuck Berry CD singles
   Chuck Berry CD albums
   Various Artists singles containing Berry material
   Various Artists EPs containing Berry material
   Various Artists LPs containing Berry material
   Various Artists CD singles containing Berry material
   Various Artists CD albums containing Berry material

Records are listed in chronological order of release (ie month/year). Where only the year of release is known, records are listed alphabetically by title after the chronological listing for that year.

Bootlegs and radio concept albums are listed separately in their own sections.

3   The US and UK discographies have been compiled from records in my personal collection and are complete, or virtually complete. Discographies for other countries are largely based on records in Malte Koch's collection and mine, and naturally are only a sample of what has been issued over the years. Having said that, France, Germany and the Scandinavian countries are virtually complete, with Australia and the Netherlands not far behind. However, countries like South Africa, New Zealand, Brazil, Japan, Israel, etc are less well represented because – apart from the occasional exception – it is difficult to obtain domestic releases anywhere other than inside their own borders. Also, no-one has ever documented what has actually been released in these countries over the years. These discographies are a first step in that direction.

4   Over the years, some of Berry's song titles have been printed differently. 'Maybellene' for instance has been mis-spelt 'Mabellene' or 'Maybelline', while 'School Day' has often been rendered as 'School Days'. To avoid confusion, I have used the spellings as shown in *Section 11 (Songs)*, *Volume 2* throughout.

USA DISCOGRAPHY

Berry's 78 rpm releases started with Chess 1604 and ended with Chess 1747. The original Chess 78 rpm labels were blue on top and white at the bottom, but later pressings carried a dark blue label. The latter now command higher prices as they were pressed in increasingly smaller quantities as 45s took over.

The earliest Chess 45 rpm releases up to and including 'Oh Baby Doll' [Chess 1664] were originally issued on a blue label with a silver top. DJ/promo copies had a white label with a blue top. From 'Rock And Roll Music' [Chess 1671] onwards, the company used a dark blue label with the word 'Chess' vertically down the left side.

Chess 1799 to 1840 were issued on a multicoloured (red/yellow/black) 'Chess' label, as well as the dark blue/silver one. Promo copies carried white labels.

1963's 'I'm Talking About You' [Chess 1853] was the first Berry single to appear with a black label with 'Chess' in gold letters across the top. 'Nadine' [Chess 1883] was the last Berry single to carry a dark blue label. The black labels with gold logo and the multicoloured 'Chess' labels continued up to Chess 1963. Promo copies had white labels. However, you can also find them in the original label colours with 'DJ Copy' printed on both sides.

Later '60s reissues of Chess 1883-1916 appeared on the new light blue-fading-to-white label with the word 'Chess' patriotically picked out in red, white and blue across top. 1970s repressings on GRT's orange Chess label carried stereo versions, except for 'Brenda Lee', which was only recorded in mono.

Chess pressed all their singles in-house, but strong sellers were often jobbed out to external pressing plants, resulting in variations in fonts and lettering size. Every single release on Chess from the silver top label in 1955 through the blue, multicoloured, black, light blue and orange labels had at least two variations. Happy hunting!

It appears that Chess pressed one-sided 7-inch 45 rpm acetates of both sides of all their singles. They also pressed one-sided 10-inch 45 rpm acetates of both sides, apparently ending in 1965 with Chess 1963. The same applies to the '50s EPs, although I have never seen any of these (only photocopies from a dubious source), so I can't vouch for their authenticity). However, it's odd that Chess pressed so many variations of each single: we're talking about the regular promo, a couple of 7-inch acetates, a couple of 10-inch acetates, and finally the commercial 7-inch release. And all of these would have been produced by each pressing plant.

In 1966, Berry went to Mercury. The first two Mercury releases had red labels with the company logo in white across the top. The last three had a tan label with wide orange borders and a black logo inside an oval. Promo copies had white labels.

I also have a Mercury *'Pre-Production Copy'* acetate of 'It Hurts Me Too'. It has a white label with 'Mercury' printed on it, but the rest looks like it was added with a typewriter.

Berry's first single after his return to Chess in 1970, 'Tulane' [Chess 2090], carried a light blue label. However, 'My Ding-A-Ling' [Chess CH-2131] and subsequent releases carried an orange label with a blue border around the outer edge and a wide bar across the middle. It is difficult to determine which are the original releases, as singles like CH-2136 and CH-2140 were also issued with light blue labels. Promo copies had white labels, but you can also find them in the normal label colours with 'DJ Copy' printed on both sides, or 'Plug Side' printed on the 'A' side. Any variations I know of are annotated below.

Chuck Berry's US EPs were all issued with a black label and silver print, with the word 'Chess' vertically down the left side. However, the earliest pressings of AFTER SCHOOL SESSION [Chess EP-5118] had a black label with a silver top and the Chess logo on top in black. ROCK AND ROLL MUSIC [Chess EP-5119] was also issued with a blue label and vertical silver 'Chess' logo, so it is possible that some of the other EPs also came with blue labels.

Berry's Chess albums carried many label variations. These are described in general terms below, however please take note of several variations which are mentioned in connection with specific pressings.

The earliest LP releases had a black label the word 'Chess' vertically down the left side. However, I have heard that ROCK, ROCK, ROCK [Chess LP-1425] was issued with a silver-top label, although I've never seen a copy, so can't verify this. The black label continued up to LP-1485 (1964). In the early to mid-1960s, Chess also used a blue label with vertical silver 'Chess' logo, and then a black label with a fancy Chess logo in gold, red, white and blue across the top. The familiar light blue label appeared in the mid-1960s and continued into the 1970s. From time to time, Chess used different pressing plants, and variations in lettering sizes and styles are therefore common.

Chess began issuing Berry's albums in stereo from 1964 onwards, using the prefix 'LPS-'. During the second half of the 1960s, all the early Chuck Berry albums were reissued in electronic stereo, also using the prefix '-LPS'. These initially appeared with light blue labels, but were later reissued with orange labels.

The orange label with a blue border around the outer edge and a wide blue band across the middle was introduced by GRT in 1971, at the same time as they changed over to a new CH- numerical series. The label sported a new Chess logo (a chess knight's head in a circle) on the upper left-hand side. GRT (1970-74) and later All Platinum (1975) eventually reissued most of Berry's catalogue with this orange label and black and white covers!

From 1982 onwards, Chess (under new owners Sugar Hill, and subsequently MCA), used a dark blue label with silver logo and a chequered border.

After MCA acquired the Chess catalogue in 1983, they reissued many of the original albums on vinyl (with prefix CH-) and CD (with prefix CHD-) in a new numerical series. In a few instances, they also changed the album cover.

Between 1966 and 1969, Berry recorded for Mercury. His first album releases appeared on a red label with 'Mercury' in white across the top and a black and white 'knight's helmet' logo to the left. From 1969 until late 1973, Mercury used a red label with twelve oval 'Mercury' logos around the perimeter. For a short while (until early/mid-1974) they used the same label but with just seven oval logos – although this may have been only for Record Club releases. After that, they adopted a completely new design, the 'coloured city' label as I call it, or 'colour skyscraper scene' label as someone else has put it. This was used until 1982, when they switched to a black label with a white oval logo on top of a 'script' Mercury logo on red background.

The 'knight's helmet logo' promo label came in white, gold or pink. The 'twelve oval logos' promo label was either white or yellow. Only the CONCERTO IN B GOODE album [Mercury SR-61223] came with the latter.

Singles

Joe Alexander & The Cubans
Oh Maria+ / I Hope These Words Will Find You Well+
Ballad AA-1008 ● September 1954
    Recorded 13 August 1954 at the Premier Studios in St. Louis. The 'A' side was written by Oscar 'Fats' Washington and Joe Alexander, the 'B' side by Washington alone. This information turned up in the US magazine, *DISCoveries* in December 1988, after someone found out that Berry had been involved in this recording as 'Charles Berryn', playing rhythm guitar. It's difficult to make him out on the 'A' Side, however, he's more audible on the 'B' side. Personally, I have always been sceptical about this. Berry himself has never admitted that he played on this record. Be that as it may, thanks to this revelation, the value of the record went sky-high! The 78 (AA-1008) and 45 (AA-1008-X45) both had maroon labels.

Maybellene / Wee Wee Hours
Chess 1604 ● July 1955
    The composer credit for 'Maybellene' on the original 78s and 45s, and on the 1957 LP ROCK, ROCK, ROCK [Chess LP-1425] was simply *'Chuck Berry'*. However, the 1960s reissues had the song credited to *'Berry–Fratto'*. The sheet music (mis-spelt 'Mabellene') was credited to *'Berry–Fratto–Feed'*. I have never seen a 78 rpm of this record with a bright and clean label – they all seem to have faded.

Thirty Days / Together (We Will Always Be)
Chess 1610 ● September 1955
    Malte Koch has a strange promo copy of this, with a blue top/white label on the 'A' side and a silver top/blue label on the 'B' Side.

No Money Down / Down Bound Train
Chess 1615 ● December 1955
    It would appear that the first issues of the three singles above didn't have *'Manufactured by Chess Recording Corp. Chicago, Il.'* at the bottom of the label. All later releases with the silver top label had this printed on them.

Roll Over Beethoven / Drifting Heart
Chess 1626 ● May 1956
    Poking fun at Beethoven in 1956 when rock'n'roll was still in its infancy was probably okay in the USA, but did not go down so well in Europe, where the song was banned from airplay in several countries including Norway.

Too Much Monkey Business / Brown Eyed Handsome Man
Chess 1635 ● September 1956
    A double-sided hit and the very first protest single by a pop artist, several years ahead of the Kingston Trio, Bob Dylan etc. These two songs also put Chuck Berry the rock'n'roll poet on the map with his fellow artists and musicians. Listen to what the Million Dollar Quartet (Lewis, Perkins, Presley) had to say about this single.

You Can't Catch Me / Havana Moon
Chess 1645 ● November 1956
    The 'A' side was featured in the movie, *Rock, Rock, Rock*.

School Day / Deep Feeling *(instr)*
Chess 1653 ● March 1957

The early 1970s light blue label reissues numbered C̲H̲-1653 were incorrectly pressed with 'Berry Pickin' ' on the 'B' side instead of 'Deep Feeling'! A real mix-up and therefore a very rare issue, as 'Berry Pickin' ' was originally never available on single. (NB Late 1960s reissues of 'School Day' on the same light blue label, but without the 'CH-' prefix, were correctly pressed.) See also *Section 4 (Bootlegs)* for a 1970s curiosity.

Oh Baby Doll / La Jaunda (Español)
Chess 1664 ● June 1957

This is the most valuable of all the Chess singles because it contains an alt. mix of 'La Jaunda' which is not available elsewhere. On this version, Berry sings a duet with himself throughout the song. The common version was first released on the 1958 LP, ONE DOZEN BERRYS [Chess LP-1432], and that's the one you will find on all other releases. Strangely, both versions were given the same master number.

Rock And Roll Music / Blue Feeling *(instr)*
Chess 1671 ● September 1957

The 'A' side had a very tricky and smart title for 1957. The lyrics said everything that was necessary to make everybody know that rock'n'roll was a musical form that you just couldn't ignore: *'Just let me hear some of that rock'n'roll music!!!'*

Sweet Little Sixteen / Reelin' And Rockin'
Chess 1683 ● January 1958

A double-sided classic although, for some unknown reason, 'Sweet Little Sixteen' was speeded up. The cut was first issued in its original form on the 1988 6-LP/3-CD CHESS BOX set [Chess CH6-/ CHD3-80001].

Johnny B. Goode / Around And Around
Chess 1691 ● March 1958

And speaking of classics...

Beautiful Delilah / Vacation Time
Chess 1697 ● June 1958

For many years, the 'B' side here never appeared on any album. However, in 1990 it finally made its way onto the MISSING BERRIES – RARITIES (VOLUME 3) LP/CD [Chess CH-/CHD-9318].

Carol / Hey Pedro
Chess 1700 ● August 1958

To get the full 'Carol' experience you either need to buy the original single, or one of the other original releases on Chess before it was destroyed in 1967 by RCA's 'electronic stereo' reprocessing. Something happened when they later tried to rechannel it back into mono. It didn't work, somebody messed it up and it always turns up with this strange sound on all the later releases – LP, CD, remastered or whatever. I have a 78 of this with the standard blue/white label, but I have also seen it with a blue label with the vertical 'Chess' logo.

Sweet Little Rock And Roller / Jo Jo Gunne
Chess 1709 ● October 1958

On the original pressings, the 'A' side was mistitled 'Sweet Little Rock And Roll', and the 'B' side 'Joe Joe Gun'.

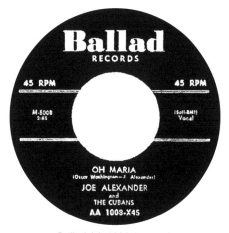

Ballad AA-1008 (78 rpm)   Ballad AA-1008 (45 rpm)

Chess 1604 (original 78 rpm pressing)   Chess 1604 (original 45 rpm pressing)

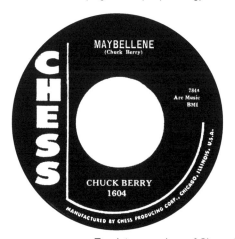

Two later pressings of Chess 1604 with variations in lettering.

Chess 1610 (promo)

Chess 1610 (original 45 rpm pressing)

Chess 1615 (original 78 rpm pressing)

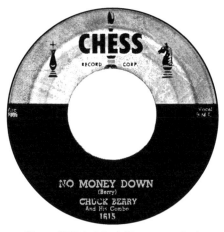

Chess 1615 (original 45 rpm pressing)

Chess 1626 (promo)

Chess 1626 (original 45 rpm pressing)

Chess 1635 (original 45 rpm pressing)

Chess 1645 (original 45 rpm pressing)

Chess 1653 (original 45 rpm pressing)

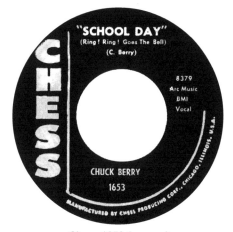

Chess 1653 (repress)

Chess 1664 (original 45 rpm pressing)

Chess 1671 (original 45 rpm pressing)

Chess 1683 (promo)   Chess 1683 (original 78 rpm pressing)

Chess 1691 (original 45 rpm pressing)   Chess 1697 (original 45 rpm pressing)

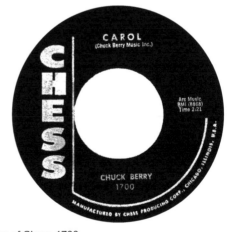

Two label variations of Chess 1700

Chess 1700 (original 78 rpm pressing)

Chess 1709 (promo)

Chess 1714 (promo)

Chess 1714 (promo)

Later pressings of Chess 1714

Chess 1716 (promo)   Chess 1716

Two label variations of Chess 1722

Two label variations of Chess 1729

Run Rudolph Run+ / Merry Christmas Baby+
Chess 1714 ● November 1958
The 'A' side was credited to '*Chuck Berry Music Inc. – M. Brodie'*. Quite what Marvin Brodie did to deserve the credit remains a mystery. Perhaps it was one of Chess' business deals. The later reissues of this single had the same accreditation.

Anthony Boy / That's My Desire+
Chess 1716 ● January 1959
The rare 'B' side was reissued as a bonus cut on the 1990 CD, MISSING BERRIES (VOLUME 3) [Chess CHD-9318]. It is also included on the 2007 4-CD set, JOHNNY B. GOODE – HIS COMPLETE '50s CHESS RECORDINGS [Hip-O Select (Geffen) B0009473-02].

Almost Grown / Little Queenie
Chess 1722 ● March 1959

Back In The USA / Memphis, Tennessee
Chess 1729 ● June 1959
It is a peculiar accident of history that the 'B' side here, which turned out to be the second most-covered Berry song in history (I have found close to 400 versions), didn't make any noise when it was first released! However, no one has ever managed to discover the secret that lies behind Berry's original version. The structure and arrangement are so simple yet effective, that it's just a pure masterpiece.

Broken Arrow / Childhood Sweetheart
Chess 1737 ● September 1959
The 'B' side was credited to '*E. Anderson'* (after Berry's middle names, Edward Anderson).

Ecuadors
Say You'll Be Mine+ / Let Me Sleep Woman+
Argo 5353 ● November 1959
This has Chuck Berry playing lead guitar on both sides. Nothing was known about the Ecuadors vocal group until very recently, when Billy Davis told Stuart Colman in 2002 that it was an *ad hoc* studio ensemble consisting of himself and Harvey Fuqua, with occasional interjections from Etta James. The composer credit on each side reads '*R. Butler'* and both songs were published by Chuck Berry Music Inc.

Too Pooped To Pop+ / Let It Rock
Chess 1747 ● January 1960
The 'B' side was credited to '*E. Anderson'* (after Berry's middle names, Edward Anderson).

Bye Bye Johnny / Worried Life Blues+
Chess 1754 ● April 1960

I Got To Find My Baby+ / Mad Lad+ *(instr)*
Chess 1763 ● August 1960
The 'A' side was a Willie Dixon tune that Berry borrowed from Little Walter. The instrumental on the 'B' side is credited to Billy Davis (who also wrote 'Too Pooped To Pop').

Jaguar And The Thunderbird / Our Little Rendezvous
Chess 1767 ● October 1960
    I have two copies of this single, one with the 'A' side timed at 1:50 and the 'B' side at 1:55, the other 1:40 and 1.58. However, the songs on both are faded out at exactly 1:49 and 1:58 respectively.

I'm Talking About You / Little Star
Chess 1779 ● February 1961
    The 'B' side is a strange choice, as it is the most unusual Berry song ever: a pop ballad with a choir that sounds like the Anita Kerr Singers.

Go, Go, Go / Come On
Chess 1799 ● October 1961
    For the avoidance of doubt: the 'A' side did not have the overdubbed audience noise that was later added for its release on the 1963 LP, ON STAGE [Chess LP-1480].

I'm Talking About You / Diploma For Two
Chess 1853 ● April 1963
    Here again Chess decided to put a pop ballad on the 'B' side, but this time it's a far better choice than 'Little Star'. Chess clearly had faith in 'I'm Talking About You'.

Sweet Little Sixteen (Surfin' USA) / Memphis (Tennessee)
Chess 1866 ● August 1963
    From the 1963 LP, ON STAGE [Chess LP-1480]. Both tracks include overdubbed audience noise.

Nadine / O'Rangutang *(instr)*
Chess 1883 ● February 1964

No Particular Place To Go / You Two
Chess 1898 ● April 1964
    Chess 1898, 1906, 1912 and 1916 were all released with the same picture sleeve, front and back.

You Never Can Tell / Brenda Lee
Chess 1906 ● July 1964
    Chess 1898, 1906, 1912 and 1916 were all released with the same picture sleeve, front and back.

Chuck Berry & Bo Diddley* / Bo Diddley & Chuck Berry*
Chuck's Beat *(instr)* /* **Bo's Beat+** *(instr)***
Checker 1089 ● August 1964
    Edited extracts from the 1964 LP, TWO GREAT GUITARS [Checker LP-2991]. Each song is faded out at 2:55. The first pressings had a maroon label with vertical 'Checker' logo, later ones appeared with a light blue label with black and red checkers around the upper perimeter and a black-and-brown checkerboard in the background. Promo copies appeared with white labels, and also light blue labels with *'DJ Copy'* printed on both sides.

Little Marie / Go, Bobby Soxer
Chess 1912 ● September 1964
    Chess 1898, 1906, 1912 and 1916 were all released with the same picture sleeve, front and back.

Chess 1737 (promo)

Argo 5353 (promo)

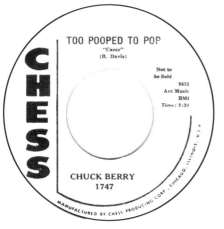

Chess 1747 (promo)

Chess 1747 (GRT repress)

Chess 1754

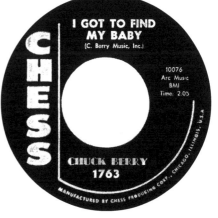

Chess 1763

Chess 1767

Chess 1779 (promo)

Chess 1799

Chess 1853 (promo)

Chess 1866 (promo)

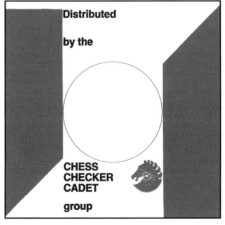

Mid-'60s sleeve

Chess 1883 (original pressing)

Chess 1883 (second pressing)

Chess 1883 (third pressing)

Chess 1883 (fourth pressing)

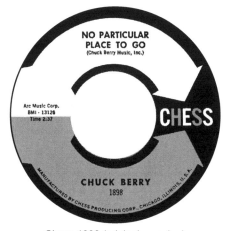

Chess 1898 (original pressing)

Chess 1898 (second pressing)

Chess 1898 (third pressing)

Chess 1898 (fourth pressing)

Chess 1906 (promo)

Chess 1906

Checker 1089 (original pressing)

Checker 1089 (second pressing)

Chess 1912 (promo)

Chess 1912

Chess 1916

Chess 1926

Chess 1926 label variation

Chess 1943

Chess 1898

Chess 1906

Chess 1912

Chess 1916

Chess 1943

Chess 1963 (promo)

First version of Chess 1963

Second version of Chess 1963

Mercury 72643 (promo)   Mercury 72680 (promo)

Mercury 72680

Mercury 72748 (promo)

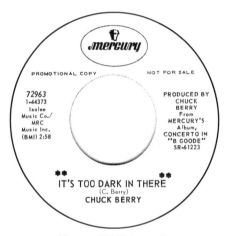

Mercury 72963 (promo)

Mercury 72963

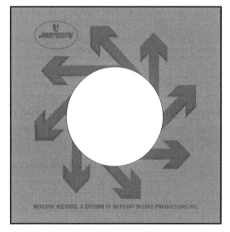

Mercury sleeve, late '60s

Mercury 72840

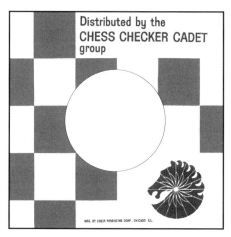

Chess, late '60s sleeve

Chess 2090 (promo)

Both sides of Chess CH-2131 – Chuck Berry's biggest ever single

Chess CH-2131 (promo)

Chess CH-2131 (GRT repress)

Chess CH-2136 (promo)

Chess CH-2140

Chess CH-2169 (promo)

Atco sleeve, late '70s

Atco 7203 (promo)

Atco 7203

Promised Land / The Things I Used To Do+
Chess 1916 • November 1964
Chess 1898, 1906, 1912 and 1916 were all released with the same picture sleeve, front and back.

Dear Dad / Lonely Schooldays *(slow version)*
Chess 1926 • March 1965
The slow version of 'Lonely Schooldays' is quite rare, only having been released on singles in the UK, West Germany, the Netherlands and Scandinavia. You will also find it on the 1991 UK 9-CD set, THE CHESS YEARS [Chess CDRED BOX-3], as well as the UK 4-CD set, POET OF ROCK'N'ROLL [Charly CDDIG-1] and UK CD OH YEAH [Charly R&B Masters CDRB-12], both from 1994.

It Wasn't Me / Welcome Back Pretty Baby
Chess 1943 • September 1965

Lonely Schooldays *(fast version)* **/ Ramona Say Yes**
Chess 1963 • June 1966
Here we have a rarity, as this version of 'Ramona Say Yes' was only released in the US on this single and the one below (although it also appeared on 45 rpm in several other countries including West Germany and Sweden). The song was also included on the 1988 6-LP/3-CD CHESS BOX set [Chess CH6-/CHD3-80001], but without the saxophone.

Havana Moon / Ramona Say Yes
Chess 1963 • June 1966
'Ramona Say Yes' was actually issued twice on Chess 1963. 'Havana Moon' is the same take as on Chess 1645 and also came as a one-sided promo. But why was this particular song released at the time? It could be because of the popularity of Richard Berry's similar-sounding 'Louie Louie', which was performed and recorded by just about every garage band in the USA around that time. The Sandpipers charted in 1966 with their version, and the Kingsmen's 1963 hit recording was also reissued that year. Malte Koch has a copy of this record with a very dark blue – almost black – label with vertical silver 'Chess' logo on the left.

Club Nitty Gritty / Laugh And Cry
Mercury 72643 *(mono)* **• November 1966**
When this single came out, I thought 'Laugh And Cry' was the worst blues I had ever heard. It sounded like a tin-can blues, because there was absolutely no bass on it. When it finally came out in 1989 on the CD reissue of FROM ST. LOUIE TO FRISCO [Mercury 836 073-2] with a remastered full bass sound, it became a completely different song.

Back To Memphis / I Do Really Love You
Mercury 72680 *(mono)* **• May 1967**
Released at the end of the '60s, this energetic rocker was doomed to fail.

Chuck Berry – The Miller Band
It Hurts Me Too+ *(live)* **/ Feelin' It** *(live, instr)*
Mercury 72748 *(mono)* **• November 1967**
Both sides are taken from the LP, LIVE AT THE FILLMORE AUDITORIUM, SAN FRANCISCO [Mercury SR-61138]. The 'A' side is a duet with Steve Miller.

4" HIP-POCKET RECORD

Maybelline
Roll Over Beethoven
CHUCK BERRY

■ Buy the hits you missed
■ 25 to 50 hip pocket records can be carried in pocket or purse
■ Hip pocket records can be mailed with greeting cards as a gift
■ They will outlast a regular 45
■ Drop them or sit on them ... they are almost indestructible
■ Take them to parties or to the beach or picnic ... they are the most portable form of music
■ Don't let the small size fool you ... the sound is amazingly big
■ Start your collection of hip pocket records today

PHILCO-FORD CORPORATION

HIP-POCKET RECORDS

DESIGNED FOR USE WITH SINGLE PLAY PHONOGRAPHS ONLY

| Philco-Ford HP-34 (front) | Philco-Ford HP-34 (back) |

Maybellene / Roll Over Beethoven
Philco-Ford Corporation HP-34 ● 1967
     Mercury recordings. This 4-inch 'hip-pocket' flexi-disc was designed to play in a special car phonograph, and was part of a series consisting mainly of '60s hits. It has a great picture of Berry on the cover.

St. Louie To Frisco / Ma Dear
Mercury 72840 *(mono)* ● **July 1968**

It's Too Dark In There *(edited)* **/ Good Lookin' Woman**
Mercury 72963 *(mono)* ● **August 1969**
     The 'A' side was edited for single release (guitar solo omitted). This was issued both with and without a single-sided black and white picture sleeve (as a matter of fact, I have only seen the picture sleeve with the promo issue). It is the most difficult Mercury single to find, especially with the picture sleeve, which is actually an advertisement for the single and also carries a picture of the album it's taken from, 1969's CONCERTO IN B GOODE [Mercury SR-61223]. The 'A' side title is at the top and reads: *'The Side YOU Requested From The Chuck Berry LP'.* There are also two reviews of the LP and 'It's Too Dark In There', one from *Rolling Stone* and one from the *Chicago Sun-Times.* The record price guides list this at a low value – around £15 – but you can expect to pay at least £30 for a mint copy.

Tulane / Have Mercy Judge
Chess [GRT] 2090 ● March 1970
     This was the first Berry single to be released only in stereo.

My Ding-A-Ling *(live, single edit)* **/ Johnny B. Goode** *(live)*
Chess [GRT] CH-2131 ● July 1972
     Both sides of this single were recorded live at the *Lanchester Arts Festival* in Coventry, England on 3 February 1972. The 'A' side was edited down to 4:18 for the single (the original album track is 11:52). After this hit No.1 on both sides of the Atlantic, it was released worldwide and almost always with a picture sleeve.

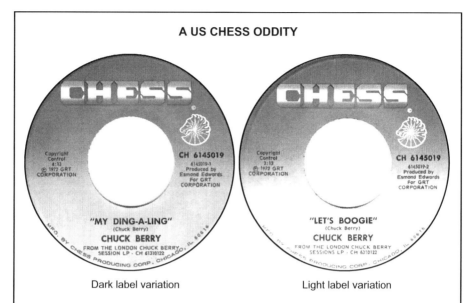

A US CHESS ODDITY

Dark label variation   Light label variation

My Ding-A-Ling+ *(live, single edit)* **/ Johnny B. Goode** *(live)*
Chess [GRT] CH-6145 019 • 1972
    This record has the same number as the UK release except for the 'CH-' prefix, and also has the same 'B' side as the original US release (the UK one has 'Let's Boogie' on the 'B' side). The label is the standard US Chess late Sixties/ early Seventies light blue one. It states that the songs are from the LONDON CHUCK BERRY SESSIONS LP [Chess CH-6310 122] – the same number as the UK LP release, apart from the 'CH-' prefix.

Reelin' And Rockin' *(live, single edit)* **/ Let's Boogie**
Chess [GRT] CH-2136 • November 1972
    The 'A' side is a 4:16 edited version for single release. The original album track is 7:10.

Bio *(single edit)* **/ Roll 'Em Pete+** *(live, single edit)*
Chess [GRT] CH-2140 • May 1973
    'Roll 'Em Pete' was recorded live on 3 February 1972 at the *Lanchester Arts Festival*, Coventry, England. Chess producer Esmond Edwards subsequently replaced the backing band tracks with overdubs by studio musicians. Only Berry's voice and guitar were retained. The complete (unreleased) version of the song is a little over five minutes long; the single was edited down to 2:50.

Shake, Rattle And Roll+ / Baby What You Want Me To Do+
Chess [GRT] CH-2169 • February 1975
    The DJ promo had a grey label.

Oh What A Thrill / California
Atco 7203 • August 1979
    The promo has the 'A' side on both sides, blue label (stereo) and white (mono). Also, the promo copy has a different label than the ordinary issue.

Reissues

GOLDEN GOODIES

Golden Goodies 1635   Chess 1653 (reissue)

In the late 1960s, Chess reissued many of the original Chess singles on the Golden Goodies label. This was gold with a vertical 'Golden Goodies' logo on the left. Although Chess catalogue numbers were used, the company name did not appear on the label at all. At the same time, they also issued the singles with a gold label and a vertical 'Chess' logo.

MERCURY 'CELEBRITY SERIES'

Mercury C-30146 (dark blue label)   Mercury C-30143 (yellow label)

The following titles were reissued by Mercury in 1972 to cash in on Berry's success after his return to Chess. The label colour was initially dark blue, but was later changed to yellow – probably in the late 1970s or early 1980s. Some of the releases carried stereo versions and some did not. You will find 'Maybellene' and 'Memphis' in both mono and stereo.

Maybellene / Sweet Little Sixteen
Mercury 'Celebrity Series' C-30143 ● 1972

School Day / Memphis, Tennessee
Mercury 'Celebrity Series' C-30144 ● 1972

Roll Over Beethoven / Back In The USA
Mercury 'Celebrity Series' C-30145 ● 1972

Rock And Roll Music / Johnny B. Goode
Mercury 'Celebrity Series' C-30146 ● 1972

CHESS 'BLUE CHIP' SERIES

Chess 'Blue Chip' Series sleeve   Chess 'Blue Chip' Series 9010

The following titles were reissued by GRT as part of the Chess 'Blue Chip' Series celebrating the company's 25th anniversary (1948–1973). Label colour was yellow with black print, and there were 62 releases during 1973-74. The entire series was subsequently reissued by All Platinum in 1975. A 'CH-' prefix was used on some releases by both GRT and All Platinum. However, you can also find them without the prefix.

Roll Over Beethoven / Nadine
Chess 'Blue Chip' Series (CH-)9010 ● 1973

Maybellene / Rock And Roll Music
Chess 'Blue Chip' Series (CH-)9020 ● 1973

Sweet Little Sixteen / Johnny B. Goode
Chess 'Blue Chip' Series (CH-)9021 ● 1973

School Day / Memphis, Tennessee
Chess 'Blue Chip' Series (CH-)9030 ● 1974

I've also seen this record with a white promo label, which may mean that promos were also produced for other releases in this series. Promotion copy for what?

 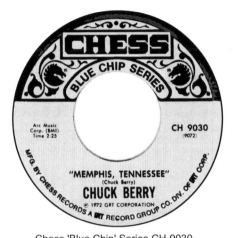

Chess 'Blue Chip' Series CH-9030 (promo) Chess 'Blue Chip' Series CH-9030

The white label differs from the commercial release, as the Chess 'Blue Chip' Series logo was not used. Instead there's a Chess 'knight' logo on the left-hand side of the label above the Chess name.

Carol / Oh Baby Doll
Chess 'Blue Chip' Series (CH-)9048 • 1974

You Never Can Tell / Promised Land
Chess 'Blue Chip' Series (CH-)9049 • 1974

Thirty Days / No Particular Place To Go
Chess 'Blue Chip' Series (CH-)9050 • 1974

My Ding-A-Ling (*live, single edit*) **/ Reelin' And Rockin'** (*live, single edit*)
Chess 'Blue Chip' Series (CH-)9051 • 1974

ERIC

The following Chess recordings were released on the Eric label in 1979, and again in 1986. The early pressings came in plain white sleeves; the later ones came in company sleeves. Label colour was black with red borders around the outer edge and the centre. These singles actually have very good sound quality. Eric Records were originally based in Philadelphia, PA. in 1979, but had moved to Westville, NJ by 1986.

Johnny B. Goode / Carol
Eric 224 • 1979, 1986

The 1986 reissue also came with a gatefold black and white picture sleeve which is very rare. The Berry-walk photo of 'Chuck' on the front is not our man after all, but someone pretending to be him. You can't see his face. The front of the sleeve proclaims: *'One record gets most of the credit for the development of rock and roll. Or most of the blame.'* Inside it says: *'Chuck Berry's Johnny B. Goode. The hit that got rock music rolling. In the spirit of such great leaps, Quantum. Louisville, July 29th, 1986.'*

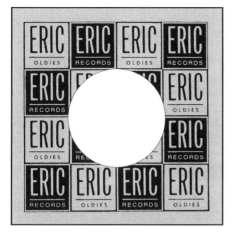

Eric sleeve, late '70s (Westville)

Eric 224

Eric 228 (Philadelphia)

Eric 228 (Westville)

School Day / My Ding-A-Ling *(live, single edit)*
Eric 225 • 1979, 1986

Rock And Roll Music / Memphis, Tennessee
Eric 226 • 1979, 1986

Roll Over Beethoven / Maybellene
Eric 227 • 1979, 1986

Sweet Little Sixteen / No Particular Place To Go *(stereo)*
Eric 228 • 1979, 1986

CHESS [Sugar Hill]

Chess sleeve, 1982

Chess CH-101

The following titles were reissued in 1982 and have excellent sound quality. The label was split in the middle with blue top and white bottom half.

Johnny B. Goode / Little Queenie
Chess CH-101 • 1982

Rock And Roll Music / Back In The USA
Chess CH-102 • 1982

Carol / Sweet Little Rock And Roller
Chess CH-103 • 1982

Maybellene / Almost Grown
Chess CH-122 • 1982

No Particular Place To Go *(stereo)* **/ You Never Can Tell** *(stereo)*
Chess CH-123 • 1982

My Ding-A-Ling *(live, single edit)* **/ Reelin' And Rockin'** *(live, single edit)*
Chess CH-133 • 1982

The following singles were reissued in 1983-84. They carried a silver label with a blue top and the Chess logo on top in silver.

Johnny B. Goode / Little Queenie
Chess CH-91000 • 1983

Rock And Roll Music / Back In The USA
Chess CH-91001 • 1983

Carol / Sweet Little Rock And Roller
Chess CH-91002 • 1983

Maybellene / Almost Grown
Chess CH-91021 ● 1983

No Particular Place To Go / You Never Can Tell
Chess CH-91022 ● 1983

My Ding-A-Ling *(live, single edit)* **/ Reelin' And Rockin'** *(live, single edit)*
Chess CH-91032 ● 1984
    Malte Koch has a promo of this with a white label and black top. A promo of 'My Ding-A-Ling' – from 1984!

CHESS [MCA]

    In 1984, MCA acquired the Chess catalogue and reissued some of Berry's output on their new Chess label, which was dark blue with the words 'Chess Records' in silver around the upper edge. They used the same numerical series as Sugar Hill. The sound quality, however, left a great deal to be desired.

Johnny B. Goode / Little Queenie
Chess CH-91000 ● 1984

Rock And Roll Music / Back In The USA
Chess CH-91001 • 1984

Carol / Sweet Little Rock And Roller
Chess CH-91002 • 1984

Maybellene / Almost Grown
Chess CH-91021 • 1984

No Particular Place To Go / You Never Can Tell
Chess CH-91022 • 1984
    Stay away from this particular single, as they left out the piano from the mix of 'You Never Can Tell'. You hear the piano intro... and then it's gone! 'You Never Can Tell' without the piano is like a sausage without the meat! On the other hand, this single is probably something of a collector's item for Berry completists.

My Ding-A-Ling *(live, single edit)* / **Reelin' And Rockin'** *(live, single edit)*
Chess CH-91032 • 1984

RIPETE GOLD NUGGETS

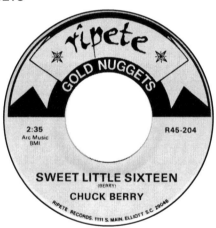

    The following Chess titles were reissued in the mid-1980s. Label colour was yellow. There were almost certainly more Berry releases in this series, but the three singles below are the only ones I have come across so far. Additionally, 'I Got To Find My Baby' was included on a Various Artists EP (see page 117).

Rock And Roll Music / Back In The USA
Ripete Gold Nuggets R45-201 • 1985

Sweet Little Sixteen / Brown Eyed Handsome Man
Ripete Gold Nuggets R45-204 • 1985

Maybellene
Ripete Gold Nuggets R45-206 • 1985
    Flip is 'Road Runner' by Bo Diddley.

COLLECTABLES 'BACK TO BACK HIT' SERIES

Collectables COL.3400   Collectables COL.3475

The Collectables series out of Narberth, PA, first appeared around 1980 and was ideal for jukeboxes and popular with buyers. The label was originally pink, but had been changed to black with a red-and-yellow logo by the time Berry's records appeared in 1986. You can still get them in specialist stores. The company has a huge catalogue of CDs and 7" vinyl singles.

All the Berry releases on the Collectables label are Chess recordings. Apart from COL.3469 and COL.3475, which have stereo 'A' sides, there is no stereo on any of the other releases, not even 'My Ding-A-Ling'.

The Berry 45s appeared two label designs. The earliest ones only referred to *'Collectable Record Corp.'* on the label. The mid-'80s reissues had *'Chess MCA Special Products'* printed in white on the left hand side. I also have several variants of the company sleeve. Happy hunting if you want them all.

Johnny B. Goode / Little Queenie
Collectables COL.3400 • 1986

Rock And Roll Music / Back In The USA
Collectables COL.3401 • 1986

School Day / Carol
Collectables COL.3402 • 1986

Sweet Little Sixteen / Promised Land
Collectables COL.3403 • 1986

Roll Over Beethoven / My Ding-A-Ling *(live, single edit)*
Collectables COL.3404 • 1986

Reelin' And Rockin' / Memphis, Tennessee
Collectables COL.3405 • 1986

Maybellene / Almost Grown
Collectables COL.3421 • 1987

No Particular Place To Go / You Never Can Tell
Collectables COL.3422 • 1987

Nadine
Collectables COL.3428 • 1987
    Flip is 'Nadine' by the Coronets, written by Alan Freed.

Run Rudolph Run+ / Merry Christmas Baby+
Collectables COL.3437 • 1987
    'Rudolph' is credited to *'C. Berry Music–M. Brodie'*. On later pressings, the credits say: *'M. Brodie–J. Marks'*.

Let It Rock / Sweet Little Rock And Roller
Collectables COL.3438 • 1987
    'Let It Rock' is credited to *'E. Anderson'*.

Too Much Monkey Business / Brown Eyed Handsome Man
Collectables COL.3439 • 1987

Thirty Days / No Money Down
Collectables COL.3440 • 1987

Little Marie *(stereo)* **/ Deep Feeling** *(instr)*
Collectables COL.3469 • 1988
    The 'A' side includes a count-in from Berry.

Oh Baby Doll / Wee Wee Hours
Collectables COL.3470 • 1988

Anthony Boy / Havana Moon
Collectables COL.3471 • 1988

Beautiful Delilah / You Can't Catch Me
Collectables COL.3472 • 1988

Joe Joe Gunne / Too Pooped To Pop+
Collectables COL.3473 • 1988
    'Too Pooped To Pop' – a Billy Davis composition – is erroneously credited to *'Chuck Berry'*.

Dear Dad / Bye Bye Johnny
Collectables COL.3474 • 1988

Go, Go, Go Johnny B. Goode *(stereo)* **/ Time Was+**
Collectables COL.3475 • 1988
    The 'A' side is the longer stereo remix version of 'Go, Go, Go' which first appeared on the 1986 LP, MORE ROCK'N'ROLL RARITIES [Chess CH-9190], with the same mis-spelling of the title. 'Time Was' is the faster 1958 take which first appeared on the 1986 2-LP, ROCK'N'ROLL RARITIES [Chess CH2-92521]. The interesting thing about this release is that it contains two songs which have not been available on a single before or since, and is therefore something of a collectors' item.

A MYSTERY BOX SET

CHUCK BERRY – A RETROSPECTIVE
BX-45367 • Germany(?), late 1990s

This box set containing nine Berry singles – eight on the Collectables label (COL.3401, 3404, 3405, 3422, 3437, 3438, 3471, 3474) and one on Eric (224) – appeared sometime in the late '90s! Some of the records came in company sleeves, others just in plain white sleeves. Some of the Collectables releases had the old label, others the newer one with '*Chess – MCA Special Products*' printed on it. The box itself was black and yellow with no picture or liner notes. Despite containing only US singles, it looks as though this package might have originated in Germany.

SPINDLE

Joe Alexander & The Cubans
Oh, Maria+ / I Hope These Words Will Find You Well+
Spindle SPN-2001 • 1995

A one-off limited edition reissue of the original Ballad 1008 single from 1954, digitally remastered by Marc Bird.

CROSLEY COLLECTORS' SERIES

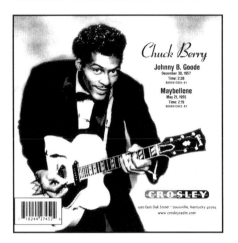

Founded in 1920, Crosley quickly became the world's largest radio manufacturer and are now a major distributor for domestic electrical appliances across the USA. The Crosley Radio Division does a neat line in repro old-time radios and record players. The following single, which was specially manufactured by Universal Music for Crosley Corporation, was given away free with some models.

Johnny B. Goode / Maybellene
Crosley Collectors' Series B0001383-21 [promo only] • **2003**
The cover has a great standard '50s picture of Berry, and the same picture on the label in colour.

EPs

AFTER SCHOOL SESSION
Chess CH-5118 • May 1957
School Day / Wee Wee Hours / Brown Eyed Handsome Man / Too Much Monkey Business

First pressings of this were issued on a black label with a silver top and the Chess logo on top in black.

HEAD OVER HEELS
Chess EP-5118 • prob. 1957
This EP includes the same cuts as the one above, but has a different title and front cover. The cover shows two people – a man and a woman – doing some kind of gymnastics where the woman is on the man's back as he's bending forward. The colour is blueish with red print and is signed by photographer/designer Don Bronstein. The reverse is identical to the AFTER SCHOOL SESSION EP. The record label is the same as AFTER SCHOOL SESSION: black with a silver top but no EP title shown, just the song titles. It is strange that this release didn't got its own master number in the Chess files, despite the fact that the songs are identical. Anyway, it is surely a rare Berry EP.

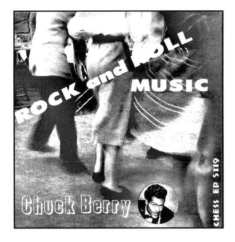

Black label

Black label variation

Blue label

ROCK AND ROLL MUSIC
Chess EP-5119 • November or December 1957
Rock And Roll Music / Blue Feeling *(instr)* / Oh Baby Doll / La Jaunda (Español)

'La Jaunda' is the usual album version. Although the back cover says 'Deep Feeling', the record plays 'Blue Feeling', as printed on the label. According to Michel Ruppli's *The Chess Labels*, this EP was initially allocated an incorrect master for Side B (#8582) with 'School Day' and 'Deep Feeling', which was then replaced by 'Oh Baby Doll' and 'La Jaunda' (#8604). Side A was #8581. It appears that someone made a mistake, since 'School Day' was already out on EP-5118. As far as I know, this EP was never released with the first coupling, but if it did, then it's extremely rare, as it must have been instantly withdrawn.

Black label

SWEET LITTLE 16
Chess EP-5121 • March 1958
Sweet Little Sixteen / Reelin' And Rockin' / Rock At The Philharmonic *(instr)* / Guitar Boogie *(instr)*

This is the most common of all the US Berry EPs.

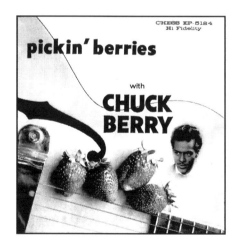 

Black label

PICKIN' BERRIES
Chess EP-5124 • August 1958
Carol / Hey Pedro / Beautiful Delilah / Vacation Time

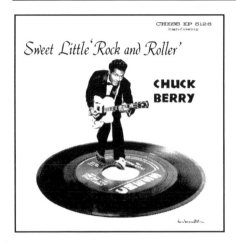

Black label

SWEET LITTLE ROCK AND ROLLER
Chess EP-5126 • November 1958
Jo Jo Gunne / Sweet Little Rock And Roller / Johnny B. Goode / Around And Around

Starting with this EP, Chess began using the 'correct' titles for the first two songs, which on all later releases would be styled in this way.

LPs

Black label

AFTER SCHOOL SESSION
Chess LP-1426 ● May 1957

School Day / Deep Feeling *(instr)* / Too Much Monkey Business / Wee Wee Hours / Roly Poly *(instr)* / No Money Down / Brown Eyed Handsome Man / Berry Pickin' *(instr)* / Together (We Will Always Be) / Havana Moon / Down Bound Train / Drifting Heart

Berry's first solo long-player was far from being a rock'n'roll album. With only three rock songs and the remainder consisting of instrumentals, ballads and blues songs, it must have disappointed a lot of people. It was reissued in 1989 on LP and CD [Chess CH-/CHD-9284] with additional liner notes and recording information.

ONE DOZEN BERRYS
Chess LP-1432 ● March 1958

Sweet Little Sixteen / Blue Feeling *(instr)* / La Jaunda (Español) / Rock At The Philharmonic *(instr)* / Oh Baby Doll / Reelin' And Rockin' / Ingo *(instr)* / Rock And Roll Music / How You've Changed / Low Feeling *(instr)* / It Don't Take But A Few Minutes

Black label, song titles in large letters

Black label, song titles in small letters

Blue label, song titles in large letters

Late '60s repress

GRT reissues: two label variations

Chess sometimes did weird things. 'Low Feeling' is actually 'Blue Feeling' under a new title, slowed down to half speed and with one 12-bar stanza omitted. Why do this, when they could have used one of the unissued songs they had in the can, or maybe even recorded another number to provide the twelfth track? Crazy, man, crazy! Here, we get only four real rock'n'roll songs, and the rest once again are a mixture of blues, ballads and instrumentals. 'Guitar Boogie' is a typical example of Chess' habit of using completely inappropriate titles. Instead of using the same title as the well-known and oft-performed classic by Arthur Smith from 1946, why didn't they just call it 'Berry Boogie' or something? The album cover is great, though.

BERRY IS ON TOP
Chess LP-1435 ● July 1959
Almost Grown / Carol / Maybellene / Sweet Little Rock And Roller / Anthony Boy / Johnny B. Goode / Little Queenie / Jo Jo Gunne / Roll Over Beethoven / Around And Around / Hey Pedro / Blues For Hawaiians *(instr)*

Now here is a true rock'n'roll album from the '50s! With the exception of the last two tracks (what are they doing on here anyway?) and possibly 'Jo Jo Gunne', the rest are all classics in their own way. It was reissued in 1987 on LP and CD [Chess CH-9256 and CHD-31260 respectively] with additional liner notes and recording information.

ROCKIN' AT THE HOPS
Chess LP-1448 ● July 1960
Bye Bye Johnny / Worried Life Blues+ / Down The Road A Piece+ / Confessin' The Blues+ / Too Pooped To Pop+ / Mad Lad+ *(instr)* / I Got To Find My Baby+ / Betty Jean / Childhood Sweetheart / Broken Arrow / Driftin' Blues+ / Let It Rock

This is almost a blues album. It has always been one of my favourite Berry long-players, although a more accurate title would have been BLUESIN' AT THE HOPS. Most of the songs were originally recorded in stereo, and some were issued as such in later years, especially on the RARITIES compilations in the '80s. I would love to have seen the whole album remixed and reissued in stereo format. The cover is terrible, though. Why didn't they use a stage shot of Berry with his blond Gibson ES-350? Reissued in 1987 on LP and CD [Chess CH-/CHD-9259] with additional liner notes and recording information.

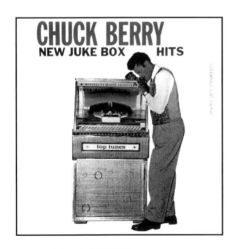

NEW JUKE BOX HITS
Chess LP-1456 ● March 1961
I'm Talking About You / Diploma For Two / Thirteen Question Method / Away From You / Don't You Lie To Me+ / The Way It Was Before / Little Star / Sweet Sixteen+ / Run Around *(instr)* / Stop And Listen / Rip It Up+

I'm not sure what Chess were thinking of when they chose the title for this album, because most of the songs were not hits at all. Perhaps it was aspirational. The well-known Tampa Red composition, 'Don't You Lie To Me', was credited to Berry. Many people don't like this album, and I must agree that it contains a rather odd selection of songs – far from what one might ordinarily expect from Berry. That said, I have always enjoyed Berry's version of 'Sweet Sixteen', although it is Matt Murphy's guitar playing that makes it special. His exquisite fills in between each line are outstanding. In reality, there is only one Berry classic here – 'I'm Talking About You' – but 'Thirteen Question Method', 'Diploma For Two' and 'Run Around' also have their attractions (the latter two even more so in their stereo incarnations, so far available only on a rare UK album [Marble Arch MALS-702] released in 1967. See UK discography for more information. Reissued (in mono) in 1984 on LP [Chess CH-9171] and in 1988 on CD [Chess CHD-9171].

CHUCK BERRY TWIST
Chess LP-1465 • February 1962
Maybellene / Roll Over Beethoven / Oh Baby Doll / 'Round And 'Round [Around And Around] / Come On / Let it Rock / Reelin' And Rockin' / School Days [School Day] / Almost Grown / Sweet Little Sixteen / Thirty Days / Johnny B. Goode / Rock And Roll Music / Back In The USA

This has the worst ever cover on any Chuck Berry album. Berry was in jail and Chess needed a long-player to meet the 'demands' for a new Berry release. What a great idea to cash in on the twist craze with probably the best and most rockin' Berry album ever released! They even threw in a couple of extra songs to bring it up to 14 tracks. Actually, it was a 'greatest hits' album by any other name. Two songs were mis-spelled here for the first time, which continued for years to come: ' 'Round And 'Round' and 'School Days'. Reissued with the same catalogue number in January 1964 as MORE CHUCK BERRY.

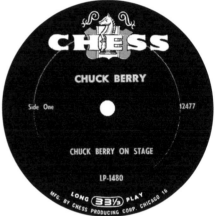

Black label (original pressing)   Black label (repress)

ON STAGE
Chess LP-1480 • August 1963
Go, Go, Go / Memphis Tennessee / Maybellene / Surfing Steel *(instr)* / Rocking On The Railroad [Let It Rock] / Brown Eyed Handsome Man *(1963 version)* / Still Got The Blues / Sweet Little Sixteen [this appears as 'Surfin' USA' on the back cover] / Jaguar And The Thunderbird / I Just Want To Make Love To You+ / All Aboard / Trick Or Treat / The Man And The Donkey / How High The Moon+ *(instr)*

When I first bought this album, I was convinced it *was* a live recording. How wrong can you be! Actually, the opening *'Welcome to the Tivoli Theatre here in Chicago…'* was so cleverly done, that, if you were not familiar with all the Berry songs, you could easily be fooled. (Remember this was 1963!) If you listen carefully, as I did back then, you can hear Berry and the band talking a little between some of the songs – 'Memphis' and 'Surfing Steel' in particular. The latter became known as 'Crying Steel' when it was reissued in 1988 on the 6-LP/3-CD CHESS BOX set [Chess CH6-/CHD3-80001]. The instrumental 'How High The Moon' fading out at the end with someone shouting *'Chuck Berry! Chuck Berry!'* sounded perfect at the time. I remember how disappointed I was when I found out the whole thing was a rip-off! Be that as it may, the dubbing was done so well that it's probably the best fake 'live' album in history. The original pressings of this LP had a sticker on the front cover saying 'including MEMPHIS & SURFIN' USA'. Furthermore, they had no song titles printed on the label, and the song sequence was incorrectly shown on the back cover. Also, 'How High The Moon' was faded out just before Berry starts playing. However, on the early '70s orange label reissue, the song lasted almost an extra minute.

MORE CHUCK BERRY
Chess LP-1465 • November 1963
This is a reissue of the 1962 *Twist* album with the same catalogue number but a different cover. The original pressings of this album had a black label with vertical silver 'Chess' logo and 'CHUCK BERRY TWIST' on the label.

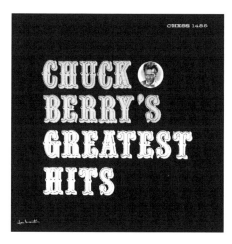 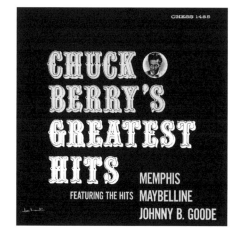

CHUCK BERRY'S GREATEST HITS
Chess LP-1485 • April 1964
Roll Over Beethoven / School Days [School Day] / Rock And Roll Music / Too Much Monkey Business / Johnny B. Goode / Oh Baby Doll / Nadine / Maybelline [Maybellene] / Memphis Tennessee / Sweet Little Sixteen / Thirty Days / Brown Eyed Handsome Man

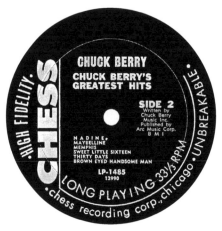 

Black label (repress)   Blue label (repress)

This was the first occasion that 'Maybellene' was spelt with an 'i', and 'School Day' again appeared as 'School Days'. The first pressings had a black label with vertical silver 'Chess' logo, but you will find all kinds of label variations (eg blue label with vertical silver 'Chess' logo, blue label with silver 'Chess' logo across the top, black label with gold 'Chess' logo across the top, the late 60s/early 70s light blue label and finally GRT's orange label). As a matter of fact, this is probably the Chuck Berry album you will find in most different label variations. The earliest issues of this album had no songs printed on the front cover. Some came with a yellow sticker which said: *'Featuring the original Hits MEMPHIS – MAYBELLINE – JOHNNY B. GOODE'.* Later issues had *'Featuring the Hits MEMPHIS – MAYBELLINE – JOHNNY B. GOODE'* printed in yellow in the bottom right-hand corner.

Chuck and Bo at the *Montreux Jazz Festival*, 16 June 1972.

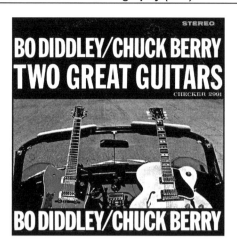

Second pressing   Third pressing

Chuck Berry & Bo Diddley
TWO GREAT GUITARS
Checker LP-2991 *(mono)* **LPS-2991** *(stereo)* ● **August 1964**
Liverpool Drive *(instr, Chuck Berry only)* / Chuck's Beat *(instr, Chuck Berry and Bo Diddley)* / When The Saints Go Marching In+ *(instr, Bo Diddley only)* / Bo's Beat+ *(instr, Bo Diddley and Chuck Berry)*

This is strictly an instrumental album and was unique when it came out, as nothing like it had been heard before. Rock music had never had a guitar jam session released on record – jam sessions were something that belonged to jazz. 'Chuck's Beat' is 10:35 long, and 'Bo's Beat' runs for an amazing 14:00 mins. Has there ever been another album like this released in the history of rock or pop music? The front cover is great, too, depicting Berry's and Diddley's guitars side by side in a sports car. The first pressings of this album had black labels with a vertical silver 'Checker' logo on the left side. I have never seen a stereo issue with this label, only mono. This was also the very first Berry recording issued in stereo in the States, though he had recorded songs in stereo as early as 1960. Reissued in 1984 on LP [Chess CH-9170] and in 1992 on CD (with bonus cuts) [Chess CHD-9170].

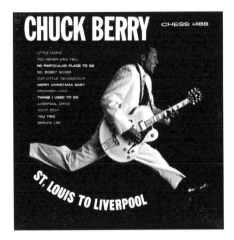

First pressing

Second pressing (promo)

Third pressing

ST. LOUIS TO LIVERPOOL
Chess LP-1488 *(mono)* LPS-1488 *(stereo)* ● November 1964
Little Marie / Our Little Rendezvous *(mono only)* / No Particular Place To Go / You Two / Promised Land / You Never Can Tell / Go Bobby Soxer / The Things I Used To Do+ / Liverpool Drive *(instr)* / Night Beat *(instr, mono only)* / Merry Christmas Baby+ *(mono only)* / Brenda Lee *(mono only)*

This was the first-ever solo Chuck Berry album released in true stereo, however, 'Our Little Rendezvous', 'Night Beat', 'Merry Christmas Baby' and 'Brenda Lee' are not stereo recordings. In view of Berry's immense popularity in Britain and a tailor-made title, this album strangely did not see a UK release (although mono versions did appear in the Netherlands and Sweden). The cover is superb – a rare treat for Berry's US fans. Rumour has it that some issues of this album include a version of 'How Great Thou Art' instead of 'Brenda Lee', however, I don't go for that. I just cannot imagine Berry doing this hymn, and there is nothing mentioned anywhere hinting that he ever performed or recorded it. Reissued in 1984 on LP [Chess CH-9186] and in 1988 on CD [Chess CHD-31261].

CHUCK BERRY IN LONDON
Chess LP-1495 *(mono)* **LPS-1495** *(stereo)* ● **April 1965**
My Little Love-Light / She Once Was Mine / After It's Over *(instr)* / I Got A Booking / Night Beat *(instr, mono only)* / His Daughter Caroline / You Came A Long Way From St. Louis+ / St. Louis Blues+ / Jamaica Farewell+ / Dear Dad / Butterscotch *(instr)* / The Song Of My Love / Why Should We End This Way / I Want To Be Your Driver

Someone once asked me which Berry album I would take with me to a desert island and I said CHUCK BERRY IN LONDON, because it contains everything from great rockers and blues to ballads and instrumentals, and a little dash of Latin and Caribbean flavour. This album has all the elements of Berry's music that you need! But why include 'Night Beat' again on this album? It was already out on the previous LP five months earlier. The unreleased track 'Do You Love Me' (1959) would have been a much better choice for this album.

Fred Rothwell's *Long Distance Information* contains a very good evaluation of all the songs, especially 'Dear Dad' – surely the most under-rated of all songs from Berry's pen. If you ever thought rock'n'roll died in 1959, then take note of what Fred has to say: *'It is the hottest thing Berry cut this side of the Fifties. Not a single note is wasted, nor a second's pause permitted during the 110 seconds Chuck sings six verses and hits two storming guitar solos.'* Fred is absolutely right. The story is about cars, Berry's favourite subject. He's driving an old Ford, and in letter form to his dad describes how badly it's behaving, angling for a replacement. At the end he signs off with, *'Sincerely, your beloved son, Henry Jr. Ford.'* That's Berry at his very best !

'Jamaica Farewell' is complete only on the stereo issue of this LP and reaches an artistic conclusion with a crash of cymbals at 2:06. On the mono version, the song is faded at 2:01. The same also applies on the European issues, where the song is faded out at 1:48. The US releases also have an extra guitar part, which is more audible in the stereo version. Part of this LP was actually recorded in London in January 1965 with English musicians (see Fred Rothwell's *Long Distance Information* for details).

The 1970s GRT orange label reissue of this LP has the front cover on both sides and poor stereo sound.

Blue label

Light blue label

FRESH BERRY'S
Chess LP-1498 *(mono)* **LPS-1498** *(stereo)* ● **November 1965**
It Wasn't Me / Run Joe+ / Everyday We Rock And Roll / One For My Baby (And One More For The Road)+ / Welcome Back Pretty Baby / It's My Own Business / Right Off Rampart Street / Vaya Con Dios+ / Merrily We Rock And Roll / My Mustang Ford / Ain't That Just Like A Woman+ / Wee Hour Blues

Many people consider this to be one of the best Berry albums. I agree that it contains some great tracks like 'It Wasn't Me', 'It's My Own Business', 'Welcome Back Pretty Baby' and 'Right Off Rampart Street'. However, I'm less keen on 'Everyday We Rock And Roll' and 'Merrily We Rock And Roll', which are based on nursery rhymes. They sound so outdated and in reality are nothing more than fillers. Moreover, the similar opening riffs and rhythm pattern on 'My Mustang Ford' and 'Ain't That Just Like A Woman' simply make these two tracks irritating to listen to and detract from some pretty good lyrics, especially those on 'My Mustang Ford'. On the plus side, the US issue again has a great cover. As well as the light blue labels with large and small lettering in both mono and stereo, you can find this with the dark blue label and silver vertical 'Chess' logo on the left. This album was also issued with a silver label with the Chess 'knight' logo in black at the top. Rumour has it that it was also issued with a red label with the same logo! A *red* Chess label !?!?

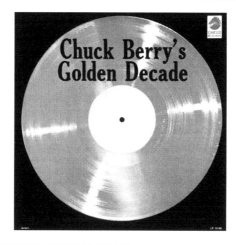

CHUCK BERRY'S GOLDEN DECADE [2-LP]
Chess LP-1514D *(mono)* **LPS-1514D** *(stereo)* ● **January 1967**
❶ Maybellene / Deep Feeling *(instr)* / Johnny B. Goode / Wee Wee Hours / Nadine / Brown Eyed Handsome Man / Roll Over Beethoven / Thirty Days / Havana Moon / No Particular Place To Go / Memphis Tennessee / Almost Grown
❷ School Day / Too Much Monkey Business / Oh Baby Doll / Reelin' And Rockin' /You Can't Catch Me / Too Pooped To Pop+ / Bye Bye Johnny / Around And Around / Sweet Little Sixteen / Rock And Roll Music / Anthony Boy / Back In The USA

At this stage of the game Chess Records made a fatal move. If you look inside the gatefold sleeve, you will find printed in very small lettering: *'Electronically rechanneled for stereo by RCA*'! For many years afterwards, we had to listen to dreadful-sounding versions of the Berry classics, because Chess used the electronic stereo 'masters' on all subsequent '70s and early '80s releases. 'Carol' in particular was destroyed forever.

The first pressings of this album had no song titles on the front cover, only the album title. They were issued with the light blue label both in mono and electronic stereo (although the latter is more common). The Billy Davis composition 'Too Pooped To Pop' was incorrectly credited to Berry. DJ copies contained one disc with a Chess label and the other with a Checker label, both light blue. However, it's unlikely there was ever a regular release in this format.

This set was reissued in 1972 [Chess 2CH-1514], initially with a 'gold record' cover, this time with all the songs printed on the record label and the heading *'The Original Two Albums'*, but was quickly replaced by a completely new gatefold design with a pink radio(!) on the front.

GOLDEN HITS
Mercury MG-21103 *(mono)* **SR-61103** *(stereo)* ● **March 1967**
Sweet Little Sixteen / Memphis, Tennessee / School Day / Maybellene / Back In The USA /
Johnny B. Goode / Rock And Roll Music / Roll Over Beethoven / Thirty Days / Carol / Club Nitty Gritty

What can I say? These re-recordings of Berry's hits (apart from 'Club Nitty Gritty', which was a new song) are far from good. The way they are done exemplifies how best to destroy classic songs! However, it seems that Berry himself had complete control in the studio, so 'nuff said. He went on to remake more of his classics during the first months at Mercury, and they were later released on various albums. I'm sure 'Club Nitty Gritty' was recorded at his own Berry Park Studio because it's only available in mono, and also has a different sound to the other songs. And why is there a question mark following the 'Thirty Days' title on the front cover?

Rumour has it that this album came out in the 1980s with the title CHUCK BERRY'S GREATEST HITS, but I can't verify that, as I've never seen it. The GOLDEN HITS album also came out as a Record Club release, using the number R-113728 in addition to the Mercury number SR-61103, and seven oval 'Mercury' logos on the label. At the bottom of the label were three small logos – Philips, Mercury and Vertigo. Of all the Mercury albums, this one has been reissued most often – always with the same catalogue number.

It was reissued on CD in 1989 with four bonus cuts and much better sound quality [Mercury 826 256-2]. However, the corresponding LP version [Mercury 826 256-1] came without the bonus cuts.

CHUCK BERRY IN MEMPHIS
Mercury MG-21123 *(mono)* **SR-61123** *(stereo)* ● **September 1967**
Back To Memphis / I Do Really Love You / Ramblin' Rose+ / Sweet Little Rock And Roller / My Heart Will Always Belong To You+ / Oh Baby Doll / Check Me Out / It Hurts Me Too+ / Bring Another Drink+ / So Long+ / Goodnight, Well It's Time To Go [It's Time To Go]

This album really was recorded in Memphis in March 1967 at the Royal Recording Studio operated by Willie Mitchell. It helps that Chuck was backed by a horn section, but the songs sound strange with almost no bass. That was a problem with all of Berry's original Mercury releases. When they were reissued on CD in 1989, they had a much fuller sound and sounded infinitely better. The two re-recorded Chess tracks are not much better than the ones he did for the GOLDEN HITS sessions, even though he didn't produce these himself (Roy Dea and Boo Frazier took care of that). Reissued in 1989 on CD (with bonus cuts and much better sound quality) [Mercury 836 071-2].

LIVE AT THE FILLMORE AUDITORIUM, SAN FRANCISCO
Mercury MG-21138 *(mono)* **SR-61138** *(stereo)* ● **November 1967**
Medley: Rockin' At The Fillmore*(instr)* – Everyday I Have The Blues+ / C.C. Rider+ / Driftin' Blues+ / Feelin' It *(instr)* / Flying Home+ *(instr)* / Hoochie Coochie Man+ / It Hurts Me Too+ *(duet with Steve Miller)* / Fillmore Blues *(instr)* / Wee Baby Blues+ / Goodnight Sweetheart – Johnny B. Goode

Except for the final song, this is strictly a blues album, on which Berry is expertly backed by the Steve Miller Blues Band. I have always enjoyed this album, especially since the musicians and Berry sound rehearsed – which they were (Miller claims he demanded three days rehearsal time with Berry prior to undertaking the concerts. And Berry agreed!) Reissued in 1989 on CD (with bonus cuts and much better sound quality) [Mercury 836 072-2].

This was the Steve Miller Band's very first appearance on album. They had formed in California in 1966 after Miller moved there that year. In 1967 they played the *Monterey Pop Festival*, backed Berry at the Fillmore, and were signed by Capitol in October. They dropped the 'Blues' from their name and in early 1968 recorded their first album, CHILDREN OF THE FUTURE [Capitol SN-16078 *(mono)* SKAO-2920 *(stereo)*].

FROM ST. LOUIE TO FRISCO
Mercury SR-61176 ● October 1968
Louie To Frisco / Ma Dear / The Love I Lost / I Love Her, I Love Her / Little Fox / Rock Cradle Rock / Soul Rockin' / I Can't Believe / Misery / My Tambourine / Oh, Captain / Mum's The Word

'All songs written by Chuck Berry. All songs published by Isalee Music (BMI). Arranged by Chuck Berry. Produced by Chuck Berry. Recorded at Berry Park Studio.'
Here, Berry had started to experiment in the studio. You can certainly hear the difference, though I have never been sure if I like it. There are some okay rockers in the shape of 'Louie To Frisco', 'Soul Rockin' ' and 'Misery', a blues tune, and daughter Ingrid helps out vocally on 'Ma Dear' and 'Little Fox', but on the rest the psychedelic influence shines through. The worst of these is 'Oh, Captain', which was actually recorded earlier at Mercury. What Berry or Mercury were thinking of when they decided to include this song will always be a mystery. It initially starts in the left channel and a few seconds later it starts again in the right channel, so you end up with two copies of the song playing simultaneously, but a few seconds out of sync. Can you imagine what this does to the listener's head? If you use both channels at the same time you'll go crazy! In an interview for *Rolling Stone*, Berry later said that Mercury spoiled 'Oh Captain' ' and that he was embarrassed to play it for his friends. It was at this time that I first realised that Berry should not be allowed to produce anything himself, and I have since been proved right on several other occasions. This album was only released in stereo and was reissued in 1989 on CD (with bonus cuts and much better sound quality) [Mercury 836 073-2].

CONCERTO IN B GOODE
Mercury SR-61223 ● October 1969
Good Looking Woman / My Woman / It's Too Dark In There / Put Her Down / Concerto In B Goode *(instr)*

Another Chuck Berry production, cut at his own studio in Berry Park. The title track is a 19-minute long instrumental blend of blues and acid rock, including various elements of strange stereo mixing with wah-wah and fuzz box used to the extreme. This is also a blues-oriented album – Berry's third – and was only available in stereo. Reissued in 1989 on CD (with much better sound quality) [Mercury 836 074-2].

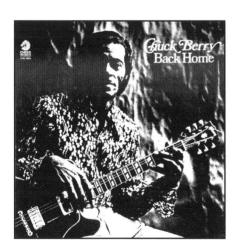

BACK HOME
Chess [GRT] LPS-1550 ● November 1970
Tulane / Have Mercy Judge / Instrumental *(instr)* / Christmas / Gun *(instr)* / I'm A Rocker / Flyin' Home *(instr)* / Fish & Chips / Some People

I'm not quite sure what happened in the studio when Berry recorded this album. Once again, Chess seem to have come up with a couple of odd titles for the instrumentals. I mean, naming a guitar instrumental 'Instrumental'! It's quite silly. And naming another one 'Flyin' Home' simply makes it stupid. Maybe they thought he was *flyin' home* to Chess? (The other 'Flying Home' (with a 'g'), which Berry recorded for Mercury on the LIVE AT THE FILLMORE album is an old Lionel Hampton tune. He also recorded a studio version, which was eventually released in 1989 as a bonus cut on the CHUCK BERRY IN MEMPHIS CD reissue.) So, what happened to being a little inventive? In his autobiography, Berry refers to all the strange titles Chess gave to his instrumentals, some of them actually being just rehearsals or warm-ups.

More positively, his 'comeback' album contained four great songs: 'Tulane' and 'I'm A Rocker' showed that Berry hadn't lost his skills as a composer; 'Have Mercy Judge' is one of his best blues songs ever; and 'Fish & Chips' is a real original and under-rated Berry tune which (although it is not an easy song to cover – and nobody has) nevertheless features some really nifty guitar-work. Berry triple-dubbed his guitar, and it is a recording he can be really proud of. Unfortunately it is a song that is usually overlooked in any review of his best work. Well, it *is* a little unusual, and far removed from rock'n'roll, but listen to the guitar pickin' the next time you have a chance.

'Christmas' was originally titled 'My Blue Christmas', and it seems that Chess even had trouble deciding what to call the album. BACK HOME is a good title, but on some issues the record labels bear two different titles: 'BACK HOME' on one side and 'HOME AGAIN' on the other. Others have 'HOME AGAIN' on both sides.

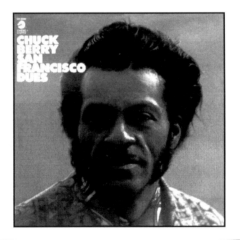

Large lettering	Small lettering

SAN FRANCISCO DUES
Chess [GRT] CH-50008 • September 1971
Oh Louisiana / Let's Do Our Thing Together / Your Lick *(instr)* / Festival / Bound To Lose / Bordeaux In My Pirough / San Francisco Dues / Viva, Viva Rock & Roll / My Dream *(poem)* / Lonely School Days *(fast version)*

'Viva, Viva Rock & Roll' and 'Lonely School Days' are from an April 1966 recording session. Even though these two songs were recorded for Chess five years earlier, there is no perceptible difference between them and the rest of the album – which makes you think.

Berry plays piano on the poem, 'My Dream'. The album has many high points – like the title track (a slow blues), 'Let's Do Our Thing Together' (a good boogie), 'Lonely School Days' (a solid Berry rocker), 'Oh Louisiana' (a wonderful, dreamlike song in which Berry tenderly sings about the Pelican State as though it were a woman) and 'Bordeaux In My Pirough' (another evocative song, though it sounds too much like Hank Williams' 'Jambalaya' for my money). Some reissues of this album had the front cover artwork on both sides.

THE LONDON CHUCK BERRY SESSIONS
Chess [GRT] CH-60020 • April 1972
Let's Boogie / Mean Old World+ / I Will Not Let You Go / London Berry Blues *(instr)* / I Love You / Reelin' And Rockin' *(live)* / My Ding-A-Ling *(live)* / Johnny B. Goode *(live)*

This is the biggest-selling Chuck Berry album ever, and his only US certified gold album. The first five tracks were cut at Pye Studios in London on 5 February 1972. The last three were recorded live at the *Lanchester Arts Festival* in Coventry on 3 February. The album was originally released in a gatefold cover, but was later packaged in a standard sleeve.

The studio recordings represent some of Berry's best '70s' output. 'Mean Old World' is one of my all-time favourite blues recordings by Berry (although it's a pity that his voice is mixed so low), and the rocking instrumental 'London Berry Blues' really couldn't be better.

It is possible that this LP was also issued with the catalogue number CH-6310 122 (see *A US Chess Oddity* on page 39), though I have never seen a copy. Reissued in 1989 on LP (without the gatefold cover) and on CD [Chess CH-/CHD-9295].

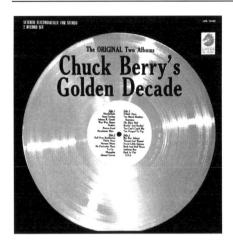

CHUCK BERRY'S GOLDEN DECADE [2-LP]
Chess [GRT] 2CH-1514 ● September 1972
    This reissue of the 1967 double album [Chess LPS-1514D] initially appeared with a 'gold record' cover, this time with all the songs printed on the record label and the heading *'The Original Two Albums'*, but was quickly replaced by a completely new gatefold design with a pink radio(!) on the front.

ST. LOUIE TO FRISCO TO MEMPHIS [2-LP]
Mercury SRM 2-6501 ● October 1972
❶ *Medley:* Rockin' At The Fillmore*(instr)* – Everyday I Have The Blues+ / C.C. Rider+ / Driftin' Blues+ / Feelin' It *(instr)* / Flying Home+ *(instr)* / Hoochie Coochie Man+ / It Hurts Me Too+ *(duet with Steve Miller)* / Fillmore Blues *(instr)* / Wee Baby Blues+ / Goodnight Sweetheart – Johnny B. Goode
❷ St. Louie To Frisco / Ma Dear / Soul Rockin' / Check Me Out / Little Fox / Back To Memphis / My Tambourine / Misery / It's Too Dark In There / I Do Really Love You / I Can't Believe / My Heart Will Always Belong To You+ / So Long+

    Disc 1 is the entire LIVE AT THE FILLMORE LP [Mercury SR-61138] from 1967, while Disc 2 contains an assortment of other Mercury tracks. This album was, of course, released to cash in on Berry's new-found fame on Chess. Mercury even

74

included the dreadful 'My Tambourine' – Berry's earlier attempt to create his own 'Ding-A-Ling'. The album features a great front cover shot of Berry in black and white with the wording *'Includes the memorable Fillmore Concert with the Steve Miller Band'* printed beneath the title. Inside the gatefold cover of the promo issue I have, someone wrote *'BULLSHIT'* on the Side 3 and 4 track list. I can understand their feelings, because when you listen to the Fillmore sides and then turn to the second album you are surely in for an anti-climax *de luxe*. Despite these shortcomings, this 2-LP set actually made the album charts (see *Section 12 (Achievements & Awards)* for details).

How come the Mercury albums always had such bad (and I mean *really* bad) sound quality? It seems like someone at the label didn't like bass. When Polygram reissued all the original Mercury albums on CD in 1989, it was a whole new ball game! It was almost like getting a new bunch of Berry recordings from the late '60s!

In the autumn of 1972, it was rumoured that Chuck Berry was working on a new album. He had reportedly recorded 35 titles, all self-composed, for an upcoming LP. This seems very strange since there are no records of any sessions which would relate to such a large number of songs. Also, at that time he would have been too busy touring the USA and Europe. Because of his new-found popularity thanks to 'My Ding-A-Ling' and the LONDON SESSIONS album, it seems odd and scarcely possible that he would have had time to spend so many hours in his recording studio at Berry Park.

JOHNNY B. GOODE
Pickwick SPC-3327 ● Late 1972
Johnny B. Goode / Memphis, Tennessee / Roll Over Beethoven / Sweet Little Sixteen / School Day / Maybellene / Reelin' And Rockin' / Rock And Roll Music / Back In The USA

Pickwick was a budget label that did not release quality records. However, the Mercury version of 'Reelin' And Rockin' ' appeared here for the first time. This album was originally issued with a silver label, then later with a black label. The covers were also slightly different: the earliest version of the silver label had only one circle in red on the left, just under *Chuck Berry,* with *'Includes Reelin' & Rocking'* in yellow; later releases (both the silver and the black label) had an additional blue circle just under the red one, with *'Roll Over Beethoven'* in white. So you actually need three variations of the album to have the full set.

Two label variations

CHUCK BERRY'S GOLDEN DECADE (VOLUME 2) [2-LP]
Chess [GRT] 2CH-60023 • February 1973
❶ Carol / You Never Can Tell / No Money Down / Together (We Will Always Be) / Mad Lad+ *(instr)* / Run Rudolph Run+ / Let It Rock / Sweet Little Rock And Roller / It Don't Take But A Few Minutes / I'm Talking About You / Driftin' Blues+ / Go, Go, Go
❷ Jaguar And The Thunderbird / Little Queenie / Betty Jean / Guitar Boogie *(instr)* / Down The Road A Piece+ / Merry Christmas Baby+ / Promised Land / Jo Jo Gunne / Don't You Lie To Me+ / Rock At The Philharmonic *(instr)* / La Jaunda / Come On

This album also made the *Billboard* album chart. It's kind-of amazing that you can release another batch of 24 tracks and call it GOLDEN DECADE (VOLUME 2). Later on there would even be a VOLUME 3! Apart for Elvis, I believe that Berry is the only artist entitled to such a magnificent honour. Three volumes with 72 tracks altogether and 75% of them stone classics (well almost). That's not bad for a black dude from St. Louis.

The original release was packaged in a gatefold sleeve, but the All Platinum reissue of this album only had a single cover. 'Run Rudolph Run' appeared here for the first time on LP. The same goes for the single version of 'Merry Christmas Baby'. 'Let It Rock' comes without Berry's solo guitar, but Johnnie Johnson's piano-playing is further up in the mix and it sounds great! 'Go, Go, Go' is taken straight from the 1963 ON STAGE album [Chess LP-1480], complete with fake audience overdub.

Promo

BIO
Chess [GRT] CH-50043 ● July 1973
Bio / Hello Little Girl, Goodbye / Woodpecker *(instr)* / Rain Eyes* / Aimlessly Driftin' / Got It And Gone* / Talkin' About My Buddy

Some issues have 'Aimlessly Driftin' ' misprinted as 'Driftin' Aimlessly' on the label. On the two songs marked * Berry was accompanied by his road band at the time: Billy Peek (guitar), Greg Edick (bass) and Ron Reed (drums), recorded 1 March 1973. The rest of the songs were recorded with members of Elephant's Memory on 3 June 1973. Seven tracks in total isn't much. However, apart from one at 3:30, all the rest last between four-and-a-half and almost seven minutes! Other titles from these sessions remain unissued.

The gatefold cover is great, with a photo of an 11 year old Chuck on the front, and a mixture of older and more recent pictures of Berry inside. However, it would have been interesting to know something about the photos. For example, how many people would know that one of them (bottom, centre) shows Berry with Johnnie Johnson and Ebbie Hardy from the late '60s or early '70s? Sadly, the 1975 All Platinum reissue with the black and white cover, and the 1984 MCA reissue [Chess CH-91510] only came in a single cover without the photos. The cover of the latter was green instead of black.

SWEET LITTLE ROCK AND ROLLER
Pickwick SPC-3345 ● 1973
Sweet Little Rock And Roller / Check Me Out / Ramblin' Rose+ / Goodnight, Well It's Time To Go [It's Time To Go] / Carol / Oh Baby Doll / Back To Memphis / It Hurts Me Too+ *(live duet with Steve Miller)* / C.C. Rider+ *(live)*

Mercury tracks. Released with two different front covers. The original issue (silver label) has one of the worst-ever covers on a Berry album – an almost-naked girl with a leather jacket and cigarette. The later issue (black label) carried a picture of Berry.

CHUCK BERRY'S GOLDEN DECADE (VOLUME 3) [2-LP]
Chess [GRT] 2CH-60028 ● April 1974
❶ Beautiful Delilah / Go, Bobby Soxer / I Got To Find My Baby+ / Worried Life Blues+ / Roly Poly *(instr)* / Down Bound Train / Broken Arrow / Confessin' The Blues+ / Drifting Heart / Ingo *(instr)* / Man And The Donkey / St. Louis Blues+
❷ Our Little Rendezvous / Childhood Sweetheart / Blues For Hawaiians *(instr)* / Hey Pedro / My Little Love-Light / Little Marie / County Line* / Viva, Viva Rock And Roll / House Of Blue Lights*+ / Time Was*+ / Blue On Blue* *(instr)* / Oh Yeah*

The songs marked * were previously unissued. This was 'Beautiful Delilah's first appearance on LP in the USA. 'Man And The Donkey' is taken straight from the ON STAGE album [Chess LP-1480], complete with the fake audience overdub. 'Blue On Blue' is a *tour de force* for Johnnie Johnson – a solid piano blues with J.J. in top form. It was probably a warm-up jam in the studio before a recording session. By rights it should have been credited to Johnson. Unfortunately Johnnie either didn't know or understand, and Berry didn't care.

According to the liner notes on the inside cover, the set contains five recently-discovered and never-before-released songs. So far, so good, but it says that 'Do You Love Me' and 'Berry Pickin' ' are included on the set – however they are not! Further on, it says that 'Our Little Rendezvous' has never been issued on an LP. Well, it's on the ST. LOUIS TO LIVERPOOL album [Chess LPS-1488] from 1964. It says the same thing about 'Broken Arrow', which was included on ROCKIN' AT THE HOPS [Chess LP-1448] in 1960. What amateurs!

The UK version of this album included 'Do You Love Me' instead of 'Time Was', and 'Berry Pickin' ' instead of 'Viva, Viva Rock And Roll'. In England they at least read the liner notes and checked the track listing before releasing it. Jolly good show!

FLASHBACK [2-LP]
Pickwick PTP-2061 • 1974

This is a repackaging of JOHNNY B. GOODE [Pickwick SPC-3327] from 1972 and SWEET LITTLE ROCK AND ROLLER [Pickwick SPC-3345] from 1973. Issued with a black label and a gatefold sleeve.

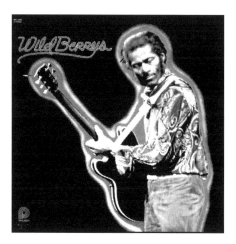

WILD BERRYS
Pickwick SPC-3392 • 1974
I Do Really Love You / So Long+ / It's Too Dark In There / My Heart Will Always Belong To You+ / Bring Another Drink+ / Good Lovin' Woman *[Good Lookin' Woman]* / My Woman / Thirty Days / Put Her Down

Mercury cuts. 'Good Lookin' Woman' is misprinted as 'Good *Lovin'* Woman' on the back cover. I have never understood what's supposed to be so 'wild' about these Berry recordings. As far as I know this album was only released with the silver Pickwick label.

CHUCK BERRY
Chess [GRT] CH-60032 • February 1975
Swanee River+ / I'm Just A Name / I Just Want To Make Love To You+ / Too Late+ / South Of The Border+ / Hi-Heel Sneakers+ / You Are My Sunshine+ / My Babe+ / Baby What You Want Me To Do+ / A Deuce* / Shake, Rattle And Roll+ / Sue Answer* [Sue Ann? Sir] / Don't You Lie To Me+

This album was originally intended to be a 2 LP-set, but for some strange reason Chess decided to release just one LP with 13 tracks. This means there are several unissued songs still in the can, mostly from August 1974 sessions in New York. The two songs marked * feature Berry's road band – Billy Peek (guitar), Greg Edick (bass) and Ron Reed (drums) – and date from the previous year's BIO sessions.

'Shake, Rattle And Roll' turns out to be the album's best and wildest rocker. The arrangement was later covered by Sweden's Jerry Williams. Berry also turns in a neat version of the Jimmy Reed classic, 'Baby What You Want Me To Do', which has a great bluesy feel. I particularly like Ingrid's voice on this one, with Chuck harmonising in the background. Apart from this particular track, I would struggle to name any other favourites. 'Too Late' is okay, but despite what the sleevenotes say, it's not a Berry original: it was written by C&W singer-songwriter Jimmy Wakely back in the '40s. The Louvin Brothers covered it on an album in 1957 and is probably where Berry picked it up. But why was Berry credited? The same goes for 'Don't You Lie To Me'. Everyone knew in 1974 that Berry didn't write this.

CHUCK BERRY'S GREATEST HITS
Everest Archive of Folk & Jazz Music FS-321 • 1976
Roll Over Beethoven / Johnny B. Goode / Sweet Little Sixteen / School Day / Maybellene / Rock And Roll Music / Ramblin' Rose+ / Carol / C.C. Rider+ *(live)* / Memphis, Tennessee

Apart from 1967's GOLDEN HITS [Mercury MG-21103/SR-61103], this was the first attempt to rip off the punters with a 'greatest hits' package of Mercury tracks. There have been so many of these over the years, that some people probably think they really *are* the originals. (But 'Ramblin' Rose' and 'C.C. Rider'? Some mistake surely? The compiler clearly didn't know what he or she was doing.) There is a statement of purpose in the liner notes which tells us a lot about the 'old' recordings – which apparently came out on 78s, no less: *'They were recorded under rather difficult conditions and most of them have been out of print for years. The Archive of Folk & Jazz Music seek out original recordings and carefully make the historic recordings available to the public on high-quality LP's. In order to transcribe these worn, poor quality 78 rpm discs, our engineers spend literally hundreds of hours splicing, editing and adjusting.'*

Chuck Berry at the Paris Olympia, 24 February 1975.

What utter tosh! When it comes to the Berry recordings above, it's an outright lie. Needless to say, there is no mention in the liner notes that these recordings happen to be from the latter part of the 1960s and are in stereo. The note-writer is happy to give the reader the impression that they are the original '50s recordings. I *hate* this! It's like knowing you are selling poison, but saying it's all very good for your health.

THE LEGENDARY MUSIC MAN – CHUCK BERRY
Candelite Music CLP-8208 ● 1977
Rock And Roll Music / Almost Grown / Thirty Days / Roll Over Beethoven / You Never Can Tell / School Day / Too Pooped To Pop+ / My Ding-A-Ling *(live, single edit)* / Nadine / Johnny B. Goode / Memphis, Tennessee / Back In The USA / Promised Land / Maybellene / Sweet Little Sixteen / Carol / Reelin' And Rockin' / No Particular Place To Go

This was probably a series of releases featuring 'legendary music men', although I haven't seen any others. This is the usual best of / greatest hits / golden hits or however you want to describe it. All Chess tracks.

THE BEST OF THE BEST OF CHUCK BERRY
Gusto GT-0004 ● 1978
Johnny B. Goode / School Day / Reelin' And Rockin' / Rock And Roll Music / Sweet Little Sixteen / Maybellene / Roll Over Beethoven / Brown Eyed Handsome Man / No Particular Place To Go / My Ding-A-Ling *(live, single edit)*

Compared to the Trip album below, this is not a good compilation of Berry's Chess output. Only 10 songs compared to Trip's 16, and one of those strange titles that makes you wonder how they ever thought of it. This release originally came out with a red label, and later with a blue one. The sound quality is okay, and only 'My Ding-A-Ling' is in stereo. I'm just wondering about one thing. The liner notes tell us that Chuck Berry was the first artist elected to the Rock & Roll Hall Of Fame on national television. In 1978? How did they know back in 1978, when it happened in 1986... or am I missing something here?

CHUCK BERRY'S 16 GREATEST HITS
Trip [Springboard] TOP16-55 ● 1978
Maybellene / Roll Over Beethoven / Sweet Little Sixteen / School Day / Reelin' And Rockin'
[Around And Around] / Back In The USA / Too Pooped To Pop+ / Almost Grown / My Ding-A-Ling*
(live, single edit) / Johnny B. Goode / Rock And Roll Music / No Particular Place To Go* / Nadine* /
Sweet Little Rock And Roller / Carol / You Never Can Tell*

This is a good selection of Berry's best from the Chess files. The cover and label
both say 'Reelin' And Rockin' ', but the track is actually 'Around And Around'. Anyway,
if they had included 'Promised Land' instead of that one, and added the live version of
'Reelin' And Rockin' ' from 1972, that really *would* have made this album his
GREATEST HITS. Tracks marked * are in original stereo. However, the sound quality
on the old mono cuts is poor due to electronic stereo reprocessing – it helps if you
push the 'mono' button.

LIVE IN CONCERT [2-LP]
Magnum MR-703 ● 1978
❶ Rock And Roll Music / Nadine / Hail, Hail, Rock And Roll [School Day] / In The Wee Wee
Hours [Wee Wee Hours] / Medley: Johnny B. Goode – Oh Carol [Carol] – Promised Land / Blues
Tune [Hoochie Coochie Man+] / Sweet Little Sixteen
❷ Memphis [Memphis, Tennessee] / Too Much Monkey Business / My Ding-A-Ling / Reelin',
Rollin' And Rockin' [Reelin' And Rockin'] / Johnny B. Goode / Maybellene

Recorded live at the *Toronto Rock & Roll Revival* concert at Varsity Stadium on
13 September 1969. Berry is backed by an awful band who don't have a clue how to
play rock'n'roll. The cover is kind-of psychedelic, but there's no photograph of Berry –
just a small drawing of his head on the front, where he looks like the Devil himself!
Some of the titles are incorrectly listed (the correct titles are shown in square
brackets). Unfortunately, this unexceptional concert (or parts of it) has been included
on dozens of album releases since 1978, and it's not particularly good testimony to
Chuck Berry or his music. (However, it is interesting to note that Berry was already
featuring 'My Ding-A-Ling' in his act as far back as 1969. Later on, when Polygram
reissued LIVE AT THE FILLMORE in 1989 with extra tracks, we discovered that the
song had already been in his repertoire as far back as 1967!)

ROCKIT
Atco [Atlantic] SD-38.118 ● August 1979
Move It / Oh What A Thrill / I Need You Baby / If I Were / House Lights / I Never Thought / Havana Moon / Wuden't Me / California / Pass Away *(poem)*

Berry signed with Atco in November 1978 and recorded this album at Berry Park Studio, Wentzville, Missouri on 14-15 February 1979. He produced, arranged, recorded and mixed it, wrote all the songs and played all the guitar parts. His backing band consisted of Johnnie Johnson on piano, Jim Marsala and Bob Wray on bass and Kenneth Buttrey on drums

Apart from 'Oh What A Thrill', this is not a well-produced album. 'California' is okay, but Berry stole the melody from Sir Douglas Quintet's 'Mendicino' and merely added new lyrics. 'Pass Away' is great, but not something you'd want to listen to too often.

Promo copies came with a 'Promo Timing Strip' on the front cover, and as far as I know, is the only Berry promo album to appear like this. No white label, but *'Promotional Copy – Not For Sale'* was stamped on the top right corner of the front cover. Reissued in 1998 on CD (with poor sound quality) [Atlantic 7567-80759-2].

This was actually Berry's very last studio album. There have been rumours for years that another album would come out, but so far nothing has happened – and now he's running out of time.

His studio and nightclub at Berry Park were destroyed by fire starting in the early hours of the morning of Saturday, 25 March 1989 and, according to Berry himself, the fire destroyed a priceless master tape with 13 numbers he had recorded off and on over the past seven years. What about all the other stuff recorded at Berry Park since the mid-'60s? Was that destroyed too? And Berry also recorded many tracks in connection with the CONCERTO IN B GOODE sessions which were not issued.

In a more recent interview (autumn 2000) Berry stated that there would be a new album coming out in connection with his 75th birthday (18 October 2001). In autumn 2006, another statement claimed that there would be a new album out in the early part of 2007. Don't you lie to me!

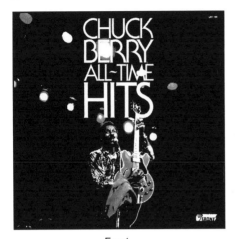 

Front   Back

ALL-TIME HITS
Up Front [Springboard] UPF-199 ● 1979
Maybellene / Roll Over Beethoven / Sweet Little Sixteen / School Day / Back In The USA / My Ding-A-Ling *(live, single edit)* / Johnny B. Goode / Rock And Roll Music / No Particular Place To Go

Budget label Springboard reduced the list to just nine Chess tracks! However, the cover features two great pictures of Berry that are worth the price of the album alone. 'My Ding-A-Ling' and 'No Particular Place To Go' are in true stereo. The rest are electronically reprocessed.

ALIVE AND ROCKIN'
Stack-O-Hits AG-9019 ● 1981
Rock And Roll Music *(demo)* / Maybellene *(live, 1956 Alan Freed radio show)* / Roll Over Beethoven *(live, 1956 Alan Freed radio show)* / How High The Moon+ *(instr)* / Vacation Time [21] / Chuck's Jam [One O'Clock Jump+] *(instr)* / Reelin' And Rockin' *(demo)* / Sweet Little Sixteen *(alt. take)* / Childhood Sweetheart *(alt. take)* / I've Changed

It's very sad that these songs saw their first official release in the US on a sloppy album like this. 'Maybellene' and 'Roll Over Beethoven' are live recordings from a 1956 Alan Freed radio show (see the 1978 Various Artists bootleg LP, ROCK'N'ROLL RADIO [Radiola MR-1087] for more information). The rest of the tracks are unreleased songs, alt. takes and demos from the Chess files overdubbed with audience noise. For the best LP release of these Chess recordings (without audience), see the 1983 UK LP, CHESS MASTERS: AMERICA'S HOTTEST WAX [Chess CXMP-2011].

It would appear that Stack-O-Hits dubbed the above songs from the AMERICA'S HOTTEST WAX bootleg [Reelin' 001], released in 1980, while the two live radio tracks from 1956 were most likely lifted from the Radiola bootleg. However, Stack-O-Hits was not a bootleg label, as far as I know.

CHUCK BERRY LIVE (VOLUME 1)
SSS International [Magnum] SSS-36 • 1981
Rock And Roll Music / Nadine / Hail, Hail, Rock & Roll [School Day] / In The Wee Wee Hours [Wee Wee Hours] / *Medley:* Johnny B. Goode – Oh Carol [Carol] - Promised Land / Blues Tune [Hoochie Coochie Man+] / Sweet Little Sixteen

The 1969 *Toronto Rock & Roll Revival* again. Same songs as the first disc of the 1978 2-LP, LIVE IN CONCERT [Magnum MR-703]. The sound quality is not good, and, as you can see, some of the songs are mistitled. VOLUME 2 in this series never appeared, however see the two Accord LPs below. (SSS International was one of the Shelby Singleton Corporation's labels out of Nashville, Tennessee. They also had the rights to all of the original material from Sun Records.)

Volume II   Volume III

TORONTO ROCK'N'ROLL REVIVAL 1969, VOLUME II
Accord SN-7171 • March 1982
Reelin' And Rockin' / Maybellene / Too Much Monkey Business / My Ding-A-Ling / Memphis, Tennessee

The 1969 *Toronto Rock & Roll Revival* again. This volume contains most of the tracks (except 'Johnny B. Goode') off the second disc of the 1978 2-LP, LIVE IN CONCERT [Magnum MR 703].

TORONTO ROCK'N'ROLL REVIVAL 1969, VOLUME III
Accord SN-7172 • March 1982
Rock And Roll Music / Nadine / School Day / In The Wee Wee Hours [Wee Wee Hours] / Johnny B. Goode [*Medley:* Johnny B. Goode – Carol – Promised Land] / Blues [Hoochie Coochie Man+] / Sweet Little Sixteen

The 1969 *Toronto Rock & Roll Revival* again. This volume contains exactly the same songs as the first disc of the 1978 2-LP, LIVE IN CONCERT [Magnum MR-703] and the 1981 LP, CHUCK BERRY LIVE (VOLUME 1) [SSS International SSS-36].

THE GREAT 28 [2-LP]
Chess [Sugar Hill] CH-8201 ● September 1982
❶ Maybellene / Thirty Days / You Can't Catch Me / Too Much Monkey Business / Brown Eyed Handsome Man / Roll Over Beethoven / Havana Moon / School Day / Rock And Roll Music / Oh Baby Doll / Reelin' And Rockin' / Sweet Little Sixteen / Johnny B. Goode / Around And Around
❷ Carol / Beautiful Delilah / Memphis Tennessee / Sweet Little Rock And Roller / Little Queenie / Almost Grown / Back In The USA / Let It Rock / Bye Bye Johnny / I'm Talking About You / Come On / Nadine / No Particular Place To Go / I Want To Be Your Driver

These 28 songs are arranged in the order they were recorded and mastered from the original session tapes. To quote from the cover: *'Chuck Berry records are power-packed plastic, intense sonic creations that sparkle and cut with the brilliance of diamonds. These twenty-eight are vital documents of the history they made. The territory Chuck Berry opened up is where pop music lives today.'*

The sound quality is *wonderful* – no electronic stereo here! The album has a gatefold cover with liner notes and recording information for each song, but don't rely too much on it. The discography in Fred Rothwell's *Long Distance Information* is far more accurate and as close to the truth as you'll ever get.

I have also seen this 2-LP set as a white label promo. It was reissued on vinyl in 1984 [Chess CH2-92500] and on vinyl and CD in 1986 [Chess CH2-/CHD-92500].

CHUCK BERRY
Phoenix 10 [Audio Fidelity] PHX-351 ● 1982
Introduction / In The Wee, Wee Hours [Wee Wee Hours] / *Medley:* Johnny B. Goode – Carol – Promised Land / Hoochie Coochie Man+ / Sweet Little Sixteen / Memphis [Memphis, Tennessee] / Hail, Hail, Rock'n'Roll [School Day]

The 1969 *Toronto Rock & Roll Revival* again. Unusually, this has very good sound quality and sort-of stereo. Actually, it's the best sound I have ever heard from this concert, and the songs are not faded out. It sounds like it may have been dubbed directly from the movie soundtrack. Pity they didn't include more selections.

CHUCK BERRY [picture disc]
Phoenix [Audio Fidelity] PD-351 ● 1982
This is a picture disc of the above Phoenix 10 album with the same songs. It has a colour picture of Berry's face (mid-'50s) on both sides – actually the same as the front cover of Phoenix PHX-351.

HAIL, HAIL, ROCK AND ROLL
Jay & Cee TLA-50143 ● 1982
Memphis, Tennessee / My Ding-A-Ling / Reelin' And Rockin' / Rock And Roll Music / Johnny B. Goode / Maybellene / Nadine / Too Much Monkey Business / Wee Wee Hours / Hail Hail Rock And Roll [School Day]

The 1969 *Toronto Rock & Roll Revival* again. 1982 was a big year for the festival, record-wise – unfortunately in my view, as it does not show Berry's best side, musically speaking. The sound is poor and the band far from rock'n'roll. The cover has a colour drawing of Berry.

REELIN' AND ROCKIN' !
Aura [Stack-O-Hits] A-1020 ● 1982
Reelin' And Rockin' / School Day / My Ding-A-Ling / Too Much Monkey Business / Memphis [Memphis, Tennessee] / Maybellene / Nadine

The 1969 *Toronto Rock & Roll Revival* again. The label says *'Stereo'*, but it's straight-ahead mono.

It was rumoured in the spring of 1982 that Berry had a double album ready for release which would contain one side of rock'n'roll, one side of blues, one side of country music and one side featuring his daughter, Ingrid. I remember hearing this too, but nothing happened. We will probably never know what became of the songs, but it sounded like an interesting concept.

20 HITS
Phoenix 20 [Audio Fidelity] P20-630 ● 1983
Introduction / In The Wee Wee Hours / Johnny B. Goode (Part I) / Johnny B. Goode (Part II) / Carol / Hootchie, Kootchie Man+ / Memphis (Version I) / Hail, Hail Rock'n'Roll / Blues+ / Rock'n'Roll Music / Nadine / School Days / Memphis (Version II) / Reelin' And Rockin' (Part I) /

Reelin' And Rockin' (Part II) / Maybelline / Too Much Monkey Business / My Ding-A-Ling (Part I) / My Ding-A-Ling (Part II)

Now, this is just *too* much crap! The songs are listed exactly as printed both on the cover and the label. It looks interesting, however it's just the 1969 *Toronto Rock & Roll Revival* yet again. The repackager mixed it all around and split several songs into 'Part I' and 'Part II' to create the illusion that there are 20 cuts here. 'Blues' is 'Hoochie Coochie Man' repeated for a second time, but mixed down to 1:50, utilizing only the beginning and ending of the song; Berry's guitar solo on 'School Day' is omitted; and, of course, 'Hail, Hail, Rock'n'Roll' is just 'School Day' again, but remixed a little to make it sound different. 'My Ding-A-Ling' is shortened to 5:18 from the original, which is over nine minutes long. And so on! It couldn't get any worse.

Chuck Berry & Bo Diddley
TWO GREAT GUITARS
Chess [MCA] CH-9170 • July 1984
Reissue. Identical to the 1964 (stereo) LP [Checker LPS-2991].

NEW JUKE BOX HITS
Chess [MCA] CH-9171 • July 1984
Reissue. Identical to the 1961 LP [Chess LP-1456]. Reissued in 1988 on CD [Chess CHD-9171].

ST. LOUIS TO LIVERPOOL
Chess [MCA] CH-9186 • December 1984
Reissue. Identical to the (stereo) 1964 LP [Chess LPS-1488]. Reissued in 1988 on CD [Chess CHD-31261].

BIO
Chess [MCA] CH-91510 • December 1984
Reissue. Identical to the 1973 LP [Chess CH-50043], except no gatefold cover and the sleeve is green.

THE GREAT 28 [2-LP]
Chess [MCA] CH2-92500 • December 1984
Reissue. Identical to the 1982 Sugar Hill release [Chess CH-8201]. The album has the catalogue number '2CH-9190' printed on the back cover and edge.

ROCK AND ROLL MUSIC [2-LP]
Pair [Polygram] PDL2-1134 • 1985
❶ *Medley:* Rockin' At The Fillmore – Everyday I Have The Blues+ *(live)* / C.C. Rider+ *(live)* / Johnny B. Goode / Club Nitty Gritty / School Day / Memphis, Tennessee / Maybellene / Sweet Little Sixteen
❷ Roll Over Beethoven / Rock And Roll Music / Carol / Thirty Days / Back In The USA / Ramblin' Rose+ / It Hurts Me Too+ / Good Lookin' Woman

Mercury recordings. Two discs packaged in a single cover. The *Medley* and 'C.C. Rider' are from the 1967 2-LP, LIVE AT THE FILLMORE AUDITORIUM [Mercury SR-61138].

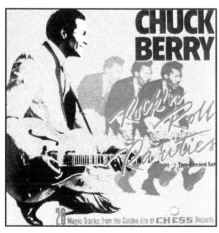

Front   Back

ROCK'N'ROLL RARITIES [2-LP]
Chess [MCA] CH2-92521 • March 1986
❶ No Particular Place To Go *(stereo remix)* / Rock And Roll Music *(prev. unissued)* / It Wasn't Me *(stereo, prev. unissued)* / Reelin' And Rockin' *(original demo)* / Come On *(stereo)* / Johnny B. Goode *(prev. unreleased)* / Bye Bye Johnny *(stereo remix)* / Little Marie *(stereo remix)* / Time Was+ *(prev. unissued)* / Promised Land *(stereo remix)*
❷ Little Queenie *(prev. unissued)* / You Never Can Tell *(stereo remix)* / Sweet Little Sixteen *(prev. unissued)* / County Line / Run Rudolph Run+ / Nadine *(stereo remix)* / Betty Jean / I Want To Be Your Driver *(stereo remix)* / Beautiful Delilah *(prev. unissued)* / Oh Yeah

Subtitled *'20 Magic Tracks From The Golden Era Of Chess Records'*. I remember when this album came out. What a feast it was! Although I didn't care much for the stereo remixes, it was a treat to hear 'Bye Bye Johnny' in true stereo for the first time! It almost became a completely new song. The sound quality on this release was tremendously good too. 'It Wasn't Me' appears without the overdubs by Paul Butterfield and Mike Bloomfield. 'Come On' is said to be *'previously unreleased'* – which is true for the US, though this alternative version had been available in stereo form in the UK since 1965, when it was included on the LP YOU NEVER CAN TELL [Marble Arch MALS-702]. See UK discography for more information.

The 'problem' with some of the titles on this album is that one is so familiar with the original releases and has heard them so many times that they simply can't compete. However, this was the very first time that we finally heard alternate takes of well known Berry classics. If you get the promo issue of this, be sure that the bio insert and the glossy black and white picture of the cover are included. There is no white or silver promo label as far as I know, just *'For promotion only'* stamped on the cover. The two discs came packaged in a single cover. Also issued on CD [Chess CHD-92521].

MORE ROCK'N'ROLL RARITIES
Chess [MCA] CH-9190 ● August 1986
Ain't That Just Like A Woman+ *(stereo remix)* / Rock And Roll Music *(original demo)* / Down The Road A Piece+ *(stereo remix)* / Brown Eyed Handsome Man *(alt. version, stereo remix)* / Route 66+ *(prev. unissued)* / Sweet Little Rock And Roller *(prev. unissued)* / My Mustang Ford *(stereo remix)* / Sweet Little Sixteen *(original demo)* / I Got To Find My Baby+ *(stereo)* / I'm Talking About You *(stereo)* / House Of Blue Lights+ / Go, Go, Go *(stereo)*

Subtitled *'From The Golden Era Of Chess Records'*, this is another great album for Berry freaks. All those stereo remixes don't sound so different from the original releases, however 'Down The Road A Piece' (appearing for the first time in stereo) is a masterpiece – with Berry's guitar in the right channel and guitar ace Matt Murphy in the left one, and it's also a little longer than the original release. 'I Got To Find My Baby', 'I'm Talking About You' and 'Go, Go, Go' are also here in stereo for the very first time. 'Go, Go, Go' is called 'Go, Go, Go (Johnny B. Goode)' on this album, and this title later also appeared like this in the Collectables single series. 'Brown Eyed Handsome Man' is the version that was used on the 1963 ON STAGE LP [Chess LP-1480], but without the overdubbed audience. Also issued on CD [Chess CHD-9190].

Berry plays Nice, 19 July 1987.

THE GREAT 28 [2-LP]
Chess [MCA] CH2-92500 • 1986
    Reissue. Identical to the 1984 2-LP [Chess CH2-92500], except for some new liner notes and a different cover design. According to MCA, THE GREAT 28 *'has justifiably become one of the most significant and best-selling reissues of its time'*. Also issued on CD [Chess CHD-92500].

BERRY IS ON TOP
Chess [MCA] CH-9256 • June 1987
    Reissue of the 1959 LP [Chess LP-1435] with additional liner notes and recording information. However, stick with Fred Rothwell's *Long Distance Information*. Also issued on CD [Chess CHD-31260].

ROCKIN' AT THE HOPS
Chess [MCA] CH-9259 • June 1987
    Reissue of the 1960 LP [Chess LP-1448] with additional liner notes and recording information. However, stick with Fred Rothwell's *Long Distance Information*. And how could Bob Schnieders write in 1987, as Don Kamerer had done on previously on CH-9256 above, that Berry was born on 15 February in San Jose, California? Accuracy is quite difficult, it seems. 18 October 1926 in St. Louis, Missouri is, of course, correct. Also issued on CD [Chess CHD-9259].

    As far back as 1982, Berry said that he had a new double album ready for release. It didn't happen. Swedish fan Johan Hasselberg talked to him four years later, and Berry said that he had a double album in progress with 14 new tracks. He added that it would be out in May or June 1987 on MCA Records. It didn't happen. Norwegian deejay Rune Halland interviewed Berry in Oslo on 1 July 1987. Again Berry mentioned that a new double album was due. This time, he said it would contain twenty-four tracks(!) – twenty of them new songs. It didn't happen.
    The following album on MCA *was* 'new', albeit not the way Berry had talked about. Only one song was completely new, but it was not written by him and it was far from being rock'n'roll or blues.

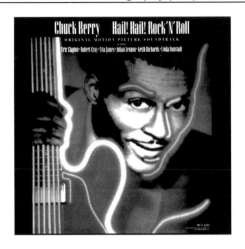

HAIL! HAIL! ROCK'N'ROLL
MCA MCA-6217 ● 1987
Maybellene / Around And Around / Sweet Little Sixteen / Brown Eyed Handsome Man *(with Robert Cray)* / Memphis, Tennessee / Too Much Monkey Business / Back In The USA *(with Linda Ronstadt)* / Wee Wee Hours *(with Eric Clapton)* / Johnny B. Goode *(with Julian Lennon)* / Little Queenie / Rock And Roll Music *(with Etta James)* / Roll Over Beethoven / I'm Thru' With Love**+**

Original soundtrack. This was actually supposed to be a double-album but it didn't happen. It was Keith Richards' final tribute to his hero. I say 'final' because I don't think Keith will ever try to do anything like it again. Berry is a tough guy to handle, and he really found that out after working with Berry for several weeks to capture the excitement of a Berry concert. Nevertheless, the movie became a big success and both Taylor Hackford who produced it, and Richards, who produced, arranged and picked the musicians for the two concerts at the Fox Theatre in St. Louis on 16 October 1986, two days before Berry's 60th birthday, can really be proud of the hard work and the final result. Thanks to Keith's efforts, Johnnie Johnson finally got the recognition he deserved too.

More songs were shown in the movie than appear on the album. Conversely, 'Around And Around' is not featured in the film but is included on the album. 'I'm Through With Love' was recorded during rehearsals at the Berry Park Studio. See *Section 7 (Chuck Berry in the Movies)* for more information. Also issued on CD [MCA MCAD-6217].

ROCK 'TILL YOU DROP – HIS GREATEST HITS [2-LP]
Silver Eagle [MCA] MSM-35099 ● 1987
❶ Maybellene / Roll Over Beethoven / School Day / Rock And Roll Music / Back In The USA / Around And Around / Johnny B. Goode / Memphis, Tennessee / Sweet Little Rock And Roller / Almost Grown / Little Queenie / Brown Eyed Handsome Man
❷ Sweet Little Sixteen / Let It Rock / Too Pooped To Pop**+** / Nadine / No Particular Place To Go / You Never Can Tell *(stereo)* / Carol / Little Marie *(stereo)* / My Ding-A-Ling *(live, single edit)* / Reelin' And Rockin'

Nothing special here, except that 'Little Marie' is not a track usually found on Chuck Berry 'greatest hits' albums. The two discs are packaged in a single cover with a couple of black and white photos on the back that are not included on the respective CD version [Silver Eagle SE-10592].

THE CHESS BOX [6-LP]
Chess [MCA] CH6-80.001 ● November 1988
❶ Maybellene / Wee Wee Hours / Thirty Days / You Can't Catch Me / No Money Down / Downbound Train / Brown Eyed Handsome Man / Drifting Heart / Roll Over Beethoven / Too Much Monkey Business / Havana Moon / School Day
❷ Rock And Roll Music / Oh Baby Doll / I've Changed *(prev. unissued in the USA)* / Reelin' And Rockin' / Rock At The Philharmonic *(instr)* / Sweet Little Sixteen *(original speed)* / Johnny B. Goode / Time Was+ *(prev. unissued slow version)* / Around And Around / Beautiful Delilah / House Of Blue Lights+ / Carol
❸ Memphis, Tennessee / Anthony Boy / Jo Jo Gunne / Sweet Little Rock And Roller / Merry Christmas Baby+ *(single version)* / Run Rudolph Run+ / Little Queenie / Almost Grown / Back In The USA / Betty Jean / Childhood Sweetheart / Let It Rock / Too Pooped To Pop+
❹ Bye Bye Johnny / Jaguar And The Thunderbird / Down The Road A Piece+ / Confessin' The Blues+ / Thirteen Question Method / Crying Steel *(prev. unissued instr)* / I'm Just A Lucky So And So+ *(prev. unissued)* / I'm Talking About You / Come On / Nadine *(stereo remix)* / Lonely All The Time [Crazy Arms]+ *(stereo, prev. unissued in the USA)* / You Never Can Tell / The Things I Used To Do+ / Promised Land
❺ No Particular Place To Go / Liverpool Drive *(instr)* / You Two / Chuck's Beat *(instr with Bo Diddley)* / Little Marie / Dear Dad / Sad Day, Long Night *(stereo instr, prev. unissued in the USA)* / It's My Own Business / It Wasn't Me / Ramona Say Yes *(prev. unissued stereo version)* / Viva, Viva Rock & Roll
❻ Tulane / Have Mercy Judge / My Dream *(poem)* / Reelin' And Rockin' *(live, album version)* / My Ding-A-Ling *(live, single edit)* / Johnny B. Goode *(live)* / A Deuce / Woodpecker *(instr)* / Bio

The songs are sequenced in the order they were recorded, session by session. It's an interesting concept and this set received an award. Looking at the titles, we've only got one new song: 'I'm Just A Lucky So And So', a pleasant, laidback blues written by Duke Ellington, with some excellent guitar-work from Berry.

It was nice to finally get 'Lonely All The Time' ['Crazy Arms'] in stereo. The song was first released in Europe (UK and the Netherlands) in 1964 on the LATEST AND THE GREATEST LP. The pedal steel instrumental, 'Crying Steel', finally shook off the overdubbed audience from the 1963 ON STAGE album [Chess LP-1480], where it was titled 'Surfin' Steel'. Billy Davis' 'Too Pooped To Pop' is credited to Berry here. 'Bye Bye Johnny' and 'Down The Road A Piece' are in mono, and the latter is faded out, as on ROCKIN' AT THE HOPS [Chess LP-1488]. 'Come On' and 'I'm Talking About You' are the mono single versions. From 'Nadine' onwards, everything is in true stereo. 'Chuck's Beat' is the complete ten-and-a-half minute take. Unfortunately, for some strange reason, 'Ramona Say Yes' appears stripped of the saxophone – the little 'extra' that made the song special. So, you will still have to get the single for comparison. 'Sad Day, Long Night' is also good to have in glorious stereo, as this was

93

previously only available in mono on European versions of FRESH BERRYS (a substitution for 'Welcome Back Pretty Baby', which was on the US release). They are actually the same song, except the US version features Berry on vocals, while the other is an instrumental.

The sound quality on this set is superb all the way through – better than on anything released previously. The cover and layout are nothing to write home about however, although there are some good pictures included in the accompanying booklet, which also contains an interview with Berry, a 'complete' illustrated Chess album discography (although they missed out ROCK, ROCK, ROCK) and a session discography). However, I recommend you stick with the one in Fred Rothwell's *Long Distance Information*. I have not seen any white promo labels for this releases, but I have a box with a sticker saying *'Sample copy'*. Also issued as a 3-CD set [Chess CHD3-80.001].

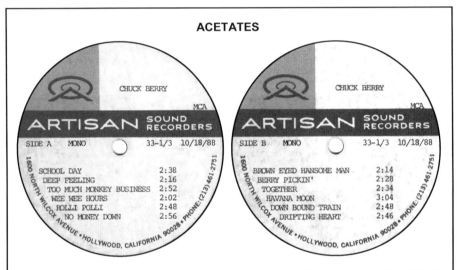

ACETATES

Pair of metal single-sided 12" acetates of the MCA reissue LP, AFTER SCHOOL SESSION [Chess CH-9284], dated 18 October 1988. Made by Artisan Sound Recorders, 1600 North Wilcox Avenue, Hollywood, California 90028. I have seen 45 rpm acetates by Berry from 1955 onwards, but I had never seen any 12" ones until I bought these in June 2004. Interesting!

AFTER SCHOOL SESSION
Chess [MCA] CH-9284 • January 1989
Reissue of the 1957 LP [Chess LP-1426] with additional liner notes and recording information. This time they *almost* got Berry's birth details correct: 19 October (it should have been 18th) 1926 in St. Louis, Missouri. I fully understand why so many people today still don't trust what's written about his birth date(s) and place(s)! Also issued on CD [Chess CHD-9284].

THE LONDON CHUCK BERRY SESSIONS
Chess [MCA] CH-9295 • June 1989
Reissue of the 1972 LP [Chess CH-60020], but no gatefold cover. Includes recording information and new liner notes by Andy McKaie. Also issued on CD [Chess CHD-9295].

Berry and the New Jordal Swingers at the Rockefeller, Oslo, Norway on 5 July 1989.

GOLDEN HITS
Mercury 826-256-1 • 1989
Reissue of 1967 LP [Mercury SR-61103]. This was also issued on CD [Mercury 826-256-2] with four bonus cuts.

MISSING BERRIES – RARITIES (VOLUME 3)
Chess [MCA] CH-9318 • 1990
Childhood Sweetheart *(alt. take)* / Do You Love Me *(alt. take)* / Big Ben Blues / Man And The Donkey *(stereo)* / One O'Clock Jump+ *(instr)* / The Little Girl From Central *(stereo)* / Untitled Instrumental *(instr)* / Let Me Sleep Woman+ *(Ecuadors)* / Vacation Time / 21 Blues

This album also has some great tracks from the Chess archives. 'Big Ben Blues' is the same as 'Big Ben' which appeared in mono on the 1964 UK LP, YOU NEVER CAN TELL [Pye International NPL-28039] and the 1967 reissue [Marble Arch MAL-702 *(mono)* MALS-702 *(stereo)*]. Ditto 'The Little Girl From Central'. 'Man And The Donkey' appears minus the overdubbed audience from the 1963 ON STAGE LP [Chess LP-1480]. 'Vacation Time' (the rare 'B' side of 'Beautiful Delilah' [Chess 1697]) appear on album in the US for the first time. '21 Blues' turns out to be a great rocker, and one can only wonder why it took so long to release it. Dig that beat and the perfect Berry guitar! Also issued on CD [Chess CHD-9318] with two bonus cuts: 'That's My Desire' and 'Blue On Blue' *(instr)*.

CDs

I remember buying my first Berry CD in 1983. It was from West Germany: a compilation of Chess tracks in electronic stereo (although I didn't find that out until six years later when I got my first CD player!). I think I had acquired about 40 Berry CDs by then, and my main reason for getting a CD player was the reissue in late 1989 of the original Mercury albums with additional, previously unreleased songs.

Many people have complained about US CDs containing fewer tracks than the ones released in Europe. There is an easy explanation for this: it is a matter of cost. In the USA, they pay for publishing by the title; in Europe the rates are based on a percentage of the list price. That's why US midline or budget titles carry fewer tracks than frontline (ie full price) releases.

However, unlike the vinyl albums, most CDs will never be collectors' items. The exceptions will be those few CDs which contain material that is unavailable elsewhere. On many CDs you will have problems finding out when and where tracks were originally released. I had originally intended to include all of Berry's CD releases in this section but came to the conclusion that it would have been too repetitive. Frankly, most of the CDs are also rather dull in presentation, with uninspiring covers, and often you don't know what you're buying until you put it in your player. They can contain Chess recordings, or the Mercury ones, or – even worse – live cuts from the 1969 *Toronto Rock & Roll Revival*. If you're 'lucky', you might end up with a CD containing a mixture of two or more of the above on one disc!

Anyway, let's start off the survey with a couple of interesting US three-inch CD singles (which MCA termed 'mini-albums').

All cuts are Chess material unless otherwise noted.

3" CD Singles

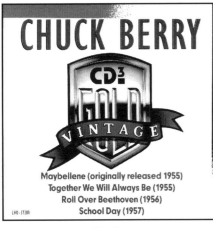

Front

Back

VINTAGE GOLD – CHUCK BERRY
Chess [MCA] CHD-37280 ● 1988
Maybellene / Together (We Will Always Be) / Roll Over Beethoven / School Day

Packaged in a clear plastic longbox. Great little picture of Berry on the back of the cover, probably from 1964.

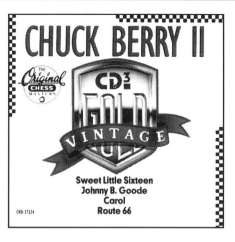

VINTAGE GOLD – CHUCK BERRY II
Chess [MCA] CHD-37324 • 1989
Sweet Little Sixteen / Johnny B. Goode / Carol / Route 66+

Packaged in a clear plastic longbox.

CD Albums

ROCK'N'ROLL RARITIES
Chess [MCA] CHD-92521 • March 1986
No Particular Place To Go *(stereo remix)* / Rock And Roll Music *(prev. unissued)* / It Wasn't Me *(stereo, prev. unissued)* / Reelin' And Rockin' *(original demo)* / Come On *(stereo)* / Johnny B. Goode *(prev. unissued)* / Bye Bye Johnny *(stereo remix)* / Little Marie *(stereo remix)* / Time Was+ *(prev. unissued)* / Promised land *(stereo remix)* / Little Queenie *(prev. unissued)* / You Never Can Tell *(stereo remix)* / Sweet Little Sixteen *(prev. unissued)* / County Line / Run Rudolph Run+ / Nadine *(stereo remix)* / Betty Jean / I Want To Be Your Driver *(stereo remix)* / Beautiful Delilah *(prev. unissued)* / Oh Yeah

Subtitled *'20 Magic Tracks From The Golden Era Of Chess Records'*. I remember when this album came out. What a feast it was! Although I didn't care much for the stereo remixes, it was a treat to hear 'Bye Bye Johnny' in true stereo for the first time! It almost became a completely new song. The sound quality on this release was tremendously good too. 'It Wasn't Me' appears without the overdubs by Paul Butterfield and Mike Bloomfield. 'Come On' is said to be *'previously unreleased'* – which is true for the US, though this alternative version had been available in stereo form in the UK since 1965, when it was included on the LP YOU NEVER CAN TELL [Marble Arch MALS-702]. See UK discography for more information.

The 'problem' with some of the titles on this album is that one is so familiar with the original releases and has heard them so many times that they simply can't compete. However, this was the very first time that we finally heard alternate takes of well known Berry classics. Also issued on 2-LP [Chess CH2-92521].

MORE ROCK'N'ROLL RARITIES
Chess [MCA] CHD-9190 ● August 1986
Ain't That Just Like A Woman+ *(stereo remix)* / Rock And Roll Music *(original demo)* / Down The Road A Piece+ *(stereo remix)* / Brown Eyed Handsome Man *(alt. version, stereo remix)* / Route 66+ *(prev. unissued)* / Sweet Little Rock And Roller *(prev. unissued)* / My Mustang Ford *(stereo remix)* / Sweet Little Sixteen *(original demo)* / I Got To Find My Baby+ *(stereo)* / I'm Talking About You *(stereo)* / House Of Blue Lights+ / Go, Go, Go *(stereo)*

Subtitled *'From The Golden Era Of Chess Records'*, this is another great album for Berry freaks. All those stereo remixes don't sound so different from the original releases, however 'Down The Road A Piece' (appearing for the first time in stereo) is a masterpiece – with Berry's guitar in the right channel and guitar ace Matt Murphy in the left one, and it's also a little longer than the original release. 'I Got To Find My Baby', 'I'm Talking About You' and 'Go, Go, Go' are also here in stereo for the very first time. 'Go, Go, Go' is called 'Go, Go, Go (Johnny B. Goode)' on this album, and this title later also appeared like this in the Collectables single series. 'Brown Eyed Handsome Man' is the version that was used on the 1963 ON STAGE LP [Chess LP-1480], but without the overdubbed audience. Also issued on LP [Chess CH-9190].

THE GREAT 28
Chess [MCA] CHD-92500 ● 1986
Same tracks as the 1982 2-LP [Chess CH-8201] and the 1984 reissue [Chess CH2-92500], but with new liner notes and the cover design. According to MCA, THE GREAT 28 *'has justifiably become one of the most significant and best-selling reissues of its time'*.

At this time, MCA packaged CDs in longboxes in the USA – something record companies did in the early days of the format, so that the CDs could be displayed in LP racks. If you can find an original US release in a longbox you will certainly have to pay a little extra, because most of these are gone now. They finally stopped this waste around 1990.

BERRY IS ON TOP
Chess [MCA] CHD-31260 ● February 1987
Reissue of the 1959 LP [Chess LP-1435] with additional liner notes and recording information. However, stick with Fred Rothwell's *Long Distance Information*. Also issued on LP [Chess CH-9256].

ROCKIN' AT THE HOPS
Chess [MCA] CHD-9259 ● May 1987
Reissue of the 1960 LP [Chess LP-1448] with additional liner notes and recording information. However, stick with Fred Rothwell's *Long Distance Information*. And how could Bob Schneiders write in 1987, as Don Kamerer had done on previously on CHD-31260 above, that Berry was born on 15 February in San Jose, California? Accuracy is quite difficult, it seems. 18 October 1926 in St. Louis, Missouri is, of course, correct. Also issued on LP [Chess CH-9259].

THE BEST OF THE BEST OF CHUCK BERRY
Hollywood HCD-100 ● 1987
This CD is the same as the 1978 LP, Gusto GT-0004 with the same cover. Originally packaged in a longbox.

HAIL! HAIL! ROCK'N'ROLL
MCA MCAD-6217 ● 1987
Maybellene / Around And Around / Sweet Little Sixteen / Brown Eyed Handsome Man *(with Robert Cray)* / Memphis, Tennessee / Too Much Monkey Business / Back In The USA *(with Linda Ronstadt)* / Wee Wee Hours *(with Eric Clapton)* / Johnny B. Goode *(with Julian Lennon)* / Little Queenie / Rock And Roll Music *(with Etta James)* / Roll Over Beethoven / I'm Through With Love+

Original soundtrack. This was actually supposed to be a double-album but it didn't happen. It was Keith Richards' final tribute to his hero. I say 'final' because I don't think Keith will ever try to do anything like it again. Berry is a tough guy to handle, and he really found that out after working with Berry for several weeks to capture the excitement of a Berry concert. Nevertheless, the movie became a big success and both Taylor Hackford who produced it, and Richards, who produced, arranged and picked the musicians for the two concerts at the Fox Theatre in St. Louis on 16 October 1986, two days before Berry's 60th birthday, can really be proud of the hard work and the final result. Thanks to Keith's efforts, Johnnie Johnson finally got the recognition he deserved too.

More songs were shown in the movie than appear on the album. Conversely, 'Around And Around' is not featured in the film but is included on the album. 'I'm Through With Love' was recorded during rehearsals at the Berry Park Studio. See *Section 7 (Chuck Berry in the Movies)* for more information. Also issued on LP [MCA MCA-6217].

ROCK 'TILL YOU DROP – HIS GREATEST HITS
Silver Eagle [MCA] SE-10592 ● 1987
Maybellene / Roll Over Beethoven / School Day / Rock And Roll Music / Back In The USA / Around And Around / Johnny B. Goode / Memphis, Tennessee / Sweet Little Rock And Roller / Almost Grown / Little Queenie / Brown Eyed Handsome Man / Sweet Little Sixteen / Let It Rock / Too Pooped To Pop+ / Nadine / No Particular Place To Go / You Never Can Tell *(stereo)* / Carol / Little Marie *(stereo)* / My Ding-A-Ling *(live, single edit)* / Reelin' And Rockin'

Nothing special here, except that 'Little Marie' is not a track usually found on Chuck Berry 'greatest hits' albums. Also issued on 2-LP [Silver Eagle MSM-35099].

ROLL OVER BEETHOVEN
Allegiance CDP-72912 ● 1987
Roll Over Beethoven / School Day / Too Pooped To Pop+ / My Ding-A-Ling *(live, single edit)* / Nadine / You Never Can Tell *(stereo)* / Sweet Little Sixteen / Almost Grown / Back In The USA / Reelin' And Rockin' / Maybellene / Sweet Little Rock And Roller / Johnny B. Goode / No Particular Place To Go / Rock And Roll Music / Carol / Thirty Days / Brown Eyed Handsome Man / Too Much Monkey Business / Promised Land *(stereo)*

According to the cover, the songs were digitally remixed and mastered at Dave Pell Digital by one Michael Boshears, but the sound quality is mostly poor. Original cover art (drawing) by Henry Neves. Art Director: Suzanne Katnik. Design: Nadre Davani. What a waste of time and space! None of these people deserved to get their names mentioned. I have never seen a vinyl album of this release.

ST. LOUIS TO LIVERPOOL
Chess [MCA] CHD-31261 ● February 1988
Reissue. Identical to the 1964 (stereo) LP [Chess LPS-1488]. Previously reissued in 1984 on LP [Chess CH-9186].

THE CHESS BOX [3-CD]
Chess [MCA] CHD3-80.001 ● November 1988

❶ Maybellene / Wee Wee Hours / Thirty Days / You Can't Catch Me / No Money Down / Downbound Train / Brown Eyed Handsome Man / Drifting Heart / Roll Over Beethoven / Too Much Monkey Business / Havana Moon / School Day / Rock And Roll Music / Oh Baby Doll / I've Changed *(prev. unissued in the USA)* / Reelin' And Rockin' / Rock At The Philharmonic *(instr)* / Sweet Little Sixteen *(original speed)* / Johnny B. Goode / Time Was+ *(prev. unissued slow version)* / Around And Around / Beautiful Delilah / House Of Blue Lights+ / Carol

❷ Memphis, Tennessee / Anthony Boy / Jo Jo Gunne / Sweet Little Rock And Roller / Merry Christmas Baby+ *(single version)* / Run Rudolph Run+ / Little Queenie / Almost Grown / Back In The USA / Betty Jean / Childhood Sweetheart / Let It Rock / Too Pooped To Pop+ / Bye Bye Johnny / Jaguar And The Thunderbird / Down The Road A Piece+ / Confessin' The Blues+ / Thirteen Question Method / Crying Steel *(prev. unissued instr)* / I'm Just A Lucky So And So+ *(prev. unissued)* / I'm Talking About You / Come On / Nadine *(stereo remix)* / Lonely All The Time [Crazy Arms]+ *(stereo, prev. unissued in the USA)* / You Never Can Tell / The Things I Used To Do+ / Promised Land

❸ No Particular Place To Go / Liverpool Drive *(instr)* / You Two / Chuck's Beat *(instr, with Bo Diddley)* / Little Marie / Dear Dad / Sad Day, Long Night *(stereo instr, prev. unissued in the USA)* / It's My Own Business / It Wasn't Me / Ramona Say Yes *(prev. unissued stereo version)* / Viva, Viva Rock & Roll / Tulane / Have Mercy Judge / My Dream *(poem)* / Reelin' And Rockin' *(live, album version)* / My Ding-A-Ling *(live, single edit)* / Johnny B. Goode *(live)* / A Deuce / Woodpecker *(instr)* / Bio

The songs are sequenced in the order they were recorded, session by session. It's an interesting concept and this set received an award. Looking at the titles, we've only got one new song: 'I'm Just A Lucky So And So', a pleasant, laidback blues written by Duke Ellington, with some excellent guitar-work from Berry.

It was nice to finally get 'Lonely All The Time' ['Crazy Arms'] in stereo. The song was first released in Europe (UK and the Netherlands) in 1964 on the LATEST AND THE GREATEST LP. The pedal steel instrumental, 'Crying Steel', finally shook off the overdubbed audience from the 1963 ON STAGE album [Chess LP-1480], where it was titled 'Surfin' Steel'. Billy Davis' 'Too Pooped To Pop' is credited to Berry here. 'Bye Bye Johnny' and 'Down The Road A Piece' are in mono, and the latter is faded out, as on ROCKIN' AT THE HOPS [Chess LP-1488]. 'Come On' and 'I'm Talking About You' are the mono single versions. From 'Nadine' onwards, everything is in true stereo. 'Chuck's Beat' is the complete ten-and-a-half minute take. Unfortunately, for some strange reason, 'Ramona Say Yes' appears stripped of the saxophone – the little 'extra' that made the song special. So, you will still have to get the single for comparison. 'Sad Day, Long Night' is also good to have in glorious stereo, as this was previously only available in mono on European versions of FRESH BERRYS (a substitution for 'Welcome Back Pretty Baby', which was on the US release). They are actually the same song, except the US version features Berry on vocals, while the other is an instrumental.

The sound quality on this set is superb all the way through – better than on anything released previously. The cover and layout are nothing to write home about however, although there are some good pictures included in the accompanying booklet, which also contains an interview with Berry, a 'complete' illustrated Chess album discography (although they missed out ROCK, ROCK, ROCK) and a session discography). However, I recommend you stick with the one in Fred Rothwell's *Long Distance Information*. Also issued as a 6-LP set [Chess CH6-80.001].

NEW JUKE BOX HITS
Chess [MCA] CHD-9171 • December 1988
    Reissue. Identical to the 1961 LP [Chess LP-1456]. Previously reissued in 1984 on LP [Chess CH-9171].

GREATEST HITS LIVE
Quicksilver QSCD-1017 • 1988
Rock And Roll Music / Nadine / School Day / Wee Wee Hours / *Medley:* Johnny B. Goode – Carol – Promised Land / Hoochie Coochie Man+ / Sweet Little Sixteen

    Toronto 1969 again. 'Nuff said. Also available on CD Up Beat Music UBCD-8. I have never seen any corresponding LP release for either of these.

VOLUME ONE: DUCKWALKIN'
Telstar TRCD-1002 • 1988
Roll Over Beethoven / Maybellene / Too Much Monkey Business / Nadine / My Ding-A-Ling *(live, single edit)* / Too Pooped To Pop+ / No Money Down / Rock And Roll Music / Almost Grown / Havana Moon / Beautiful Delilah / Thirty Days / Sweet Little Rock And Roller / Merry Christmas Baby+ / Around And Around / Wee Wee Hours / Carol / No Particular Place To Go

    It says on the cover that these cuts are digitally remastered. The sound is okay, but unexceptional, and the cover is so dull it's almost unbelievable. And whatever happened to VOLUME TWO?

AFTER SCHOOL SESSION
Chess [MCA] CHD-9284 • January 1989
    Reissue of the 1957 LP [Chess LP-1426] with additional liner notes and recording information. This time they *almost* got Berry's birth details correct: 19 October (it should have been 18th) 1926 in St. Louis, Missouri. I fully understand why so many people today still don't trust what's written about his birth date(s) and place(s)! Also issued on LP [Chess CH-9284].

THE LONDON CHUCK BERRY SESSIONS
Chess [MCA] CHD-9295 • June 1989
Reissue of the 1972 LP [Chess CH-60020]. Includes recording information and new liner notes by Andy McKaie. Also issued on LP [Chess CH-9295].

———————————

I remember when the following five Polygram reissues came out in 1989. What a big surprise! Here, they had the good idea to re-release the Mercury recordings along with previously unissued tracks from the sessions at which the original album tracks were recorded (only one alt. take is missing) – and in superb sound quality! All of a sudden, the tracks sounded completely different and so much better! The credit for this goes to Dennis Drake at Polygram Studios, who did such a good job of the mastering. The reissues used the original covers and liner notes, so anyone who didn't look closely enough at the track listings probably missed the fact that they included previously unreleased songs.

GOLDEN HITS
Mercury [Polygram] 826-256-2 • June 1989
Sweet Little Sixteen / Memphis Tennessee / School Day / Maybellene / Back In The USA / Around And Around *(prev. unissued)* / Brown Eyed Handsome Man *(prev. unissued)* / Johnny B. Goode / Rock And Roll Music / Roll Over Beethoven / Thirty Days / Carol / Let It Rock / Reelin' And Rockin' / Club Nitty Gritty

Reissue of the 1967 (stereo) LP [Mercury SR-61103] with four bonus cuts, packaged in a clear plastic longbox. For a Berry fan who just has to have everything, it's okay. Personally, however, I have never liked these new recordings. Okay, some are not so bad, but they're nowhere compared to the original Chess recordings – and the two unissued cuts are unfortunately no better. What happened to the exciting beat? There was also an LP version of this reissue [Mercury 826-256-1], but without the bonus cuts. The other CDs in this reissue series were not available on vinyl.

CHUCK BERRY IN MEMPHIS
Mercury [Polygram] 836 071-2 • June 1989
Back To Memphis / I Do Really Love You / Ramblin' Rose+ / Sweet Little Rock And Roller / My Heart Will Always Belong To You+ / Oh Baby Doll / Check Me Out / It Hurts Me Too+ / Bring Another Drink+ / So Long+ / Goodnight, Well It's Time To Go [It's Time To Go] / Flying Home+ *(prev. unissued)*

Reissue of the 1967 (stereo) LP [Mercury SR-61123] with just one bonus cut – 'Flying Home' – but it's a good one from the pens of Benny Goodman and Lionel Hampton. Again, there was a tremendous improvement to the sound quality! Packaged in a clear plastic longbox.

LIVE AT FILLMORE AUDITORIUM
Mercury [Polygram] 836 072-2 • June 1989
Medley: Rockin' At The Fillmore *(instr)* – Everyday I Have The Blues+ / C.C. Rider+ / Driftin' Blues+ / Feelin' It *(instr)* / Flying Home+ *(instr)* / Hoochie Coochie Man+ / It Hurts Me Too+ *(duet with Steve Miller)* / Good Morning Little Schoolgirl+ *(prev. unissued)* / Fillmore Blues *(instr)* / Wee Baby Blues+ / Bring Another Drink+ *(prev. unissued)* / Worried Life Blues+ *(prev. unissued)* / Reelin' And Rockin' *(prev. unissued)* / My Ding-A-Ling *(prev. unissued)* / Goodnight Sweetheart – Johnny B. Goode

Reissue of the 1967 (stereo) LP [Mercury SR-61138] with five bonus cuts. It's abundantly clear that the Miller Band were not a rock'n'roll outfit, and that was perhaps one of the reasons that Mercury left out the more rockin' stuff in the first place. There are a few mistakes here and there (especially Berry's guitar playing) on the previously unissued cuts. So, although we get the full concert, it is still predominantly a blues album. However, it would have been nice if Berry had performed more of his own blues tunes like 'No Money Down', 'Childhood Sweetheart' and 'Wee Wee Hours'. Note also that Berry was already performing 'My Ding-A-Ling' back in 1967, though it doesn't make the song any more interesting on record. 'Reelin' And Rockin' ' is also very close lyric-wise to the version that was recorded live in England in 1972.

The album title was shortened for this release. Packaged in a clear plastic longbox.

FROM ST. LOUIE TO FRISCO
Mercury [Polygram] 836 073-2 ● June 1989
Louie To Frisco / Ma Dear / The Love I Lost / I Love Her, I Love Her / Little Fox / Rock Cradle Rock / Soul Rockin' / I Can't Believe / Misery / Almost Grown *(prev. unissued)* / My Tambourine / Laugh And Cry *(prev. unissued on album)* / Oh Captain / Campus Cookie *(prev. unissued)* / Mum's The Word / Song Of My Love *(prev. unissued)*

Reissue of the 1968 (stereo) LP [Mercury SR-61176] with four bonus cuts. 'Laugh And Cry' (the 'B' side of the single 'Club Nitty Gritty') is a song I had never liked, but here it had a completely new sound! 'Song Of My Love' is a song Berry originally recorded for the 1965 LP, CHUCK BERRY IN LONDON [Chess LP-/LPS-1495]. Here, however, it gains a new dimension with a very light backing, two guitars and a bass, plus harmony vocals from daughter Ingrid. But the dreadful 'Oh Captain' should have been put at the end.

The only known unreleased Mercury cut now remaining is an alternative longer version of 'Rock Cradle Rock'.

CONCERTO IN B GOODE
Mercury [Polygram] 836 074-2 ● June 1989
Good Lookin' Woman / My Woman / It's Too Dark In There / Put Her Down / Concerto In B Goode *(instr)*

Reissue of the 1969 (stereo) LP [Mercury SR-61223]. No bonus cuts, but again vastly improved sound quality. Mercury forgot to put a marker between the last two tracks, so your CD player will list only four tracks. Berry recorded the songs for this album at Berry Park Studios and sent the tape to Mercury. It is known that other songs were also recorded, but they were probably not available to Mercury, and may have been lost when his studio burned down in 1989. Packaged in a clear plastic longbox.

MISSING BERRIES – RARITIES (VOLUME 3)
Chess [MCA] CHD-9318 ● July 1990
Childhood Sweetheart *(alt. take)* / Do You Love Me *(alt. take)* / Big Ben Blues / Man And The Donkey *(stereo)* / One O'Clock Jump+ *(instr)* / The Little Girl From Central *(stereo)* / Untitled Instrumental *(instr)* / Let Me Sleep Woman *(Ecuadors)* / Vacation Time / 21 Blues / That's My Desire+ / Blue On Blue *(instr)*

This album also has some great tracks from the Chess archives. 'Big Ben Blues' is the same as 'Big Ben' which appeared in mono on the 1964 UK LP, YOU NEVER CAN TELL [Pye International NPL-28039] and the 1967 reissue [Marble Arch MAL-702 *(mono)* MALS-702 *(stereo)*]. Ditto 'The Little Girl From Central'. 'Man And The Donkey' appears minus the overdubbed audience from the 1963 ON STAGE LP [Chess LP-1480]. 'Vacation Time' and 'That's My Desire' (rare 'B' sides off the singles 'Beautiful Delilah' [Chess 1697] and 'Anthony Boy' [Chess 1716] respectively) appear on album in the US for the first time. '21 Blues' turns out to be a great rocker, and one can only wonder why it took so long to release it. Dig that beat and the perfect Berry guitar! Also issued on LP [Chess CH-9318] but without the two bonus cuts, 'That's My Desire' and 'Blue On Blue'.

Chuck Berry & Bo Diddley
TWO GREAT GUITARS
Chess [MCA] CHD-9170 ● October 1992
Liverpool Drive *(instr, Chuck Berry only)* / Chuck's Beat *(instr, Chuck Berry and Bo Diddley)* / When The Saints Go Marching In+ *(instr, Bo Diddley only)* / Bo's Beat+ *(instr, Chuck Berry and Bo Diddley)* / Fireball *(prev. unissued instrumental, Bo Diddley)* / Stay Sharp *(prev. unissued instrumental, Bo Diddley)* / Chuckwalk *(prev. unissued instrumental, Chuck Berry)* / Stinkey *(prev. unissued in USA instrumental, Bo Diddley)*

Here, MCA included one previously unissued Berry track and three by Bo Diddley. The Berry instrumental came from the same December 1957 session that produced 'Rock At The Philharmonic' and 'Guitar Boogie'. 'Chuckwalk' sounds similar to 'Berry Pickin' ' and is probably one of those many instrumental warm-ups in the Chess studio. So why didn't they use that one instead of the dreadful 'Low Feeling' on ONE DOZEN BERRYS [Chess LP-1432]? Previously reissued in 1984 on LP (without bonus cuts) [Chess CH-9170].

LIVE AT THE FILLMORE AUDITORIUM – SAN FRANCISCO
Rebound 314 520 203-2 ● 1994
Medley: Rockin' At The Fillmore *(instr)* – Everyday I Have The Blues+ / C.C. Rider+ / Driftin' Blues+ / Feelin' It* *(instr)* / Flying Home+ *(instr)* / Hoochie Coochie Man+ / It Hurts Me Too+* *(duet w/Steve Miller)* / Good Morning Little Schoolgirl+ / Fillmore Blues *(instr)* / Reelin' And Rockin' / My Ding-A-Ling / Johnny B. Goode

Second CD reissue of the 1967 (stereo) LP [Mercury SR-61138], this time with two bonus cuts: 'Reelin' And Rockin' ' and 'My Ding-A-Ling'. However, the cover proclaims that the two songs marked * are '*CD bonus tracks*' on this issue. There was also a cassette release [Mercury 314 520 203-4] minus these tracks.

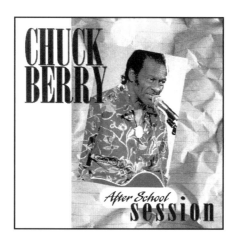

AFTER SCHOOL SESSION
MCA Special Products MCAD-20873 ● 1995
Too Much Monkey Business / Wee Wee Hours / Roly Poly *(instr)* / Deep Feeling *(instr)* / School Day / No Money Down / Brown Eyed Handsome Man / Havana Moon / Berry Pickin' *(instr)* / Drifting Heart

Reissue of the original 1958 LP [Chess LP-1426] minus two songs ('Down Bound Train' and 'Together (We Will Always Be)') and with a different cover. The remaining songs are in a different sequence. Special Products? Give me a break!

> Lest there should be any misunderstanding: if it's possible to speak of a 'final' Chuck Berry studio recording, then it is his guest appearance on Shabba Ranks' 'Go, Shabba, Go'. This track was included on European pressings of Ranks' 1995 CD, A MI SHABBA [Epic 477482-2], but *not* on the US version. See the French discography (page 315) for more info.

36 ALL-TIME GREATEST HITS [3-CD]
MCA [Universal] Special Products 1526 MSD3-36066 ● 1996
❶ Maybellene / Roll Over Beethoven / School Day / Oh Baby Doll / Anthony Boy / Little Queenie / Back In The USA / Too Pooped To Pop+ / Let It Rock / Nadine / No Particular Place To Go / You Never Can Tell
❷ Little Marie / Promised Land / Dear Dad / My Ding-A-Ling *(live, single edit)* / Reelin' And Rockin' / Sweet Little Sixteen *(original speed)* / Johnny B. Goode / Rock And Roll Music / Memphis, Tennessee / Sweet Little Rock And Roller / Brown Eyed Handsome Man / Carol
❸ Almost Grown / Too Much Monkey Business / Beautiful Delilah / Berry Pickin' *(instr)* / Drifting Heart / Night Beat *(instr)* / Time Was+ *(slow version)* / I've Changed / Vacation Time / Wee Wee Hours / Oh Yeah / Thirty Days

   3-CD set containing only 12 tracks per disc. Simple and cheap layout with no info whatsoever except for the titles. However, all tracks originally recorded in stereo are in very good sound quality.

   The following two albums were released under the '*Chess 50th Anniversary Collection*' banner. They are good compilations, and genuinely digitally remastered, albeit 'Carol' (VOLUME 1) still sounds strange. Good pictures and detailed liner notes and recording information (but again stick to the sessionography in Fred Rothwell's *Long Distance Information*). You could look upon these two collections of tracks as one of rock'n'roll's most enduringly important pieces of musical work. These songs have been covered by everyone from the Beatles to the Grateful Dead, the Beach Boys to Linda Ronstadt, and the Rolling Stones to Buck Owens: you name it, they've played it. Chuck Berry laid down the law for playing rock'n'roll music, plus '*It was the lyrics, man, the lyrics!*' as Paul McCartney once told him. There is little doubt that Berry made Chess Records what it was, and rock'n'roll what it is.

CHUCK BERRY – HIS BEST (VOLUME 1)
Chess [MCA] CHD-9371 • February 1997
Maybellene / Thirty Days / You Can't Catch Me / Downbound Train / Brown Eyed Handsome Man / Roll Over Beethoven / Too Much Monkey Business / Havana Moon / School Day / Rock And Roll Music / Oh Baby Doll / Reelin' And Rockin' / Sweet Little Sixteen / Johnny B. Goode / Around And Around / Beautiful Delilah / Carol / Anthony Boy / Jo Jo Gunne / Memphis Tennessee

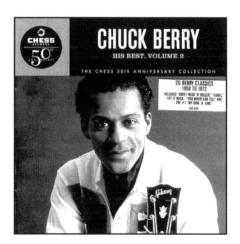

CHUCK BERRY – HIS BEST (VOLUME 2)
Chess [MCA] CHD-9381 • February 1997
Sweet Little Rock And Roller / Little Queenie / Almost Grown / Back In The USA / Let It Rock / Too Pooped To Pop+ / Bye Bye Johnny / Jaguar And The Thunderbird / Confessin' The Blues+ / Down The Road A Piece+ / I'm Talking About You / Come On / Nadine / You Never Can Tell / Promised Land / No Particular Place To Go / I Want To Be Your Driver / Tulane / My Ding-A-Ling *(live, single edit)* / Reelin' And Rockin' *(live album version)*

ROCKIT
Atlantic 7567-80759-2 • 1998
Reissue of the 1979 LP [Atco SD38-118]. It comes with additional liner notes and a brief history of Atlantic Records, and was one of fifty digipak titles that were reissued to commemorate Atlantic's 50th anniversary. When I played this CD, I thought there was something wrong with my CD player, but there wasn't. I don't know what they did, but the original album on Atco sounds much better. You have been warned! See also August 2007 reissue [American Beat Records 24182].

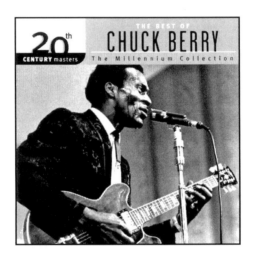

THE BEST OF CHUCK BERRY
MCA [Universal] MCAD-11944 • 1999
Maybellene / Roll Over Beethoven / Brown Eyed Handsome Man / School Day / Rock And Roll Music / Sweet Little Sixteen / Johnny B. Goode / Carol / You Never Can Tell / My Ding-A-Ling *(live, single edit)* / No Particular Place To Go

Compilation issued as part of MCA's *'20th Century Masters – The Millennium Collection'* series. With just 11 songs and only half of the CD's playing time filled up, this is a total rip-off! The sound is great, although there is the same old problem with 'Carol'. And MCA have once again come up with some great '50s and '60s pictures of Berry. It makes me wonder where these pictures were when the original Chess albums came out? They sure could have used them back then, because most of the old album covers had rather unimaginative pictures of Berry, and rather unexciting designs. I don't know how much Don Bronstein received for producing all those lousy covers, but he will never earn any stars in my book.

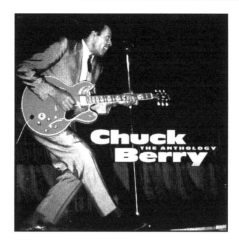

ANTHOLOGY [2-CD]
MCA [Universal] 088 112 304-2 ● June 2000
❶ Maybellene / Wee Wee Hours / Thirty Days / You Can't Catch Me / Down Bound Train / No Money Down / Brown Eyed Handsome Man / Roll Over Beethoven / Too Much Monkey Business / Havana Moon / School Day / Rock And Roll Music / Oh Baby Doll / Sweet Little Sixteen / Guitar Boogie *(instr)* / Reelin' And Rockin' / Johnny B. Goode / Around And Around / Beautiful Delilah / The House Of Blue Lights**+** / Carol / Jo Jo Gunne / Memphis, Tennessee / Sweet Little Rock And Roller / Little Queenie / Almost Grown
❷ Back In The USA / Do You Love Me / Betty Jean / Childhood Sweetheart / Let It Rock / Too Pooped To Pop**+** / I Got To Find My Baby**+** / Don't You Lie To Me**+** / Bye Bye Johnny / Jaguar And The Thunderbird / Down The Road A Piece**+** / Confessin' The Blues**+** / I'm Talking About You / Come On / Nadine / You Never Can Tell / Promised Land / No Particular Place To Go / Dear Dad / I Want To Be Your Driver / Tulane / My Ding-A-Ling *(live, single edit)* / Reelin' And Rockin' *(live, single edit)* / Bio

This nice 50-track 2-CD set is a must for the music fan who for some odd reason does not have much Berry music in their collection. As far as rock'n'roll goes, this is the real deal. The set is very similar to the two HIS BEST volumes released in 1997, so it seems that the latter were quickly withdrawn from the market, otherwise I can't see the reason for this release. All that aside, it contains great music from beginning to end and the sound is superb – although not all songs recorded in stereo are in stereo, which they should have been. There are extensive liner notes and individual track info, and some great pictures.

Now, here's something to think about. Of the 45 tracks here written by Berry all but *two* – 'Do You Love Me' and 'Bio' – have been recorded by other artists and groups. And the five songs not written by Berry have been covered in the Chuck Berry style, except maybe for 'Confessin' The Blues'.

CHUCK BERRY BLUES
MCA [Universal] B0000530-02 ● September 2003
House Of Blue Lights+ / Wee Wee Hours / Deep Feeling *(instr)* / I Just Want To Make Love To You+ / How You've Changed / Down The Road A Piece+ / Worried Life Blues+ / Confessin' The Blues+ / I Still Got The Blues / Driftin' Blues+ / Run Around / Route 66+ / Sweet Sixteen+ / All Aboard / The Things I Used To Do+ / St. Louis Blues+

Interesting concept from MCA, and it would have been good to finally have a proper Berry blues album out in the USA. However, this is so hopeless I don't know how to express my dismay. Why didn't they use the best and original masters? Instead they went for the easy way out. No searching in the files, just grab the first take they find and use it. Nothing is in stereo apart from the last two tracks. If a song was originally recorded in stereo, then that is the 'original' version to me – not the mono mixes which were released in the early '60s. Titles like 'Down The Road A Piece', 'I Still Got The Blues' and 'Run Around' have all been out before in stereo, so why not use those? 'Down The Road A Piece' is even faded at 2:08, like in the old days, despite the fact that it appeared more recently with a longer playing time.

On the positive side, 'All Aboard' is now available without the overdubbed 'live' audience from the 1963 ON STAGE LP [Chess LP-1480], although I have a feeling that this was originally recorded in stereo too. The same goes for 'I Just Want To Make Love To You', which likewise sees its first release in the USA without the fake audience overdub. 'Trick Or Treat' is now the only remaining track from the infamous ON STAGE album that has not been reissued without the audience noise. There are also some good photos on the cover and in the booklet.

Back in 1993, the UK reissue label Ace released a compilation called ON THE BLUES SIDE [Ace CDCH-397] containing 21 goode blues recordings by Mr. Berry (see UK discography for more info). However, there wasn't too much duplication: the Ace CD contained ten songs not included on this US release, and this US release contained five other songs not included in the Ace CD.

CROWN PRINCE OF ROCK'N'ROLL
American Legends ALE-100101 ● 2003
Roll Over Beethoven / Johnny B. Goode / Brown Eyed Handsome Man / Everyday I Have The Blues+*/ School Day / Rock And Roll Music *(with Tina Turner)* / Sweet Little Sixteen / *Medley:* Carol – Little Queenie* / *Medley:* Maybellene – Mountain Dew+* / Nadine / Promised Land / Memphis, Tennessee / Let It Rock / Johnny B. Goode*

This is one of those irritating releases that combines recordings from two different sources, which again means variable sound quality. Tracks marked * were recorded live at the *Rock'n'Roll Spectacular* in Peterborough, England on 3 September 1983; the rest are from the *Live At The Roxy* show in 1982 (see *Section 8 (Chuck Berry on TV)* for more information). And what about the album title? CROWN PRINCE? Is that because Elvis is the KING? My oh my, what ingenuity!

50TH ANNIVERSARY OF ROCK'N'ROLL: AFTER SCHOOL SESSION
Geffen [Universal] B0001685-02 ● March 2004
School Day / Deep Feeling *(instr)* / Too Much Monkey Business / Wee Wee Hours / Roly Poly *(instr)* / No Money Down / Brown Eyed Handsome Man / Berry Pickin' *(instr)* / Together (We Will Always Be) / Havana Moon / Down Bound Train / Drifting Heart / You Can't Catch Me* / Thirty Days* / Maybellene*

Compilation issued as part of Geffen's *'50th Anniversary Of Rock'n'Roll'* series. Reissue of the 1957 LP [Chess LP-1426] with three bonus cuts (marked *). Nice layout and *perfect* sound! The three additional tracks are taken from the very first Chess album, ROCK, ROCK, ROCK [Chess LP-1425] from 1956, but why leave out 'Roll Over Beethoven'?

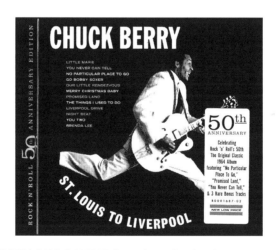

50TH ANNIVERSARY OF ROCK'N'ROLL: ST. LOUIS TO LIVERPOOL
Geffen [Universal] B0001687-02 ● March 2004
Little Marie / Our Little Rendezvous *(mono)* / No Particular Place To Go / You Two / Promised Land / You Never Can Tell / Go, Bobby Soxer / The Things I Used To Do+ / Liverpool Drive *(instr)* / Night Beat *(instr, mono)* / Merry Christmas Baby+ *(mono)* / Brenda Lee *(mono)* / Fraulein+* / O'Rangutang* *(instr, mono)* / The Little Girl From Central*

Another release in Geffen's *'50th Anniversary Of Rock'n'Roll'* series. Reissue of the 1964 LP [Chess LPS-1488] with three bonus cuts (marked *). Nice layout and perfect sound, mostly stereo. The additional tracks are interesting in that 'O'Rangutang' is not faded and runs for 3:02 (see the UK 1998 release THE LATEST AND THE GREATEST/YOU NEVER CAN TELL [BGO BGOCD-428]), and 'The Little Girl From Central' is also a little bit longer, fading out at 2:39.

GOLD
Geffen [Universal] B0004364-02 ● May 2005
    Tracks identical to the 2000 2-CD, ANTHOLOGY [MCA 088 112 304-2]. Different cover and pictures in the booklet, but same liner notes.

THE DEFINITIVE COLLECTION
Geffen [Universal] B0004417-02 ● October 2005
Maybellene / Thirty Days / You Can't Catch Me / Too Much Monkey Business / Roll Over Beethoven / Brown Eyed Handsome Man / Havana Moon / School Day / Rock And Roll Music / Oh Baby Doll / Reelin' And Rockin' / Sweet Little Sixteen / Johnny B. Goode / Around And Around / Beautiful Delilah / Carol / Memphis, Tennessee / Sweet Little Rock And Roller / Little Queenie / Almost Grown / Back In The USA / Let It Rock / I'm Talking About You / Come On / Nadine / You Never Can Tell / Promised Land / No Particular Place To Go / I Want To Be Your Driver / My Ding-A-Ling *(live, single edit)*

    30 certified Chess classics on one CD! Nice booklet with some unusual pictures which I haven't seen before, including the front cover. This CD is a real gem for any music collector.

YOW [2-CD]
Primo PRMCD-2016 ● May 2007
❶ Roll Over Beethoven / Johnny B. Goode / Maybellene / Too Much Monkey Business / Brown Eyed Handsome Man / Sweet Little Sixteen / Thirty Days / School Day / Rock And Roll Music / Reelin' And Rockin' / Promised Land / Nadine / No Particular Place To Go / Little Queenie / Carol / You Never Can Tell / Back In The USA / Wee Wee Hours
❷ *Live:* Reelin' And Rockin' / Maybellene / Memphis, Tennessee / Rock And Roll Music / School Day / Johnny B. Goode / Too Much Monkey Business / Chuck's Jam *(instr)* / Sweet Little Sixteen / How High The Moon**+** *(instr)* / Vacation Time / Childhood Sweetheart / I've Changed / Wee Wee Hours / My Ding-A-Ling *(single edit)*

Keep away from this double CD!!! I bought it because of the strange title, but although Disc 1 has the best of and greatest hits and even goode sound quality, Disc 2 is so annoying: a mess of Toronto tracks and original Chess tracks with overdubbed audience noise plus the live hit version of... 'My Ding-A-Ling'. Hey, look at the track listing. Why on earth would people buy a Berry CD set to get almost the same songs on both CDs and with inferior 'live' versions on Disc 2? Who came up with such an idea in 2007?

ROCKIT
American Beat Records [Elektra] 24182 ● August 2007
Reissue of the 1979 LP [Atco SD38-118] and 1998 CD [Atlantic 7567-80759-2]. It comes with additional information about Berry's singles chart activity, both pop and R&B. And a few extra liner notes containing short statements from John Lennon, Jerry Lee Lewis and Stevie Wonder. Again, the original album on Atco has better sound.

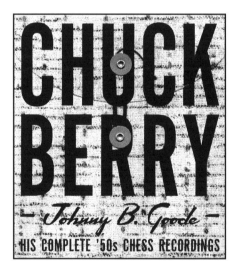

JOHNNY B. GOODE – HIS COMPLETE '50S CHESS RECORDINGS [4-CD]
Hip-O Select [Geffen] B0009473-02 ● December 2007
❶ Maybellene / Wee Wee Hours / Thirty Days / Together (We Will Always Be) / You Can't Catch Me / Roly Poly *(instr)* / Down Bound Train / Berry Pickin' *(instr)* / No Money Down / I've Changed / Drifting Heart / Brown Eyed Handsome Man / Roll Over Beethoven / Too Much Monkey Business / Maybellene *(live, 1956 Alan Freed radio show)* / Roll Over Beethoven *(live, 1956 Alan Freed radio show)* / Havana Moon / Rock And Roll Music *(demo)* / Untitled Instrumental *(instr)* / Deep Feeling *(instr)* / School Day / Low Feeling *(instr)* / La Jaunda *(single version)* / Blue Feeling *(instr)* / How You've Changed / Oh Baby Doll

❷ Rock And Roll Music *(alt. take)* / Rock And Roll Music / 13 Question Method *(early version - prev. unissued in USA)* / How High The Moon+ *(instr)* / Sweet Little Sixteen *(demo)* / Sweet Little Sixteen *(alt. take 3 - prev. unissued)* / Sweet Little Sixteen *(alt. take 11)* / Sweet Little Sixteen *(original master with unissued dialogue)* / Sweet Little Sixteen *(original speeded-up single version)* / Rock At The Philarmonic *(instr)* / Guitar Boogie *(instr)* / Night Beat *(instr, alt. take 3 with Phil Chess dialogue - prev. unissued)* / Night Beat *(instr)* / Time Was+ *(alt. take 4, slow version - prev. unissued)* / Time Was+ *(slow version)* / Reelin' And Rockin' *(alt. take 1 with dialogue)* / Reelin' And Rockin' *(alt. takes 7 and 8 with dialogue - prev. unissued)* / Reelin' And Rockin' / Chuckwalk *(instr)* / Johnny B. Goode *(alt. takes 2 and 3)* / Johnny B. Goode / Around And Around *(alt. take 2 overdub - prev. unissued)* / Around And Around *(alt. take 3 overdub - prev. unissued in USA)* / Around And Around / Ingo *(instr, alt. take 3 overdub - prev. unissued)* / Ingo *(instr)*
❸ It Don't Take But a Few Minutes / Blues For Hawaiians *(instr)* / Beautiful Delilah *(alt. takes 15 and 16)* / Beautiful Delilah / Vacation Time / 21 Blues / 21 *(prev. unissued in USA)* / 21 *(alt. take 14 - prev. unissued)* / Oh Yeah / Hey Pedro / Time Was+ *(fast version)* / House Of Blue Lights+ / Carol / Jo Jo Gunne / Memphis, Tennessee / Anthony Boy / Sweet Little Rock And Roller *(alt. take 5)* / Sweet Little Rock And Roller / Long Fast Jam *(instr, prev. unissued)* / Long Slow Jam *(instr, prev. unissued)* / Merry Christmas Baby+ *(take 9A, single version)* / Merry Christmas Baby+ *(alt. take 16 - LP version)* / Run Rudolph Run+
❹ Little Queenie *(alt. take 8)* / Little Queenie / That's My Desire+ / Do You Love Me *(alt. take)* / Do You Love Me *(prev. unissued in USA)* / Almost Grown *(alt. take 14 - prev. unissued)* / Almost Grown *(alt. take 28 - prev. unissued)* / Almost Grown / Back In The USA / Blue On Blue *(instr)* / Blue On Blue *aka* Upchuck *(instr, prev. unissued)* / Betty Jean *(alt. take 14)* / Betty Jean *(alt. take 17 - prev. unissued)* / Betty Jean / County Line / Childhood Sweetheart *(alt. take)* / Childhood Sweetheart / One O'Clock Jump+ *(instr)* / I Just Want To Make Love To You+ *(alt. take 3 - prev. unissued)* / I Just Want To Make Love To You+ / Broken Arrow / *(alt. take 21 - prev. unissued)* / Broken Arrow / Let It Rock *(alt. mix without lead guitar)* / Let it Rock / Too Pooped To Pop+ *(alt. take 4A - prev. unissued)* / Too Pooped To Pop+ / Say You'll Be Mine+ *(Ecuadors)* / Let Me Sleep Woman+ *(Ecuadors)*

Of course this set is unique and very special to a Berry collector, as we finally get all of his '50s recordings in one place, in chronological order, plus fourteen alt. takes and two unreleased tracks! However, CD 1 is missing the original single version of 'La Jaunda', which is a little different in the mix. On CD 2 we finally get the much better alternative version of 'Around And Around', which is also a few seconds longer than the one first featured on the UK LP Marble Arch MLS-702. CD 3 is the the most interesting, as it contains two long jams (which is why this CD contains fewer tracks, in case you were wondering). I think 'Blues Jam' is the best of these. CD 4 omits the third Ecuadors cut, 'Up There', which couldn't be located in the vaults. Also, the two versions of 'Blue On Blue' are transposed in the booklet – the previously issued take comes first. And hey, 'Run Rudolph Run' is credited to *'Berry–Brodie'*, in 2007. Thank you guys!

This is a very important piece of musical history and I think there will be more releases in the future (if this one sells well enough), like a '60s set and one from the '70s. This is very exciting, as there are several songs from both decades which the public have never heard. The accompanying booklet is well written by Fred Rothwell, but of the six pictures only one is new. If you haven't got this set yet for some strange reason, run and buy it!

Hopefully it will sell like hot cakes and we will subsequently see a complete '60s set, and then one for the '70s. Go to *Section 11 (Songs)* in *Volume 2* and check out all the unissued tracks from those two decades.

There are interesting album releases from various countries (UK, Japan, and even Sweden) which contain material that has not been issued in the USA. These are, of course, included in the discographies for those countries. Additionally, the rarest and most valuable releases from across the globe are listed in *Section 6 (Rarest Berrys)*. You will also find a few interesting items in the *Section 4 (Bootlegs)*.

Cassettes / 8-Tracks / Reel-To-Reel Tapes

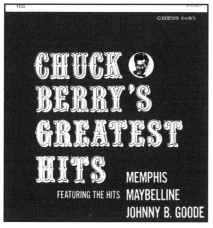

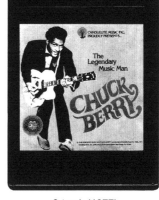

Chess reel-to-reel tape (1964)   8-track (1977)

I have never been a collector of tapes in any format, nor are they of great interest to most collectors (although nowadays you will have to pay quite a bit for an original reel-to-reel tape of Chuck Berry's music), so I will restrict myself to some brief notes on the subject.

I'm not certain what Berry material was released on 7" reel-to-reel, but one of the first was CHUCK BERRY'S GREATEST HITS [Chess 1485], issued by GRT (General Recorded Tape, Inc.) in the mid-'60s, and one of the last was 1972's CHUCK BERRY LONDON SESSIONS. As far as I know, all of Berry's Mercury albums also came out on reel-to-reel (one example is GOLDEN HITS [Mercury STC-61103]).

8-track cartridges are also somewhat confusing. AFTER SCHOOL SESSION was released as an 8-track [Chess 1426], which suggests that probably all of the original Chess albums from the '50s and '60s came out as 8-tracks between the mid-'60s and around 1972, and you can find LONDON SESSIONS as a quadraphonic 8-track cartridge [Chess C8033-60020]. Curiously, the CHUCK BERRY'S GOLDEN DECADE 8-track [Chess 1514-8] was released in 1972 with the 'gold record' cover, rather than the 'pink radio' design used on that year's vinyl reissue [Chess 2CH-1514]. There's also another 8-track of Chess material – of which I have never seen an LP version – titled GREATEST HITS [Solid Sounds 451].

All of Berry's Mercury material was issued on 8-tracks. To give you an idea, CHUCK BERRY'S GOLDEN HITS was numbered Mercury MC-8-61103, but came without the liner notes, and ST. LOUIE TO FRISCO TO MEMPHIS came out as

   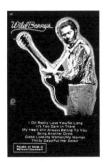

Mercury Twin-Pak MCT-8-2-6501. Both had the same covers as the original albums.

I have also seen a Pickwick 8-track called JOHNNY B. GOODE, a Pickwick Twin Tape of the 1974 FLASHBACK double album, and an 8-track of Pickwick's SWEET LITTLE ROCK AND ROLLER (first issue), P8-1188. I also have an 8-track of an LP titled THE LEGENDARY MUSIC MAN – CHUCK BERRY, released by Candelite Music Inc. in 1977 (see LP section for details).

Norwegian Berry collector Per Arvesen has a whole bunch of Berry music cassettes (he really *does* collect them!), many from the US. From the late '60s onwards, all of Berry's albums came out on cassette as well as LP, all with the same covers as the LPs – almost. One exception was 1973's BIO [Chess 5033-50043-M], which came in a blue hard plastic case without any pictures apart from the front cover (top left above). The song sequence was also different (*Side A:* Bio / Rain Eyes / Hello Little Girl, Goodbye / Got It And Gone; *Side B:* Woodpecker / Talkin' About My Buddy / Aimlessly Driftin').

A few months ago, I came across a release called CHUCK BERRY'S GIANT HITS in an unusual tape format called 'Mini Twin' [Mini Twin MT-E-125]. This contains four songs: 'Maybellene' and 'Sweet Little Sixteen' *(Programme One),* and 'School Day' and 'Roll Over Beethoven' *(Programme Two).* It was manufactured by Munitz Stereo-pak, Van Nuys, California, and, judging by its strange size, I think you needed a special player for it. Mercury Records may also have had some involvement, as all the recordings are from that label.

116

Various Artists EPs

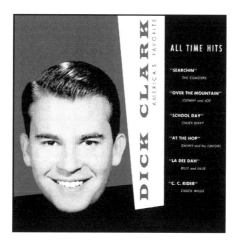

DICK CLARK PRESENTS ALL TIME HITS
August B-100/101 • 1958
School Day

This was the first in a series of four volumes. On the one above Dick Clark is billed as '*America's Favorite*'. The other tracks were 'At The Hop' by Danny & The Juniors, 'Over The Mountain, Across The Sea' by Johnnie & Joe, 'C.C. Rider' by Chuck Willis, 'La Dee Dah' by Billie & Lillie' and 'Searchin' ' by the Coasters.

Ripete Gold Nuggets REP-1033 • 1991
I Got To Find My Baby+

4-track EP, no cover. Label is white with blue print, and the vinyl is a golden yellow. Other artists are the Moonglows ('Over And Over Again' – uptempo version), Champion Jack Dupree ('Shake Baby Shake') and King Arthur Epps ('Depending On You').

Various Artists LPs

This is not intended to be a complete survey of American compilation albums featuring Chuck Berry tracks, as would be quite impossible to trace them all and it's not of immense interest in any case. I have therefore confined myself to the albums which are of special interest to Berry fans or are particularly collectable. However, the fact that Berry's music was included on so many albums does give a good indication of his importance. All the soundtrack albums are also listed in *Section 7 (Chuck Berry in the Movies)*, although they are dealt with in more detail here. All cuts are the Chess originals unless otherwise stated.

ROCK, ROCK, ROCK
Roost, no number • 1956
You Can't Catch Me

Promotional soundtrack album distributed to movie theatre managers and radio stations. It was never released commercially and is therefore highly sought after by Berry collectors. See *Section 7 (Chuck Berry in the Movies)* for more information.

First pressing   Second pressing

ROCK, ROCK, ROCK
Chess LP-1425 ● December 1956
Maybellene / Thirty Days / You Can't Catch Me / Roll Over Beethoven

Touted by Chess Records as the first rock music film soundtrack album, this in fact only contains tracks by Chess artists – Berry, the Moonglows and the Flamingos – and most of the tracks weren't even in the movie! (The only Berry song featured was 'You Can't Catch Me'.) Picture of Berry on the cover. Reissued in 1986 on LP [Chess CH-9254] and in 1988 on CD [Chess CHD-31270]. See *Section 7 (Chuck Berry in the Movies)* for more information.

GO, JOHNNY, GO!
No label, no number ● 1959
Go, Johnny, Go! [Johnny B. Goode] / Memphis, Tennessee / Little Queenie

Promotional soundtrack album distributed to movie theatre managers and radio stations, featuring tracks by Jimmy Clanton, Sandy Stewart, Jackie Wilson, Chuck Berry, the Cadillacs, the Flamingos, Eddie Cochran, Ritchie Valens, Harvey Fuqua and Jo Ann Campbell. It was never released commercially and is therefore sought after by collectors. See *Section 7 (Chuck Berry in the Movies)* for more information.

MURRAY THE K'S BLASTS FROM THE PAST
Chess LP-1461 ● 1961
Sweet Little Sixteen

Also on the album are songs by the Chantels, Bobby Lester & The Moonglows, Bo Diddley, the Flamingos, Nat Kendrick & The Swans, the Fiestas, the Orchids, Ritchie Valens, the Moonlighters and the Pastels.

ALAN FREED'S GOLDEN PICS
End LP-313 ● 1962
Maybellene

15 tracks including songs by the Cadets, the Turbans, the Flamingos, Little Richard, the Nutmegs, Gloria Mann, the Magnificents, the El Dorados, the Hearts, the Rivileers, Jimmy McCracklin, Little Walter, the Willows and the Chantels.

HOUND DOG'S OLD GOLD
Atlantic 8068 ● 1962
Wee Wee Hours

Interesting that Berry was actually on Atlantic as early as 1962. He's in good company here with other people like Willie 'Big Mama' Thornton, the Mello-Kings, the Coasters, Jack Scott, Chuck Willis, Wilbert Harrison, the Shirelles, the Spaniels, the Fiestas, Al Brown & The Toppers and Clyde McPhatter. The album concept was the idea of Buffalo-based disc jockey George 'Hound Dog' Lorenz. Royalties from this album were donated to the Working Boys' Home in Buffalo, NY, which assisted boys from all over the United States and Canada.

TREASURE TUNES FROM THE VAULT
Chess LP-1474 ● 1962
Sweet Little Sixteen

Album co-promoted with radio station WLS, seven of whose presenters are pictured on the cover. Other artists on the album include Kathy Young, Ritchie Valens, Clarence 'Frogman' Henry, the Fiestas, Maurice Williams & The Zodiacs, the Tokens, Sammy Turner, Barrett Strong, the Monotones, the Crescendos and Lee Andrews & The Hearts.

THE BLUES (VOLUME 1)
Argo LP-4026 • 1963
Worried Life Blues+

Highlights from the Chess vaults with Sonny Boy Williamson, Buddy Guy, Little Walter (2), John Lee Hooker, Muddy Waters (2), Lowell Fulson, Howlin' Wolf (2) and Jimmy Witherspoon. The front cover depicts Otis Rush, although he's not included in this volume.

THE BLUES (VOLUME 2)
Argo LP-4027 • 1963
Thirty Days / Wee Wee Hours

More Chess highlights by artists like John Lee Hooker, Howlin' Wolf, Muddy Waters, Bo Diddley, Little Walter (2), Jimmy Witherspoon, Buddy Guy and Otis Rush.

———————————

The following two LPs were part of a series released in 1963-64 consisting of 19 volumes. I remember back in the late '60s when I bought several of these in used record stores, they were truly a Golden treasure to a collector, because many of the songs were hard to find anywhere else. The albums came out before the horrible 'electronic stereo' madness took over for almost 20 years and destroyed most of the great music that was recorded in glorious mono. (Incidentally, note the strange numerical series here: VOLUME 8 really is 25214, and VOLUME 9 is 25213.)

GOLDEN GOODIES (VOLUME 8)
Roulette R-25214 • 1963
Roll Over Beethoven / School Day

Other artists include Jimmie Rodgers (3), Faye Adams (2), Ral Donner, Bo Diddley, Maxine Brown, Jesse Belvin and Ronnie Hawkins with his Berry cover, 'Forty Days' ['Thirty Days'].

GOLDEN GOODIES (VOLUME 9)
Roulette R-25213 • 1963
Maybellene

Other artists include Buddy Knox (2), Joey Dee, Jimmie Rodgers, Frankie Lymon, Jimmy Bowen, Lee Allen, Lou Christie, Ral Donner, Dee Clark and Maxine Brown.

———————————

JERRY BLAVAT PRESENTS FOR DANCERS ONLY –
RECORDED LIVE AT CHEZ-VOUS & WAGNERS • Lost Nite LPS-108 • 1966
Almost Grown / Little Queenie

Jerry Blavat was a disc jockey in Philadelphia, Pennsylvania in the 1960s, and the two big spots for his giant record hops on Friday nights and Sunday afternoons were Chez-Vous and Wagners. According to the liner notes, the 18 songs included on the album were the most-requested records of the past four years, 1962-66. It is therefore interesting to note that the majority of them date from the late '50s and early '60s! The album is 'live' inasmuch as it features Blavat playing the records live. Other artists include the Du-Ettes, Bobby Comstock, Paul Gayten, Five Du-Tones, Clarence

'Frogman' Henry, Gary 'US' Bonds, Ron Holden, Oscar Wills, Jessie Hill, Dreamlovers, Frankie Lymon, the Versatones, the Videos, and Johnny & The Hurricanes.

HEAVY HEADS VOYAGE 2
Chess LP-1528 *(mono)* LPS-1528 *(stereo)* ● 1969
Wee Wee Hours

More highlights from Chess Records including Willie Mabon, Muddy Waters (2), Sonny Boy Williamson (2), Howlin' Wolf (2), Little Walter (2), John Lee Hooker, and Lowell Fulson. How come Berry's 'Wee Wee Hours' is picked so often? It's not the song with which Berry influenced a whole world of rock groups and artists. The cover design here is just terrible, by the way.

POP ORIGINS (VOLUME 1)
Chess LP-1544 ● 1969
Memphis Tennessee / Rock And Roll Music / Roll Over Beethoven

'Buy Chess Records – often imitated, never duplicated. Yes kids, 14 original classics by the artists who invented rock & roll.' This is a very good and interesting compilation. During the '60s there were so many rock groups (and also solo artists) who were inspired by and covered songs originally written and recorded by Chess artists. The cover is kinda unusual and the notes on the back list the songs on the album and which artist covered them (or *'pop-ulized'* them, according to Chess), and when: 'Mona' by Bo Diddley (January 1957) covered by the Rolling Stones (May 1965); 'Spoonful' by Howlin' Wolf (July 1960) covered by Cream (June 1968); and so on. Includes songs by Bo Diddley (2), Lowell Fulson, Howlin' Wolf (5), Dale Hawkins, Muddy Waters, and Little Milton.   (NB: This is often shown in price guides as a Chuck Berry & Howlin' Wolf album, but that's not the case.)

The following two albums are listed principally because of Berry's unusual presence on the Capitol label:

SUPER SOUL-DEES (VOLUME 3) [2-LP]
Capitol STBB-178 • 1969
Nadine

The gatefold cover is typical of the time, with a black, semi-naked lady with feathers gracing the front and back. Of the 17 black artists included, only seven are pictured on the inside (no Berry), and there are no liner notes. Other artists include Lou Rawls (2), the Larks, Bettye Swann (2), Billy Preston, Clara Ward, Nancy Wilson (2), Dobie Gray, Patti Drew (2), Willie Hightower, King Curtis, the Ohio Players, Cannonball Adderley, the Salty Peppers, Gene Chandler and KaSandra.

SUPER OLDIES (VOLUME 6) [2-LP]
Capitol STBB-401 • 1969
Nadine

The cover is very dull with no pictures of the artists, no liner notes or info at all, but *does* feature the obligatory semi-naked lady on the front of the gatefold cover. The set includes 20 tracks by 20 different artists from the '50s and '60s: Sam Cooke, the Johnny Otis Show, Peggy Lee, Gene Vincent, the Beach Boys, Cilla Black, Sonny James, Billy Bland, Ferlin Husky, Gene Chandler, the Beau Brummels, Ed Townsend, Peter & Gordon, Thomas Wayne, Bill Parsons (Bobby Bare), Bobby Freeman, Nelson Riddle, Terry Stafford and Jack Scott... but why include the same Berry song on two compilations released almost at the same time?

Now, the following was a great series at the time it was released. The first seven volumes (1956-62) came out in June 1970; 1955 and 1963 appeared in January 1972; and 1964-1967 were released in September 1973. Each album is a re-creation of a radio show aired during the year indicated, with commercials and everything... although I'm not quite sure how accurate they are/were. The 1961 volume especially is a strange one, as it includes 'Nadine' – which was not recorded until January 1964! All volumes were distributed by Chess/GRT – maybe that's why most of the artists were black, even though the deejays were all white.

(NB: When these volumes were reissued in later years they included fewer songs, and some songs were also switched around. For example, if you buy the original 1970 pressing of the 1957 volume, you'll get 12 songs by the likes of Chuck Berry, Dale Hawkins, the Tuneweavers, the Heartbeats, Buddy Knox, the Spaniels, the Diamonds, Johnnie & Joe, Larry Williams, the Five Satins, Jimmie Rodgers and Lee Andrews & The Hearts, but, if you buy the 1983 reissue, you get just 10 songs, the Coasters replace the Tuneweavers, Jimmy Dorsey(!) replaces Dale Hawkins, and Bill Justis replaces Lee Andrews & The Hearts. Gone are the Heartbeats and Johnnie & Joe. Then, if you buy the 1986 reissue, you'll find that Dale Hawkins, the Tuneweavers and Lee Andrews & The Hearts are back, but Buddy Knox and Jimmie Rodgers have disappeared to be replaced by Jerry Lee Lewis. Confusing, huh?)

CRUISIN' 1956
Increase [GRT] INCM-2001 • June 1970
Roll Over Beethoven

Re-creation of a radio show featuring deejay Robin Seymour, WKMH, Detroit: *'Let there be music! – Yeah! that was a real mover. By the way, Chuck Berry is coming to the Riviera Theatre in three weeks, so you can get that Chuck Berry record at your recommended record store.'*

Cruisin' (krew-zin) v. Teen-age custom of driving around, primarily to listen to pop music stations on the car radio, while observing other kids and cars doing the same thing; popular all over the United States beginning in the mid-Fifties.

The word Cruisin' doesn't appear in the dictionary, but it's a familiar word to millions of people who did it. The new seven-record series on Increase Records, CRUSIN' THE FIFTIES AND SIXTIES, is a year-by-year recreation of pop-music radio during the years 1956 through 1962.

Each album is not just a collection of the top pop music of a particular year, but a total recreation by a top disc jockey (of that year) doing his original program over a major pop music station. That means actual commercials, promotional jingles, sound effects, newscast simulations and even record hop announcements, in addition to the original records themselves.

If albums are not available at your local record shop, you can purchase any of them by sending a check or money order for $4.98 to: **CRUISIN', 320 E. 21st Street, Chicago, Illinois 60616**

CHECK THE ALBUMS YOU WANT BELOW:

☐ **1956: ROBIN SEYMOUR,** WKMH, Detroit . . . . . INCREASE #INCM: 2001
☐ **1957: JOE NIAGARA,** WIBG, Philadelphia . . . . INCREASE #INCM: 2002
☐ **1958: JACK CARNEY,** WIL, St. Louis . . . . INCREASE #INCM: 2003
☐ **1959: HUNTER HANCOCK,** KGFJ, Los Angeles . INCREASE #INCM: 2004
☐ **1960: DICK BIONDI,** WKBW, Buffalo . . . . INCREASE #INCM: 2005
☐ **1961: ARNIE "WOO WOO" GINSBURG,**
WMEX, Boston . . . . INCREASE #INCM: 2006
☐ **1962: RUSS "WEIRD BEARD" KNIGHT,**
KLIF, Dallas . . . . INCREASE #INCM: 2007

Send $4.98 (Check or Money Order) for each album you want to:
CRUISIN', 320 EAST 21ST STREET, CHICAGO, ILLINOIS 60616
Enclosed is my check or money order for $_____
NAME_____
ADDRESS_____
CITY_____STATE_____ZIP_____

CRUISIN' 1957
Increase [GRT] INCM-2002 ● June 1970
School Day

Re-creation of a radio show featuring deejay Joe Niagara, WIBG, Philadelphia: *'This is the one you do not get enough of. May I present the merry Mr. Chuck Berry.'* Picture of Berry on the cover. Niagara died on 11 June 2004 aged 76.

CRUISIN' 1958
Increase [GRT] INCM-2003 • June 1970
Rock And Roll Music

Re-creation of a radio show featuring deejay Jack Carney, WIL, St. Louis: *'That was St. Louis' own, our very own Chuck Berry and 'Rock And Roll Music' from the Silver Dollar Survey. Have you ever seen the automobile that Chuck Berry drives around town? Hoo-hoo, that is something to see!'*

CRUISIN' 1959
Increase [GRT] INCM-2004 • June 1970
Almost Grown

Re-creation of a radio show featuring deejay Hunter Hancock, KGFJ, Los Angeles: *'You should have seen Chuck Berry recently at the Firefall Ballroom – he was a gaaas!'* *Huntin' With Hunter* was his most famous show, a Top 20 survey. Hancock died in August 2004 aged 88.

CRUISIN' 1961
Increase [GRT] INCM-2006 • June 1970
Nadine

Re-creation of a radio show featuring deejay Arnie 'Woo Woo' Ginsburg, WMEX, Boston: *'We're gonna play this one for everyone saying "Woo Woo Ginsburg" tonight at the Adventure Car Hop. Here it is, the No. 4 score on the WMEX Top Thirty'.* That's good for 'Woo Woo' Ginsburg, but 'Nadine' in the Top Thirty in *1961*? Give me a break! Who's responsible for such nonsense? It got even worse later when the album was reissued in 1983 and they included a faded live version of 'Johnny B. Goode' by Berry from the 1969 *Toronto Rock & Roll Revival*! Picture of Berry on the cover.

WMID / THE JERSEY GIANT – GIANT SOUVENIRS
Post 7202 • 1971
School Day

WMID was a leading force in South Jersey broadcasting. They played current hits and also programmed plenty of nostalgia items including a rock'n'roll revival show on Friday, Saturday, and Sunday nights. The station started playing the hits back in the mid '50s. This album contains a collection of the best from then and now. Other artists include Johnnie & Joe, Lee Andrews & The Hearts, Santo & Johnny, the Sheppards, the Heartbeats, the Five Satins, the Quin-Tones, Steam, the Intrigues, Tony Joe White, the Winstons, the Cowsills, Fuzz, Neil Diamond, and Runt (Todd Rundgren).

CRUISIN' 1955
Increase [GRT] INCM-2000 • January 1972
Maybellene

Re-creation of a radio show featuring deejay 'Jumpin' George Oxford, KSAN, San Francisco: *'You can call it rhythm & blues or rock'n'roll, but here is one that's a hit under any name... What magic that man does with lyrics!'* Picture of Berry on the cover.

CHESS/JANUS LP SAMPLER [promo only]
Chess/Janus [GRT] 2259/2260 ● 1972
Let's Boogie

White label radio station promo. A collection of tracks from various current Chess albums. 10 songs by 10 different artists, including the Dells, the Gospel Six, Muddy Waters, Aretha Franklin, Bo Diddley, Jack McDuff, Gloria Spencer, Harvey Mandel and Rev. C.L. Franklin. Exciting music, but a very dull cover. The numbers 2259 and 2260 are the matrix numbers of the two sides of the album.

OLDE GOLDE / WABY RADIO 14 – ALBANY
Post 7210 ● 1972
Sweet Little Sixteen

There's nothing special about this, except that it was compiled by WABY in Albany, NY from thousands(?) of phone calls. Apparently, it was their way of saying 'Thank you' to the good folks in Capital Country for their acceptance of the 'new' WABY, which on 1 February 1972 hopped on the nostalgia trend sweeping the nation and switched to playing '*All The Hits, All The Time*'. Other artists include Frankie Avalon, Jimmy Charles, Shelley Fabares, the Dixie Cups, Sam The Sham & The Pharaohs, the Righteous Brothers, Tommy James & The Shondells, the Animals, the Box Tops, Jeannie C. Riley, Neil Diamond, the Five Stairsteps, Ocean, Van Morrison, the Ides of March, Gallery and Melanie.

CRUISIN' 1965
Increase [GRT] INCM-2010 ● September 1973
Sweet Little Sixteen

Re-creation of a radio show featuring deejay Robert W. Morgan, KHJ, Los Angeles. This song provided a '*93/KHJ Golden*' interlude in the show. Berry's name is not mentioned at all. The song starts directly after a KHJ-TV *Beatle Special* promo and the *Golden* jingle.

AMERICAN GRAFFITI [2-LP]
MCA MCA2-8001 ● 1973
Almost Grown / Johnny B. Goode

'*41 original hits from the soundtrack*'. The film has become a cult movie, and the album, a good compilation of '50s and '60s classics, was a best seller on both sides of the Atlantic. A few of the songs are introduced by the howling, prowling deejay Wolfman Jack (died July 1995). There was also a follow-up compilation, MORE AMERICAN GRAFFITI (1975), but this featured no Berry material. The album was reissued in 1993 as a 2-CD set [MCA MCD-8001-2]. In 1998, MCA issued a 20-track HIGHLIGHTS OF AMERICAN GRAFFITI single CD to commemorate the 25th anniversary of the film's release [MCA 11871]. Both of Berry's tracks were included on this also. See *Section 7 (Chuck Berry in the Movies)* for more information.

HEAVY TRAFFIC
Fantasy F-9436 ● 1973
Maybellene

A very unusual soundtrack compilation, especially for Berry's music to be included on. Here he's joined by the Isley Brothers, Sergio Mendes & Brazil '66, the Dave Brubeck Quartet, Merle Saunders, Ed Bogas and Ray Shanklin. See *Section 7 (Chuck Berry in the Movies)* for more information.

CHUCK AND HIS FRIENDS [3-LP]
Aristocrat/Brookville [GRT] BR-100 ● 1974
Roll Over Beethoven / Memphis, Tennessee / Viva, Viva Rock And Roll / Bordeaux In My Pirough /
You Never Can Tell / Lonely School Days *(fast version)* / My Ding-A-Ling *(live, single edit)* / Johnny B.
Goode / Nadine / School Day / Sweet Little Sixteen / Maybellene / Rock And Roll Music

The cover says 'Brookville', but the label is 'Aristocrat'. These three LPs were
issued in a single cover. The first disc contains Chess cuts by Berry, the second and
third are by various other artists (*'Chuck's Friends'*) including Little Richard, Billy
Stewart, the Teen Queens, the Platters (2), Dale Hawkins, the Chiffons, the
Moonglows (2), the Kingsmen, the Penguins, Johnny Ace, the Champs, Fontella Bass,
Hank Ballard, Little Willie John, Ramsey Lewis, the Shangri-Las, the Shirelles and Bo
Diddley. The cover has some great pictures of Berry on stage with photos of his
friends in the background which could be from a TV show, or more likely it's just
promotion for the album, as it was advertised on TV and Berry himself did the
commercial for it. Unusually, Berry is depicted holding a small black Gibson guitar.
'My Ding-A-Ling' is credited to Dave Bartholomew and Chuck Berry. This is the only
time I have seen it credited like this (which is absolutely correct, by the way).

ONLY YOU – THE ORIGINALS
Pickwick SPC-3512 ● 1975
Johnny B. Goode / Reelin' And Rockin' *(Mercury recordings)*

Originals? Apart from two songs by the Platters, there aren't any originals at all
among the songs by Jerry Lee Lewis, Fats Domino (live), Bill Haley or Berry!
However, there is a picture of Berry on the back of the cover.

SUPER OLDIES OF THE 50'S (VOLUME 2) / THE BEST OF CHUCK BERRY [2-LP]
Trip TOP 50-2 / GS-777 ● 1975
Maybellene / Roll Over Beethoven / Sweet Little Sixteen / School Day / Reelin' And Rockin'
[Around And Around] / Back In The USA / Too Pooped To Pop+ / Almost Grown / My Ding-A-Ling
(stereo) (live, single edit) / Johnny B. Goode

This is a 2-LP set packaged in a single cover. SUPER OLDIES features 20
different artists from the '50s, but no Berry. The Berry LP has 10 songs from the
Chess files – mono takes ruined by electronic stereo – which are the same as the first
10 tracks on the later Trip album, CHUCK BERRY'S 16 GREATEST HITS [Trip
TOP 16-55], released in 1978.

The Berry record [GS-777] has no label identification, other than the legend *'Produced by F&G Marketing Inc.'* The title and picture on the front cover are similar to the soundtrack album of the AMERICAN GRAFFITI 2-LP set (*'Songs of American Graffiti and other Rock Favorites'*), but it says in small letters at the bottom *'Not the Original Sound Track Album'*. The back has the standard 1950s black and white picture of Berry with guitar, and here the title is the same as that shown on the record. A typical cheap album set destined for sale in supermarkets.

AMERICA'S MUSICAL ROOTS
Festival FR-1008 • 1976
Blue Feeling *(instr)* / Wee Wee Hours

This is actually a Chess 'greatest hits' compilation, featuring artists like Little Walter, Howlin' Wolf, Muddy Waters, Sonny Boy Williamson, Lowell Fulson, John Lee Hooker, Bo Diddley – all with two songs apiece – plus Elmore James and Memphis Slim with one song each. This is a real goodie. Informative liner notes on the inner sleeve with info on each song. Deejay Jim Pewter did the concept and research, and also produced the set with Rick Donovan.

THE HAPPY DAYS OF ROCK'N'ROLL
Pickwick SPC-3517 • 1976
Johnny B. Goode *(Mercury)*

12 songs by 12 different artists, with more originals than Pickwick SPC-3512 above. Not bad! There are pictures of Berry on both the front and back cover.

JIM PEWTER'S 10TH ANNIVERSARY SALUTE TO ROCK'N'ROLL
Festival FR-1006 • 1976
Rock And Roll Music

Jim Pewter was the winner of the 1974 *Billboard 'Program Director Award – Oldies'* category, as well as host of the *Jim Pewter Radio Show*, heard throughout the world through the facilities of the American Forces Radio and Television Service out of Los Angeles, California. In 1961, he made recordings for Circus, and later for both RCA and MGM. The album above features 20 songs by various '50s and '60s artists. The inner sleeve has good liner notes with info on each song.

RHYTHM AND BLUES CHRISTMAS
United Artists UA-LA654-R • 1976
Run Rudolph Run+

A very good 10-track Xmas compilation by producer Snuff Garrett with great liner notes on each artist/song. Other artists include Charles Brown, Baby Washington, Clyde McPhatter & The Drifters, the Five Keys, B.B. King, the Orioles, Amos Milburn, Lowell Fulson and Marvin & Johnny. 'Rudolph' is credited to Marvin Brodie and Johnny Marks. Berry has been featured on hundreds of Xmas compilations over the years with either this or his version of 'Merry Christmas Baby' – or sometimes both on the same album. See also 1986.

AMERICAN HOT WAX [2-LP]
A&M SP-6500 • February 1978
Medley: Reelin' And Rockin' – Roll Over Beethoven *(live)* / Sweet Little Sixteen *(Chess)*

Original soundtrack. A film about a week in the life of deejay Alan Freed, who is putting together a *Rock & Roll Anniversary Show* at the Brooklyn Paramount in 1958. The live medley was specially recorded for the film. Berry appears as himself, as do Jerry Lee Lewis and Screamin' Jay Hawkins. One record contains live cuts from the film, the other original '50s recordings. See *Section 7 (Chuck Berry in the Movies)* for more information.

ROCK & ROLL SHOW
Gusto GT-0002 • 1978
Reelin' And Rockin' / Roll Over Beethoven / Sweet Little Sixteen

The front cover gives the impression that this is a live album, but all the songs are studio recordings and some are not even the originals! Berry's songs are, though. Other artists include Bill Doggett, Sammy Turner, Jerry Lee Lewis (2), the Moonglows, Billy Ward & His Dominoes, Screamin' Jay Hawkins, the Coasters and Frankie Ford. There are pictures of Berry and Jerry Lee on the front cover, and liner notes about both artists on the back.

SHAKE, RATTLE & ROLL – ROCK'N'ROLL IN THE 1950s
New World NW-249 *(mono)* • 1978
Maybellene

A *'Recorded Anthology of American Music'* according to the label – and a very good compilation it is too! Gatefold cover with a four-page booklet and every song neatly detailed with recording information, history and even lyrics. Unfortunately there are very few pictures, but what the heck. Apparently they didn't get the permission to include Elvis' recordings or Little Richard's Specialty material. Elvis is therefore missing completely; however, Richard is represented by a recording he did in 1952, 'Every Hour', originally released on RCA-Victor. Actually, the whole concept is a combination of a book and LP, and the music is in glorious mono. Who else did that in the '70s? Other artists include Joe Turner, Johnny Ace, Billy Ward & His Dominoes, Faye Adams, Bill Haley & His Comets, Lloyd Price, Fats Domino, the Silhouettes, Buddy Holly, Jerry Lee Lewis, Jackie Wilson, the Shirelles, Dee Clark, Ray Charles, the Coasters and Gary 'US' Bonds.

ROCK'N'ROLL HIGH SCHOOL
Sire SRK-6070 • 1979
School Day

Original soundtrack. Berry is in unusual musical company on this album, rubbing shoulders with the likes of the Ramones, Brian Eno, Nick Lowe, P.J. Soles, Devo, Eddie & The Hot Rods, Brownsville Station, Todd Rundgren and Alice Cooper.

CHESS IS BACK! – SAMPLER [promo only]
Chess [Sugar Hill] CH-333 • 1982
Maybellene / Little Queenie

White label promo released to radio stations and stores to promote new releases of old tracks. *'Suggested cuts for programming and in-store play. Chess Records have never sounded better.'* THE GREAT 28 2-LP [Chess CH-8201] is depicted on the back cover. Other albums mentioned include Muddy Waters'/Howlin' Wolf's MUDDY & THE WOLF [Chess CH-8200], John Klemmer's BLOWIN' GOLD [Chess CH-8300], the Dells' THE DELLS [Chess CH-8400], Aretha Franklin's ARETHA GOSPEL [Chess CH-8500] and the WIZARDS FROM THE SOUTHSIDE compilation [Chess CH-8203] featuring Muddy Waters, Howlin' Wolf, Sonny Boy Williamson, Little Walter, John Lee Hooker and Bo Diddley.

The following was a series of 14 volumes with 12 tracks apiece featuring various '50s and '60s acts. For Berry fans the most interesting release is VOLUME 11, as it includes a picture of Chuck with Los Angeles deejay Art Laboe, taken at the *Oldies But Goodies* concert at the Hollywood Palladium on 31 July 1971.

OLDIES BUT GOODIES (VOLUME 10)
Original Sound OSR LP-8860 • 1982
Roll Over Beethoven

OLDIES BUT GOODIES (VOLUME 11)
Original Sound OSR LP-8861 • 1982
Maybellene

Picture of Berry on the cover.

OLDIES BUT GOODIES (VOLUME 12)
Original Sound OSR LP-8862 • 1982
Sweet Little Sixteen

The following was very similar to the 1960s Roulette 'GOLDEN GOODIES' series. I'm not going to list all the artists included, however VOLUMES 1-10 include mostly doo-wop groups. No pictures of the artists were included on the covers.

THE ORIGINAL ROCK'N'ROLL HITS OF THE '50S (VOLUME 1)
Roulette SR-59001 • 1982
Roll Over Beethoven

THE ORIGINAL ROCK'N'ROLL HITS OF THE '50S (VOLUME 2)
Roulette SR-59002 • 1982
You Can't Catch Me

THE ORIGINAL ROCK'N'ROLL HITS OF THE '50S (VOLUME 3)
Roulette SR-59003 • 1982
Johnny B. Goode

THE ORIGINAL ROCK'N'ROLL HITS OF THE '50S (VOLUME 4)
Roulette SR-59004 • 1982
Maybellene

THE ORIGINAL ROCK'N'ROLL HITS OF THE '50S (VOLUME 5)
Roulette SR-59005 • 1982
Sweet Little Sixteen

THE ORIGINAL ROCK'N'ROLL HITS OF THE '50S (VOLUME 6)
Roulette SR-59006 • 1982
School Day

THE ORIGINAL ROCK'N'ROLL HITS OF THE '50S (VOLUME 7)
Roulette SR-59007 • 1982
Rock And Roll Music

THE ORIGINAL ROCK'N'ROLL HITS OF THE '60S (VOLUME 11)
Roulette SR-59011 • 1982
No Particular Place To Go

THE ORIGINAL ROCK'N'ROLL HITS OF THE '60S (VOLUME 13)
Roulette SR-59013 • 1982
You Never Can Tell

PARTY TIME FIFTIES
JCI *(Jeito Concepts Inc.)* JCI-3201 • 1985
Johnny B. Goode

This was one of a series of LPs of at least 11 volumes covering mostly '60s music, apart from the one above, which was strictly '50s. Other artists on the album above included Wanda Jackson, the Crickets, the Everly Brothers, Dion & The Belmonts, Bobby Darin, Little Richard, Bill Haley & His Comets, Freddy Cannon, the Fiestas, the Diamonds and Danny & The Juniors.

ROCK AND ROLL: THE EARLY DAYS
RCA-Victor AFM1-5463 • 1985
Maybellene

As far as I know, this was the first time Elvis was featured on a compilation with the other greats from the '50s. A very good album including one song each from the likes of Berry, Presley, Holly, Lewis, Richard, Perkins, Diddley, Haley, Joe Turner, the Chords, Big Mama Thornton, Wynonie Harris and Muddy Waters. A video with a running time of 59 minutes was also released and featured more artists including Fats Domino and the Everly Brothers. So why weren't these two included on the album (and Eddie Cochran and Gene Vincent)? If you give or take a year or two, the package was released to mark the 30th birthday of the Big Beat, any old way you choose it! Picture of Berry on the cover.

ROCK, ROCK, ROCK
Chess [MCA] CH-9254 ● September 1986
Reissue of the 1956 LP [Chess LP-1425]. MCA used two different pictures of Berry from those which appeared on the original album. One is from 1965! If you come across a promo issue of this album (stamped on the back cover), these also contained a promo sheet for the *Original Chess Masters* series and two glossy sheets of pictures of various Chess/Checker artists (no Berry, though). Reissued in 1988 on CD [Chess CHD-31270].

COOL YULE – A COLLECTION OF ROCKIN' STOCKING STUFFERS
Rhino RNLP-70073 ● 1986
Run Rudolph Run+

Here 'Rudolph' is credited to Berry! This is also a good compilation with liner notes and info on each artist/song. Other artists include the Marquees (2), Solomon Burke, Bud Logan, Clyde McPhatter & The Drifters, Ike & Tina Turner, Jack Scott, Booker T. & The MG's, the Surfaris, Paul & Paula, Clarence Carter, James Brown and Edd 'Kookie' Byrnes. Altogether there are 14 songs on the album – not a bad deal for 1986. Picture of Berry on the cover.

ROCKIN' LITTLE CHRISTMAS
MCA 25084 ● 1986
Merry Christmas Baby+ / Run Rudolph Run+

Both of Berry's famous Yuletide recordings on one album. A good compilation with recording information on each song and liner notes by Brenda Lee. However, I'm not too keen on the 'ROCKIN' ' title, as at least half of the songs are far removed from rock'n'roll. Other artists include Brenda Lee, of course (2), the Moonglows (2), Dodie Stevens, Lord Douglas Byron, the Gems, Bobby Helms, the Enchanters and the Surfaris.

Now, the following was a lo-o-ong series. 20 volumes with 10 songs from the '50s and '60s on each, many of them in stereo, and all in *great* sound quality. Berry does not appear on the volumes which are not listed below. I remember buying the first four volumes when I was in the USA in 1988, and I thought the sound was extremely good – better than I'd heard on any other compilations up to that point. When I was back in the jungle, sorry the *States*, the following year I bought the remaining 16 volumes.

131

All the songs were originally released on singles, and the year, record label and catalogue number of each is listed – but that's all. There are no liner notes or pictures of the artists. However, the original master tapes were used throughout, and they are a joy to listen to. I just don't have the space to mention all the artists and songs (although I would really love to). However, on VOLUME 20 you'll find rarities like a stereo version of 'Ding Ding Dong' by the Jivetones, originally released on Apt 25020 in 1958, the Bay Bops on Coral from 1959 with a stereo version of 'Follow The Rock', and Steppenwolf with 'Sookie Sookie' from 1968. On VOLUME 12 you get a stereo version of Big Danny Oliver's 1958 rocker, 'Sapphire', and Three Dog Night's 'Easy To Be Hard' from 1969. On VOLUME 4 you get 'Born Too Late' by the Poni-Tails from 1958 and 'Personality' by Lloyd Price from 1959 – again both in true stereo. VOLUME 19 has Little Walter with 'My Babe' from 1955, 'Crazy' by Patsy Cline from 1961, and 'The Unicorn' by the Irish Rovers from 1968. This should give you an example of the variety and quality of the series. The only regret is the short playing time, with just five songs per side. In later years, the series was available on CD with two volumes (20 tracks) on each - for example VINTAGE MUSIC (VOLUMES 13 & 14) [MCA MCD-5937]. That's good value for money!

VINTAGE MUSIC – COLLECTORS' SERIES (VOLUME 1)
MCA MCA-1429 • 1986
Maybellene

VINTAGE MUSIC – COLLECTORS' SERIES (VOLUME 2)
MCA MCA-1430 • 1986
Roll Over Beethoven

VINTAGE MUSIC – COLLECTORS' SERIES (VOLUME 3)
MCA MCA-1431 • 1986
School Day

VINTAGE MUSIC – COLLECTORS' SERIES (VOLUME 4)
MCA MCA-1432 • 1986
Johnny B. Goode

VINTAGE MUSIC – COLLECTORS' SERIES (VOLUME 5)
MCA MCA-25023 • 1986
Sweet Little Sixteen

VINTAGE MUSIC – COLLECTORS' SERIES (VOLUME 6)
MCA MCA-25024 • 1986
Rock And Roll Music

VINTAGE MUSIC – COLLECTORS' SERIES (VOLUME 7)
MCA MCA-25025 • 1986
No Particular Place To Go *(stereo)*

VINTAGE MUSIC – COLLECTORS' SERIES (VOLUME 8)
MCA MCA-25026 • 1986
You Never Can Tell *(stereo)*

VINTAGE MUSIC – COLLECTORS' SERIES (VOLUME 11)
MCA MCA-25120 • 1987
Carol

VINTAGE MUSIC – COLLECTORS' SERIES (VOLUME 12)
MCA MCA-25121 • 1987
Back In The USA

VINTAGE MUSIC – COLLECTORS' SERIES (VOLUME 15)
MCA MCA-25124 • 1987
Come On *(single version)*

VINTAGE MUSIC – COLLECTORS' SERIES (VOLUME 16)
MCA MCA-25125 • 1987
Too Much Monkey Business

VINTAGE MUSIC – COLLECTORS' SERIES (VOLUME 18)
MCA MCA-25127 • 1987
Nadine *(stereo)*

VINTAGE MUSIC – COLLECTORS' SERIES (VOLUME 20)
MCA MCA-25129 • 1987
Reelin' And Rockin'

THE BEST OF CHESS ROCK'N'ROLL [2-LP]
Chess [MCA] CH2-6024 • 1987
Maybellene / Johnny B. Goode

This is in a series of four *'Best Of Chess'* packages, covering R&B, blues, jazz and rock'n'roll. 20 tracks, gatefold cover and great liner notes. Other artists include Bo Diddley (2), Jackie Brenston, Bobby Charles, Dale Hawkins, the Moonglows (2), Clarence 'Frogman' Henry, the Flamingos, the Tuneweavers, the Students, the Monotones, Lee Andrews & The Hearts, the Sensations, Johnnie & Joe, Tommy Tucker, Dave 'Baby' Cortez and the Jaynetts. Berry picture on the cover. Also released in Italy by Green Line [Chess GCH2-6024] and distributed in the UK by Charly.

FRAT ROCK! (VOLUME 2)
Rhino RNLP-70183 • 1987
Reelin' And Rockin' *(live, album version)*

This is the version on 1972 LONDON SESSIONS LP [Chess CH-60020]. Apart from this Berry song which was included because of its risqué lyrics, 'La Bamba' by Ritchie Valens and 'Tequila' by The Champs, the rest of this 12-track album consists of '60s stuff by the likes of Sly & The Family Stone, the Spencer Davis Group, Bill Deal & The Rhondels, Paul Revere & The Raiders, the Music Explosion, the Bobby Fuller Four, the Premiers, the Blendells and the Marathons. Picture of Berry on the cover.

CLASSIC ROCK (VOLUME 2)
MCA MCA-25186 • 1988
Johnny B. Goode

This is interesting because Berry appears here alongside an unusual mixture of pop and rock heroes like Elton John, Steely Dan, Dave Mason, Steppenwolf, Lynyrd Skynyrd, Smith, Three Dog Night, the James Gang, and Detroit with Mitch Ryder. Picture of Berry on the cover.

SPUDS MACKENZIE'S PARTY FAVES
Capitol C1-48993 • 1988
Johnny B. Goode

Released by Capitol Special Markets in conjunction with Anheuser-Busch Inc. (brewers of Budweiser beer), who advise that 'party animals' should party often, but party cool, drinking Bud-Light. Apart from Berry's classic, the album includes songs by the Human Beinz(!), the Spencer Davis Group, the Beach Boys, Dion, the Johnny Otis Show, Ritchie Valens, Eddie Cochran, the Kingsmen, Jerry Lee Lewis, the Rivingtons and the Outsiders.

The following three releases were part of a series of great compilations by Joel Whitburn, the world's leading chart researcher. His company, Record Research Inc, publishes books based on *Billboard*'s weekly chart data. Each volume contains good liner notes and pictures of all featured artists – though they are short on playing time, with only 10 songs per album. But why didn't they include Berry in 1958? 'Sweet Little Sixteen' peaked at No. 2 and stayed there for three weeks. See also 1989.

1955 BILLBOARD TOP ROCK'N'ROLL HITS
Rhino R1-70598 • 1988
Maybellene

Berry's first hit is featured alongside recordings by Bill Haley & His Comets, the Penguins, Fats Domino, the Fontane Sisters, the Cheers, the Platters, LaVern Baker, the El Dorados and the Moonglows. Picture of Berry on the back cover. Also issued on CD [Rhino R2-70598].

1957 BILLBOARD TOP ROCK'N'ROLL HITS
Rhino R1-70618 • 1988
School Day

Other artists include Elvis Presley (2), the Everly Brothers, Paul Anka, Buddy Knox, the Crickets, the Diamonds, Buddy Holly and Jerry Lee Lewis. Picture of Berry on the back cover. Also issued on CD [Rhino R2-70618].

1972 BILLBOARD TOP ROCK'N'ROLL HITS
Rhino R1-70633 ● 1989
My Ding-A-Ling *(live, single edit)*

Another interesting mixture of styles, with hits by Gilbert O'Sullivan, Johnny Nash, Three Dog Night, Looking Glass, America, the Hollies, the Temptations, the Moody Blues and the O'Jays. Picture of Berry on the cover. Also issued on CD [Rhino R2-70633].

GREATEST R&B CHRISTMAS HITS
Rhino R1-70638 ● 1989
Run Rudolph Run+

Also includes hits by Johnny Moore's Three Blazers, the Orioles, Mabel Scott, Amos Milburn, Lou Rawls, Brook Benton, the Cadillacs, the Jackson 5 and Sister Rosetta Tharpe. Picture of Berry on the cover. Also issued on CD [Rhino R2-70638].

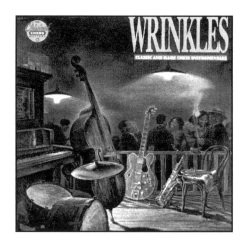

WRINKLES – CLASSIC AND RARE CHESS INSTRUMENTALS
Chess [MCA] CH-9293 ● 1989
How High The Moon+ *(instr, prev. unissued in USA)*

Great compilation and great cover! Informative liner notes, recording session details and a great little picture of Berry on the back. A fragment of Berry's take on the famous Les Paul instrumental was included as the playout track on the 1963 ON STAGE album [Chess LP-1480] with overdubbed audience noise. This was the first occasion that the cut was issued complete and without the audience overdub in the USA – officially at least (it first appeared in 1980 on the AMERICA'S HOTTEST WAX bootleg [Reelin' 001], which was subsequently legally issued in the UK in 1982 under the same title [Chess CXMP-2011]). Picture of Berry on the cover. Also issued on CD [Chess CHD-9293].

Various Artists CD Singles

CALIFORNIA UNCORKED – BLOSSOM HILL
Universal UPR-2001 ● 2001
Back In The USA *(Chess)*

This 5-track CD was specially compiled by Universal for Blossom Hill to promote their fruity wine (California's fastest-growing wine). The winery, located at Paicine, just south of San Francisco, was founded in 1986. Other artists include the Mamas & Papas ('California Dreamin'), Bachman Turner Overdrive ('You Ain't Seen Nothing Yet'), Howlin' Wolf ('California Blues') and Shirley Horn ('Peel Me A Grape').

Various Artists CD Albums

ROCK, ROCK, ROCK
Chess [MCA] CHD-31270 ● February 1988
Reissue of the 1956 LP [Chess LP-1425]. MCA used two different pictures of Berry from those which appeared on the original album. One is from 1965! Previously reissued in 1986 on LP [Chess CHD-31270].

WRINKLES – CLASSIC AND RARE CHESS INSTRUMENTALS
Chess [MCA] CHD-9293 ● 1989
How High The Moon+ *(instr, prev. unissued in USA)*

Great compilation and great cover! Informative liner notes, recording session details and a great little picture of Berry on the back. A fragment of Berry's take on the famous Les Paul instrumental was included as the playout track on the 1963 ON STAGE album [Chess LP-1480] with overdubbed audience noise. This was the first occasion that the cut was issued complete and without the audience overdub in the USA – officially at least (it first appeared in 1980 on the AMERICA'S HOTTEST WAX bootleg [Reelin' 001], which was subsequently legally issued in the UK in 1982 under the same title [Chess CXMP-2011]). Picture of Berry on the cover. Also issued on LP [Chess CH-9293].

A RAGE IN HARLEM
Sire 9-26617-2 ● 1991
Brown Eyed Handsome Man

Original soundtrack. The album starts with Berry's classic and continues with 23 musical performances by various black artists (of course). Some songs (notably Little Richard's 'Elevator Operator' and LaVern Baker's 'Sugar Daddy Blues') were specially recorded for the movie. Others were mostly original '50s recordings by the Solitaires, Fats Domino (2), Robert & Johnny, Little Walter, Clarence 'Frogman' Henry, James Brown, the Willows, Jimmy Reed, Johnny Ace, Lloyd Price, Elmore James, Howlin' Wolf, Bo Diddley and Shirley & Lee. See *Section 7 (Chuck Berry in the Movies)* for more information.

BLUES MASTERS (VOLUME 15: SLIDE GUITAR CLASSICS)
Rhino R2-71126 ● November 1993
Deep Feeling *(instr)*

In 1993 Rhino released a 15-CD box set titled BLUES MASTERS: THE ESSENTIAL BLUES COLLECTION (VOLUMES 1-15) [Rhino R2-71121-71135], consisting of everything from urban blues, post-war Chicago blues, Texas blues, jump blues and blues women to Memphis blues, New York City blues and slide guitar classics. The music here really is essential. It's probably the best blues collection ever issued. You could also buy the CDs individually. This volume also contained 18 gems by Berry, Elmore James, Muddy Waters, Hound Dog Taylor, Robert Nighthawk, Homesick James, Earl Hooker, Johnny Winter, the Paul Butterfield Blues Band, Ry Cooder and many more. Rhino subsequently released a few more volumes, including another of particular interest to Berry fans, BLUES MASTERS (VOLUME 18: MORE SLIDE GUITAR CLASSICS) [Rhino R2-75348] in 1998 (see below for details).

AMERICAN GRAFFITI [2-CD]
MCA MCD-8001-2 • 1993
Almost Grown / Johnny B. Goode

Reissue of the original 41-track original soundtrack 2-LP from 1973, sort-of a '20th Anniversary' issue.

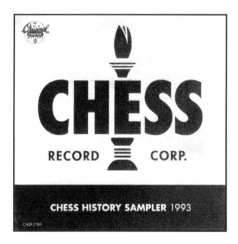 

CHESS HISTORY SAMPLER 1993 [promo only]
Chess [MCA] CH3P-2789 • 1993
Johnny B. Goode

Promotional release featuring 18 prime cuts from the Chess Record Corporation. These are the roots of modern popular music: Muddy Waters, John Lee Hooker, Forrest Sykes, Lowell Fulson, Little Walter, the Moonglows, Clarence 'Frogman' Henry, Bo Diddley, Buddy Guy, Sonny Boy Williamson, Detroit Junior, Howlin' Wolf, Etta James, Fontella Bass, the Dells, Little Milton and Koko Taylor. One song each.

CHESS RHYTHM & ROLL [4-CD]
Chess [MCA] CHD4-9352 • December 1994
Maybellene / Too Much Monkey Business / School Day / Johnny B. Goode / Do You Love Me / Let It Rock / No Particular Place To Go

Nothing new from Chuck here except for a nice unpublished '50s photo, although the set contains 14 previously unissued cuts by the likes of Bo Diddley, the Flamingos, the Four Tops, the Moonglows and Bull Moose Jackson. This longbox set contains 77 artists and 99 tracks reviewing the label's R&B and rock'n'roll output from its boogie beginnings through to the early stirrings of soul music, 1947-67. The music is complemented by extensive liner notes and a 64-page booklet crammed with photos. MCA also released a similar 4-CD set titled CHESS BLUES [Chess CHD4-9340]. This contained no Berry material, but it should have.

PULP FICTION
MCA MCAD-11103 • 1994
You Never Can Tell

This has now become a cult movie, and the Berry track almost became a cult song because of the movie. Thanks to producer Quentin Tarantino, Berry's 1964 classic became one of the musical highlights of the film and also appeared on various CD singles and promos. The album itself sold over three million copies and spent 107 weeks on the Billboard album chart. See *Section 7 (Chuck Berry in the Movies)* and *Section 12 (Achievements & Awards)* for more information.

THE ULTIMATE CHRISTMAS ALBUM
Collectables COL-2512CD • 1994
Run Rudolph Run+

25-track compilation by deejay Joe McCoy of WCBS Oldies radio station in New York. This album spent six weeks on the *Billboard* album chart.

THE MUSIC NEVER STOPPED: ROOTS OF THE GRATEFUL DEAD
Shanachie 6014 • October 1995
Promised Land

This CD is a unique compilation of 17 versions of cover tunes that the Grateful Dead recorded or frequently performed in concert, and introduces Dead fans to the group's seminal influences – and there were many! Great cover with a colour drawing of many of the artists standing on stage in front of a bunch of Deads. Produced by Henry Kaiser and David Gans. Liner notes by Blair Jackson, who says that the band have two Berry covers in their repertoire, 'Promised Land' and 'Johnny B. Goode'. Excuse me Mr. Jackson, haven't you heard them doing 'Around And Around'? Also includes Bobby 'Blue' Bland, Gus Cannon's Jug Stompers, Rev. Gary Davis, the Dixie Cups, Bonnie Dobson, Bob Dylan, Woody Guthrie, Merle Haggard, Buddy Holly, Howlin' Wolf, Charlie Patton, the Pindar Family with Joseph Spence, Obray Ramsey, Jimmy Reed, Marty Robbins and Henry Thomas. Picture of Berry on the cover. See also *Covers (Volumes 3 and 4)*.

JAILHOUSE ROCK (HITS FROM THE BIG HOUSE)
Sony AK-66393 • 1995
Have Mercy Judge

Unusual compilation with all tracks related to prison in one way or another: 'I Fought The Law', 'Folsom Prison Blues', 'Nine Pound Steel', 'Life In Prison', 'Jailbreak', and so on. Other artists include the Bobby Fuller Four, 10cc, Pacific Gas & Electric, Johnny Cash, Merle Haggard, Joe Simon, Thin Lizzy, Three Dog Night, the Byrds, Henson Cargill, and REO Speedwagon. A variety of music, but... only 12 songs on a CD, isn't that a crime?

SOUL TRAIN – 25TH ANNIVERSARY HALL OF FAME [3-CD]
MCA MCAD3-11329 • 1995
Johnny B. Goode

A soul and R&B collection with a little bit of rock'n'roll thrown in c/o Chuck Berry and his original version of the rock'n'roll classic. 58 tracks with good sound quality and a 52-page booklet with many rare colour pictures from *Soul Train*, including one of Berry. The set was issued to celebrate the 25th Anniversary of *Soul Train*, the longest-running, uninterrupted, first-run syndicated US TV show in history. I wonder why didn't they make the set really interesting by using original recordings from the TV shows? I have a video of a *Soul Train* show from 1973 featuring Berry playing live in front of a dancing black audience. Original live recordings from the show would have made this set a real collector's item. As it is, it's just another in a long run of uninteresting soul compilations. Rhino also released a *Soul Train* 20th anniversary set in 1990, but Berry was not on it. Picture of Berry on the cover.

Chuck Berry & Bo Diddley
GUITAR LEGENDS
MCA Special Products MCAD-20974 • 1996
I'm A Man *(Bo Diddley)* / Carol *(Chuck Berry)* / Who Do You Love *(Bo Diddley)* / Thirty Days *(Chuck Berry)* / Roll Over Beethoven *(Chuck Berry)* / Road Runner *(Bo Diddley)* / Almost Grown *(Chuck Berry)* / You Can't Judge A Book By Its Cover *(Bo Diddley)* / My Ding-A-Ling *(Chuck Berry) (live, album version)* / Ooh Baby *(Bo Diddley)*

I like it when Berry and Diddley are combined on records, but I don't agree when the title of the album is GUITAR LEGENDS and it includes the execrable 'My Ding-A-Ling'! To make matters worse, it is the full-length album version at 11:32! Surprisingly, there is no songwriter accreditation on the album at all. I was under the impression that you were not allowed to release anything without printing the composer's name – and here we are talking about MCA, one of the biggest record companies in the world.

JINGLE ALL THE WAY
TVT Soundtrax 8070-2 • 1996
Run Rudolph Run+

Original soundtrack with other seasonal tracks by the Brian Setzer Orchestra, Lou Rawls, Darlene Love (2), Johnny Mathis, Charles Brown, Clarence Carter, Nat 'King' Cole, Bobby Helms and David Newman (2). See *Section 7 (Chuck Berry in the Movies)* for more information.

ROCK AND ROLL FESTIVAL (VOLUME ONE – SUPERSTARS LIVE IN CONCERT)
Anansi/Black Tiger BLT-109-2 • 1996
Too Much Monkey Business / My Ding-A-Ling / Reelin' And Rockin'

Another compilation featuring some of Berry's live Toronto recordings. Other artists include Cat Mother & The All Night Newsboys (2), Chicago (2), Alice Cooper (2), Bo Diddley (2), Jerry Lee Lewis (3 songs associated with Elvis Presley!) and Tony Joe White (2). No picture of Berry, so it's nothing to have or keep. It's appropriate that they picked 'Too Much Monkey Business'. I hope VOLUME 2 never appeared.

Jive Bunny & The Mastermixers
CAN CAN YOU PARTY
Stardust 26666 • 1996
Chuck Berry Medley: My Ding-A-Ling – Rock And Roll Music – Sweet Little Sixteen – Reelin' And Rockin' – Johnny B. Goode – Roll Over Beethoven – My Ding-A-Ling

This is the same four-minute mix featured on the 1994 UK Various Artists CD, PARTY MEGAMIX 2 [Prism Leisure PLATCD-3933] and also on the 1991 Danish Various Artists LP, ROCK'N'ROLL HALL OF FAME [Mega MRLP-3191].

A CHILD'S CELEBRATION OF CHRISTMAS
Rhino R2-72878 • August 1997
Run Rudolph Run+

It's that time of year again! Other artists include Stevie Wonder, the Beach Boys, the Roches, the Singing Dogs, Odds Bodkin, Spike Jones, Robin & Janie Williams, Tish Hinojosa, Pete Seeger, Gene Autry, Art Mooney, Run DMC and the Jackson 5.

HOME ALONE 3
Hollywood HR-62138-2 • 1997
Almost Grown / School Day

Another movie soundtrack album, which interestingly features two Berry songs. Also includes one song each by Jim Croce, the Wailers and Dean Martin. See *Section 7 (Chuck Berry in the Movies)* for more information.

CHRISTMAS FAVORITES
Rhino Music For Little People R2-75539 • August 1998
Run Rudolph Run+

A CHILD'S CELEBRATION OF DANCE MUSIC
Rhino Music For Little People R2-75542 • September 1998
No Particular Place To Go

15-track compilation including Chuck Berry, the Beach Boys (2), Chubby Checker (2), the Jackson 5, Claudine Clark, Earl Chandler, Freddy Cannon, Johnny Horton, Clarence 'Frogman' Henry, Major Lance, Sam The Sham, Taj Mahal and Rick Dees & His Cast Of Idiots.

BLUES MASTERS (VOLUME 18: MORE SLIDE GUITAR CLASSICS)
Rhino R2-75348 • 1998
Blues For Hawaiians *(instr)*

Another great volume following in the footsteps of the 1993 BLUES MASTERS box set. 16 tracks presenting Berry in the company of Muddy Waters, Elmore James, Hound Dog Taylor, J.B. Hutto, Robert Junior Lockwood, Tampa Red, Earl Hooker, Johnny Winter and others.

HIGHLIGHTS FROM THE COMPLETE SOUNDTRACK OF AMERICAN GRAFFITI
MCA 11871 • 1998
Almost Grown / Johnny B. Goode

Reissue to coincide with the 25th Anniversary of the original motion picture, reduced to a single CD selection with 20 tracks. The original 2-LP set and the 1993 2-CD 20th Anniversary reissue both contained 41 tracks.

YULETIDE SOIREE PARTY PACK [2-CD]
Rhino R2-75216 • 1998
Run Rudolph Run+

Various artists from the '50s and '60s. The unusual thing about this set is that one of the CDs features a singalong for party carolling – sort-of karaoke (no Berry). It's interesting to note how many Christmas compilation albums there are featuring 'Run Rudolph Run'. Actually, you can expect the cut to be on almost every other Christmas album release. Royalty-wise, it's a great pity Berry couldn't keep his writing credits.

THE CHESS STORY 1947-75 [15-CD]
MCA [Universal] 3805962 • December 1999
Maybellene / Thirty Days / No Money Down / Roll Over Beethoven / Brown Eyed Handsome Man / Too Much Monkey Business / School Day / *(Rock And Roll Music)* / Sweet Little Sixteen / Carol / Sweet Little Rock And Roller / Almost Grown / Back In The USA / Let it Rock / Come On / Nadine / Promised Land / My Ding-A-Ling *(live, single edit)* / Bio

15-CD set tracing the history of the Chess label. There are 13 CDs containing 330 tracks, one CD containing interviews with Phil and Marshall Chess, and one CD-ROM. This set comes in a solid box with three 'books' inside containing five CDs each, plus a small booklet containing a track listing. There's also a 70-page book of the same size containing essays by Tony Russell (the blues side), Colin Escott (the rock'n'roll side) and Robert Pruter (the soul side). Also included is an interview with Phil Chess.

Berry is reasonably well represented, but guys – a Chess story without 'Johnny B. Goode' is like a gun without bullets! Moreover, 'Rock And Roll Music' is listed but missing on the original issue (for some reason, we get a Cookie & The Cupcakes track that also appears elsewhere in the set).

The CD-ROM includes footage of Chess Records, a story of the label accompanied by pictures of Berry, Bo Diddley, the Flamingos, Etta James, the Moonglows and Muddy Waters, and a listing of the current US Chess catalogue, although Berry is missing! However there *is* a track listing of the *Legendary Masters* series, and two Berry CDs – HIS BEST (VOLUME 1) and HIS BEST (VOLUME 2) – are included, as are snippets of 'Maybellene' and 'Johnny B. Goode'. The disk also contains a video archive with black and white footage of Berry performing 'Johnny B. Goode' live on a *Hullabaloo* TV show with Trini Lopez in 1965.

For people who don't have any knowledge of Chess, this set might be a winner, but to the rest of us who have followed the company's history throughout the years it comes as something of a disappointment. At least, it was to me. The three boxes cover three periods: 1947-56, 1957-64 and 1965-75. However, would you believe there is no recording information whatsoever! The only references are to the various original Chess singles or albums, without any release dates. Such an exclusive box set should also have included exclusive material such as unissued tracks, etc. It says *'Limited Edition'* on the box. Mine is numbered '08081'.

Rockin' in Gothenburg, Sweden – 30 August 1976.

HOT RODS & CUSTOM CLASSICS [4-CD]
Rhino R2-75688 ● 1999
Maybellene / No Money Down / No Particular Place To Go

What a release! 87 full-throttle rock'n'roll and R&B hits spanning 1946-98, plus sound bites from vintage drive-in movies, TV and radio – even an interview with James Dean from 1955! It comes with a massive book packed with information and rare photos, plus a fuzzy dice, moon-eyes, a custom accessories catalogue and a key chain. I won't list all the artists, but Berry fans might like to note the inclusion of Dave Edmunds' version of 'Dear Dad', 'SS-396' by Paul Revere & The Raiders and a few other Berry soundalikes. There are so many rare and great songs about cars on this set, you'll burn out your four carburettors if you listen to it all at once!

LOUD, FAST & OUT OF CONTROL [4-CD]
Rhino R2-75704 ● 1999
Johnny B. Goode / Roll Over Beethoven / Maybellene

The incendiary sounds of the '50s! Rhino have released the ultimate rock'n'roll set. If you just need one rock'n'roll compilation, this is it! *'4 CDs that scared the hell out of mom and dad'.* 104 tracks featuring the best of the greatest including Presley, Lewis, Richard, Cochran, Holly, Haley, Vincent, Domino, Perkins, Diddley, the Everly Brothers, LaVern Baker, Hank Ballard, Larry Williams, the Coasters, Roy Orbison, Bobby Darin, Joe Turner... the list goes on and on. For Berry freaks this also includes 'Forty Days' by Ronnie Hawkins and 'Brown Eyed Handsome Man' by Buddy Holly. What more could you possibly want? Well, there's also an 80-page booklet packed with rare photos and true tales of teenage vice. A hands-down winner!

AMERICAN BANDSTAND OFFICIAL LIBRARY OF ROCK'N'ROLL [8-CD]
Atlantic Q-92904 ● 2000
Sweet Little Sixteen

Longbox containing eight CDs and a 35-page booklet. 120 original master recordings from 1950s to 1980s.

GREEN BAY PACKERS: GREATEST HITS (VOLUME 2) [2-CD]
Alphabet City Sports 4025 ● 2000
Johnny B. Goode *(Mercury)*

This is a 24-track compilation to celebrate the Green Bay Packers baseball team. Besides tracks by James Brown, Jerry Lee Lewis, the Shangri-Las, Free, Steam, the Village People, the Troggs, Martha Reeves & The Vandellas and Lipps Inc. there are highlights from various game reports. It's a pity though that they didn't use the original Chess 'Johnny'.

BLUES GUITAR GREATS
Universal Special Products 314556719 ● 2001
Everyday I Have The Blues+ *(Mercury)*

It's gratifying to see this song included on a blues compilation. It's from the 1968 LP, LIVE AT THE FILLMORE AUDITORIUM [Mercury SR-61138], and it's a very goode Berry track. Others are by the likes of Elvin Bishop, Roy Buchanan, Luther Allison, Albert Collins, Robert Cray, Buddy Guy, Freddie King, Little Milton and Otis Rush.

COLD FEET
Global TV 72607 • 2001
You Never Can Tell

Official soundtrack from the popular NBC TV series.

HEARTS IN ATLANTIS
Decca 440015035 • 2001
Carol

Original soundtrack. Other artists include Chubby Checker, Santo & Johnny, the Platters (3), the Crew Cuts and Percy Faith. See *Section 7 (Chuck Berry in the Movies)* for more information.

THE JAMES DEAN ERA [CD+DVD]
Stardust CLP-1072-2 • 2001
Maybellene

Nice release containing a CD with 22 tracks from the '50s and a DVD including rare movie clips of James Dean, also commercials, a photo gallery and interview with Dean talking about the making of *Rebel Without A Cause.*

BACK TO BLACK: 1900-99 [10-CD]
Universal 541518 • 2002
Johnny B. Goode / Sweet Little Sixteen

This concept is very interesting as it demonstrates how important black music has been to American culture – as if there were any doubt. This starts off with Scott Joplin's 'Maple Leaf Rag' and ends with DJ Luck/MC Neat. 220 tracks plus a 64-page booklet. This is *real* musical history!

THE SANTA CLAUSE 2
Buena Vista 500860069 • 2002
Run Rudolph Run+

Original soundtrack. Other artists include SheDaisy, Brian Setzer, Louis Armstrong, Brenda Lee, the Shirelles, Hilary Duff, Steve Tyrell and Smokey Robinson & The Miracles. See *Section 7 (Chuck Berry in the Movies)* for more information.

SAY IT LOUD! A CELEBRATION OF BLACK MUSIC IN AMERICA [2-CD]
Rhino RN-76660 • 2002
Brown Eyed Handsome Man

A superb tribute starting with Scott Joplin and Bessie Smith and ending with Living Color and Coolio. In between we get all the great black artists who set the standards in the Twentieth Century for jazz, blues, rock'n'roll, soul, rap, hip-hop – you name it. 108 digitally remastered tracks plus a 72-page book including historical essays, timeline and many photos. The Berry picture (a great stage shot) was new to me. Between the songs there are spoken interludes from people like Jesse Owens, John F. Kennedy, Joe Louis, Malcolm X and others.

CHUCK BERRY – THE ARC CLASSICS [promo only]
Arc Music Group AMC CB-0402 ● February 2004
All Aboard / Come On *(Groovie Ghoulies)* / Adulteen *(prev unissued)* / You Never Can Tell *(Emmylou Harris)* / Go, Go, Go / Hey Good Looking *(Bo Diddley)* / I'm In The Twilight Zone *(prev unissued)* / The Little Girl From Central / Nadine *(Carson City Playboys)* / Brenda Lee / Liverpool Drive *(instr)* / Nadine *(Dr. Feelgood)* / You Two / Brown Eyed Handsome Man *(Taj Mahal)* / Come On / Big Ben / O'Rangutang *(instr)* / Trick Or Treat *(Groovie Ghoulies)* / The Man And The Donkey / Brown Eyed Handsome Man *(Nina Simone)* / No Particular Place To Go

'I'm In The Twilight Zone' is incorrectly titled 'I'm In The Danger Zone'. Actually, Berry recorded the song twice using a different title. It's a very good blues, recorded (in stereo!) at the 'Nadine' session in November 1963, and one can only wonder why it was never released. 'Adulteen' was laid down in July 1961 at the 'Come On' session, but the song is not rock'n'roll – a banal *'live your life like an adulteen'* ditty which is soon forgotten. 'Come On' is the mono version. 'All Aboard' is, of course, without the dubbed on audience and 'O'Rangutang' is the complete, unfaded track. The cover versions are all listed in *Covers (Volumes 3* and *4)*.

This promo CD was made as part of Arc's efforts to place the songs with film producers/TV commercial makers (lots of money in this), and possibly other artists.

50TH ANNIVERSARY OF ROCK'N'ROLL: ROCK, ROCK, ROCK
Geffen B0001751-02 ● June 2004
Similar to the 1956 LP [Chess LP-1425], but with three additional tracks: Frankie Lymon & The Teenagers' 'I'm Not A Juvenile Delinquent', Alan Freed & His Rock'n'Roll Orchestra's 'Rock & Roll Boogie' and the Johnny Burnette's Rock'n'Roll Trio's 'Lonesome Train (On A Lonesome Track)'. Again with a nice layout and perfect sound quality.

FROM CLARKSDALE TO CLEVELAND (VOLUME 1: THE ROADHOUSE)
Kejo CD-3000 ● 2004
Around And Around

15 tracks including the Doors, Howlin' Wolf, Bill Wyman's Rhythm Kings, Jimmy Rogers, Stevie Ray Vaughan, George Thorogood, Koko Taylor, John Hammond, John Lee Hooker, the J. Geils Band, Lynyrd Skynyrd, Willie Dixon, Foghat and Slim Harpo.

HAPPY BIRTHDAY NEWPORT! 50 SWINGING YEARS
Columbia/Sony Legacy CK-92377• **2004**
Sweet Little Sixteen *(live)* [on promo copies only]

This 3-CD set contains 27 cuts, but does not include 'Sweet Little Sixteen'. However, advance promos of this set did include the Berry track on Disc 1, which for some reason was deleted from the final package. Strange, because Berry's performance at the 1958 *Newport Jazz Festival* made many people who were not interested in jazz in the first place aware of that musical form through the movie, *Jazz On A Summers Day* (1960).

CARS
Disney Pixar 61349-7 • 2006
Route 66+ *(alt. stereo version)*

Original Soundtrack. Interesting to see this track included. There is also another version of this classic song on the album, performed by John Mayer. It's an okay rockin' tune with some Berry resemblance though not enough to qualify for inclusion in the *Soundalikes* section in *Volume 4.* This album peaked at No. 6 in the *Billboard* 'Top 200 Albums' chart in 2006.

On 15 October 2007, the US newspaper *Salem News* published a very interesting article about Merle Haggard, who figured he'd done just about everything in music except for making a bluegrass album and a rock'n'roll album. The first of these is already out, but the latter project – if it ever happens – should be of great interest to any Chuck Berry fan. In the article, Haggard states that he's working on the rock'n'roll album. Keith Richards has already signed up, and Haggard hopes that Chuck Berry will be able to contribute as well. He doesn't say what the 'contribution' will be, but it *is* an inspiring thought.

Just imagine, a country legend recording with a rock'n'roll legend!!! I am not quite sure how this would sound, as rock'n'roll is not something anyone would ordinarily associate with Merle Haggard – far from it. However, Haggard is a legend in his own time and since 1963 has written and recorded a host of country classics including 'Okie From Muskogee', 'Workin' Man Blues', 'Mama Tried', 'Hungry Eyes' and 34 other No.1 country hits! He says: *'I like to write something that you can photograph.'* Well folks, that's Chuck Berry music in a nutshell. Will it be a Haggard song ('Workin' Man Blues'?), a Berry song ('Nadine' perhaps?) or a completely new song? It's anybody's guess.

If Haggard can pull this off and get Berry to say yes, it will be a milestone in musical history. *Sing me back home...*

UK DISCOGRAPHY

Chuck Berry's earliest UK releases came out on the London label (a subsidiary of Decca), but represented only a fraction of his US output. His first two US singles, 'Maybellene' *b/w* 'Wee Wee Hours' and 'Thirty Days' *b/w* 'Together (We Will Always Be)', were not issued in the UK until they were belatedly wheeled out for the 1956 RHYTHM AND BLUES WITH CHUCK BERRY EP. 'Too Much Monkey Business' *b/w* 'Brown Eyed Handsome Man' wasn't released at all. Ditto the likes of 'Oh Baby Doll', 'Merry Christmas Baby' *b/w* 'Run Rudolph Run' and 'Anthony Boy', to mention the most well-known (although 'Run Rudolph Run' was later coupled with 'Johnny B. Goode' and released on Pye International in 1963).

The London label (which began licensing US recordings from October 1949) is arguably the most collectable label in Europe, and the '50s releases in particular command high prices. The label colour was black. The first two Berry releases appeared with gold print, after which silver print was introduced. All singles up to and including HLM-8921 were released both in 78 rpm and 45 rpm formats. (45 rpm pressings were given a "45-" prefix, to differentiate them from 78s. For ease of reference, I have ignored these prefixes, as strictly speaking they were not part of the catalogue number.) All earliest pressings of Berry's 45 rpm singles up to and including HLM-8921 had triangular centres. HLM-9069 ('Too Pooped To Pop') was the first to be issued only with a round centre.

London promo 45s were single-sided, which meant you got two separate records, each with one side only; the other side was blank. Promo labels were orange, and the discs were pressed with a triangular centre, or later on with small centre hole (although I do have a copy of HLN-8375 with a small centre hole). They were numbered according to matrix numbers: so, for example, promo copies for HLU-8275 ('Down Bound Train' *b/w* 'No Money Down') were numbered MSP.1204 and MSP.1205 respectively.

For EPs and LPs, London used a maroon label with silver print (apart from the first EP, which had gold print). It's very easy to tell if you have an original pressing, because the month and year are always printed at the bottom of the back cover. For instance, my two copies of the LP ONE DOZEN BERRYS say *'58.11'* (November 1958) and *'8/59'* (August 1959) respectively. My two copies of the RHYTHM & BLUES WITH CHUCK BERRY EP read *'10/56'* and *'6/57'*.

Although Berry managed a couple of minor hits in the '50s, it wasn't until Chess agreed a UK distribution deal for their product with Pye at the height of the British R&B boom that he really hit it big in Britain (up until that time, all his UK releases – including his 1961 Pye International single – had been licensed on an individual basis). 'Go, Go, Go' [Pye International 7N.25209] provided him with a hit in the summer of 1963, and was followed by a string of others into early 1965.

The Pye International label was red and yellow with black print. From April 1963, 'R&B Series' was also overprinted as necessary to distinguish black music releases on the label from pop material. The earlier Pye singles had round push-out centres, but later releases came with small centre holes. Pye EPs came both styles of centre.

Promo 45s all had small centre holes and the colour was a dirty pink with only 'Pye International' printed across the top and 'Advance Promotion Copy' printed on the left. The 'A' side had a big black 'A' printed on the label.

I also have an 'Advance Pressing' acetate of 'Nadine' (see illustration on page 157).

In 1965, Chess launched their own UK label, which was distributed by Pye. Berry's recordings appeared on this label up until he signed to Mercury in 1966 and beyond. The label was black with gold print with a 'chess knight' logo behind the Chess name across the top, and was the same for all formats. Promo labels were white and used the same layout as the Pye International Advance Promotion Copies, with Chess across the top and a big black 'A' on the 'A' side. Promos came both with round push-out centres and small centre holes.

The Mercury label was black with silver print and promo labels were white. Commercial releases and promos both came with round push-out centres and large centre holes.

In 1971, Phonogram took over distribution of the UK Chess label. A new numerical series was initiated and a light blue label design similar to the US one (except that the word 'Chess' was all in white, instead of pink, white and blue) was adopted. Some singles also appeared with a pastel blue embossed 'label' pressed into the vinyl, again with the Chess logo across the top. Singles carrying the light blue label came either with a push-out centre or a large centre hole; those carrying the darker blue embossed label came with a push-out centre or a small centre hole.

As in the USA, Chess product dried up in the mid-'70s following the demise of All Platinum until the label's relaunch in 1982 by Sugar Hill, and its sale soon after to MCA. In the UK, PRT (Precision Records & Tapes Ltd.) – formerly Pye – launched a cheaply-packaged but very welcome Chess Masters compilation series which ran from 1982 to 1987. However, they were soon overtaken by reissue specialist Charly, who initially distributed Chess albums reproduced under licence in Italy by Green Line, but after 1987 flooded the market with their own – often superb – compilations of Chess product. This caused much consternation in the US and resulted in a series of court battles with MCA, who alleged that Charly had no rights to the Chess catalogue. For their part, Charly claimed the material been licensed to them by Marshall Sehorn and Red Dog Express, who in turn claimed to have derived their rights from an agreement with Joe Robinson of All Platinum. MCA ultimately emerged victorious in April 1996, but for the best part of a decade UK fans of Chuck Berry and other Chess artists enjoyed an unexpected bonanza. Ironically, the majority of MCA's UK (and US) Chess releases since then have been nothing to write home about.

Singles

Down Bound Train / No Money Down
London HLU-8275 • May 1956
The original release had a black label with gold print and a triangular centre. Later pressings came with silver print and both triangular and round centres. Rumour has it that this single was first issued with a maroon label, but no one has ever seen a copy.

You Can't Catch Me / Havana Moon
London HLN-8375 • February 1957
The original release had a black label with gold print and a triangular centre. Later pressings came with silver print and both triangular and round centres.

Roll Over Beethoven / Drifting Heart
London HLU-8428 • May 1957
The original release had a black label with silver print and a triangular centre. Later pressings came with a round centre.

School Day / Deep Feeling *(instr)*
Columbia DB-3951 • June 1957
The 78 rpm version of this single had a green label. The 45 rpm version had a purple label with gold print. It's hard to find a copy with clean and legible labels.

Rock And Roll Music / Blue Feeling *(instr)*
London HLM-8531 • December 1957

Sweet Little Sixteen / Reelin' And Rockin'
London HLM-8585 • March 1958

Johnny B. Goode / Around And Around
London HLM-8629 • May 1958

Beautiful Delilah / Vacation Time
London HL-8677 • August 1958

Carol / Hey Pedro
London HL-8712 • October 1958

Sweet Little Rock And Roller / Jo Jo Gunne
London HLM-8767 • December 1958
The title on Side A was mis-spelt 'Sweet Little Rock And Roll', and the title on Side B was mis-spelt 'Joe Joe Gun'.

Almost Grown / Little Queenie
London HLM-8853 • April 1959

Back In The USA / Memphis, Tennessee
London HLM-8921 • July 1959

Too Pooped To Pop+ / Let It Rock
London HLM-9069 • March 1960

Bye Bye Johnny / Mad Lad+ *(instr)*
London HLM-9159 ● July 1960

I'm Talking About You / Little Star
Pye International 7N.25100 ● September 1961
    Unlike later Pye International releases, the label colour was dark turquoise with gold print.

I'm Talking About You / Little Star
Pye International 7N.25100 ● May 1963
    Reissue of above with the new red/yellow label.

Go, Go, Go / Come On
Pye International 7N.25209 ● July 1963
    'Go, Go, Go' is the clean studio cut. 20 July 1963 was the date that Chuck Berry's 'Go, Go, Go' hit the British Top Thirty and opened the door for Mr. Berry and real rhythm & blues to the English public.

Let It Rock / Memphis, Tennessee
Pye International 7N.25218 ● September 1963
    It might seem strange that 'Let It Rock' was the 'A' side, but I have the promo of this with a big fat 'A' on that side. Either way, it was a double-sided hit. The record entered the British charts on 10 October 1963 – the day the author celebrated his 14th birthday – so naturally, this particular single became the start of my Chuck Berry collection.

Run Rudolph Run+ / Johnny B. Goode
Pye International 7N.25228 ● December 1963
    The promo copy I have indicates that 'Run Rudolph Run' is the 'A' side, but the original commercial release states it's the 'B' side. However, it was Christmas time and it was 'Rudolph' that charted.

Nadine / O'Rangutang *(instr)*
Pye International 7N.25236 ● February 1964

No Particular Place To Go / Liverpool Drive *(instr)*
Pye International 7N.25242 ● April 1964
    Except for the dreadful 'Ding-A-Ling' in '72, this was Berry's biggest selling single in the UK, reaching No. 3.

You Never Can Tell / Brenda Lee
Pye International 7N.25257 ● August 1964

Little Marie / Go, Bobby Soxer
Pye International 7N.25271 ● October 1964
    This was the first of the Pye International R&B Series releases that didn't chart.

Promised Land / The Things I Used To Do+
Pye International 7N.25285 ● January 1965
    And this was the last one that did.

Lonely Schooldays *(slow version)* **/ I Got A Booking**
Chess [Pye] CRS-8006 ● March 1965

Dear Dad / My Little Love Light
Chess [Pye] CRS-8012 ● April 1965

It Wasn't Me / It's My Own Business
Chess [Pye] CRS-8022 ● October 1965

Ramona Say Yes / Lonely Schooldays *(fast version)*
Chess [Pye] CRS-8037 ● June 1966
　　As mentioned in the US discography, 'Ramona Say Yes' in this form is one of the few songs still only available as a single release (UK, Australia, Canada, (West) Germany and Sweden). The version included on the 1988 US 6-LP/3-CD CHESS BOX set [Chess CH6-80.001/CHD3-80.001] is without the saxophone which is very audible on the single and makes the song special.

Club Nitty Gritty / Laugh And Cry
Mercury MF-958 ● December 1966

Back To Memphis / I Do Really Love You
Mercury MF-994 ● July 1967

Johnny B. Goode / Sweet Little Sixteen
Chess [Pye] CRS-8075 ● May 1968
　　Same as the previous Chess label releases, with black and gold print. However, the promo label was yellow with a push-out centre. There's a reference on the label to the 1967 LP, CHUCK BERRY'S GREATEST HITS [Marble Arch MAL-660].

St. Louie To Frisco / Ma Dear
Mercury MF-1057 ● October 1968

No Particular Place To Go / It Wasn't Me
Chess [Pye] CRS-8089 ● April 1969
　　This was issued as a spin-off single from the 1969 LP, CHUCK BERRY'S GREATEST HITS [Chess CRL-4548].

Roll Over Beethoven / Back To Memphis
Mercury MF-1102 ● May 1969
　　Chuck's last Mercury release was one of a series of reissues marketed as *'Revived 45's – Don't Miss 'em This Time Round'*, and came in an art sleeve. The story goes that Mercury UK thought the 'B' side actually was 'Memphis, Tennessee'. However, as this was actually the very first Berry single in UK that came with anything other than a ordinary company sleeve, it must have some rarity value.

Rock And Roll Music / Johnny B. Goode / School Day [maxisingle]
Chess [Phonogram] 6145 007 ● March 1972

Chuck Berry – Bo Diddley
BIG DADDIES [maxisingle]
Chess [Phonogram] 6145 012 ● August 1972
See *Various Artists Singles*

My Ding-A-Ling *(live, single edit)* **/ Let's Boogie**
Chess [Phonogram] 6145 019 ● October 1972
　　'My Ding-A-Ling' was recorded live at the *Lanchester Arts Festival* in Coventry, England on 3 February 1972. Unfortunately this became Berry's first and only UK No.1, and is very different in style to what really put his name on the musical map. It

came out with at least two different label variations. First of all, with the light blue label with both large and small centre holes, and then with a moulded blue label and small centre hole. (See also my comments in the US singles discography.)

Reelin' And Rockin' *(live, single edit)* **/ I Will Not Let You Go**
Chess [Phonogram] 6145 020 ● January 1973
     The 'A' side is of course the live version from the 'Ding-A-Ling' concert in 1972. This one also came with the same label variations as 'My Ding-A-Ling'. Some of the light blue issues were incorrectly labelled on the 'B' side with Ramsey Lewis' 'Ain't That Peculiar' [Chess 6145 004], although it is Berry's song that plays.

South Of The Border+ / Bio *(single edit)*
Chess [Phonogram] 6145 027 ● November 1973
     The top deck is a BBC-TV recording from the 1972 *Sounds For Saturday* show (originally bootlegged on LP as SIX TWO FIVE), and was surely issued to cash in on the 'My Ding-A-Ling' craze. The song has additional lyrics by Berry which are very much in the same 'Ding-A-Ling' mould, and this particular single is actually quite collectable. It was also released on the 1991 9-CD set, THE CHESS YEARS [Chess CDRED BOX-3], but this is now also very hard to find.

Shake, Rattle And Roll+ / I'm Just A Name
Chess [Phonogram] 6145 038 ● March 1975

Sweet Little Rock And Roller / No Particular Place To Go / Back In The USA [maxisingle]
Chess [Phonogram] 6198 080 ● May 1976
     This was issued both with blue and purple labels, and had a small centre hole.

Sweet Little Sixteen / Guitar Boogie *(instr)*
Chess [Phonogram] 6078 707 ● March 1977
     Issued in connection with the 1977 LP, MOTORVATIN' [Chess 9286 690]. But the catalogue number is surely wrong. 6078 707 would indicate a release year around 1971, but the MOTORVATIN' album came out in 1977.

Oh What A Thrill / California
Atlantic K-11354 ● August 1979
     This was the last original single to be released with new songs from Berry's hand.

No Particular Place To Go / Sweet Little Sixteen
Flashbacks [PRT] FBS-18 ● January 1983
     Picture sleeve.

Memphis, Tennessee / No Particular Place To Go
Old Gold [PRT] OG-9296 ● April 1983

My Ding-A-Ling *(live, single edit)* **/ School Day**
Chess [Green Line/Charly] GCHN-01 ● 1988
     Italian pressing distributed in the UK by Charly. This was released to tie in with the 1987 2-LP, HAIL! HAIL! ROCK'N'ROLL [Chess DETD-207] (not the movie soundtrack) and came in a picture sleeve. See also the 1988 12" EP, Chess GCHX-101. Both releases had the same sleeve art.

───────────────

By this time Old Gold had become a distinct company who licensed songs from all kinds of '50s-'70s record companies. They released singles in generic company sleeves and picture sleeves with liner notes:

No Particular Place To Go / Memphis, Tennessee
Old Gold OG-9843 ● 1989

My Ding-A-Ling *(live, single edit)* **/ Reelin' And Rockin'**
Old Gold OG-9845 ● 1989

Roll Over Beethoven / Johnny B. Goode
Old Gold OG-9847 ● 1989

Sweet Little Sixteen / Rock And Roll Music
Old Gold OG-9849 ● 1989

Hail, Hail, Rock'n'Roll – The Mix
Dino 7CHUCK1 ● November 1991
Medley: Johnny B. Goode – My Ding-A-Ling – Let It Rock – Rock And Roll Music – Reelin' And Rockin' – Roll Over Beethoven – Sweet Little Sixteen – No Particular Place To Go – School Day (4:41) / My Ding-A-Ling (5:04)

This was released during the megamixes. It was done by one Allan Coulthard and I think he did a splendid job, although one mix is enough. Picture sleeve.

Hail, Hail, Rock'n'Roll – The Mix [12" single]
Dino 12CHUCK1 ● November 1991
This contains the same medley as Dino 7CHUCK1 above and in addition has the complete Chess recording of 'School Day' on the 'B' side. Also issued on CD [Dino CDCHUCK1].

Maybellene / Wee Wee Hours
Chess [Universal] 9830034 ● July 2005
'50th anniversary limited edition single, celebrating a pivotal moment in modern guitar music that changed the lives of both the people who heard it and the direction of music itself. The platform from which rock music sprang blistering!' So say the liner notes on the back. That's a pretty accurate assessment, if you ask me. The cover has a great 1955 picture of Berry holding the Gibson he recorded the songs with.

London HLU-8275 (one-sided demo)

London HLU-8275 (original pressing)

London HLU-8275 (later pressing)

London HLN-8375 (one-sided demo)

London HLN-8375 (original pressing)

London HLN-8375 (later pressing)

Columbia DB-3951 (78 rpm)

Columbia DB-3951 (45 rpm)

London sleeve, late '50s

London HLM-8629 (promo)

London HLM-8629: two tri-centre label variations

London HL-8677 (78 rpm)

London HL-8712 (promo)

London HLM-8767 (78 rpm)

London HLM-9159

Pye International sleeve, early '60s

Pye Int. 7N.25100 (original pressing)

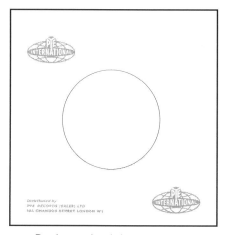

Pye International sleeve, mid-'60s

Pye Int. 7N.25100 (second pressing)

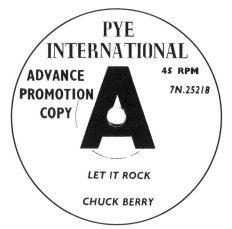

Pye Int. 7N.25218 (promo)

Pye Int. 7N.25218

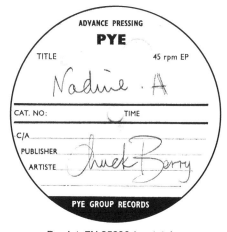

Pye Int. 7N.25236 (acetate)

Pye group sleeve, mid-'60s

Chess sleeve, late '60s

Chess CRS-8006 (promo)

Chess CRS-8012 (promo)

Chess CRS-8012

Chess CRS-8037 (promo)

Chess CRS-8037

Mercury sleeve, late '60s

Mercury MF-994

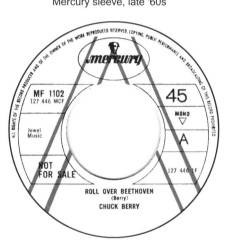

Mercury MF-1102 (promo)

Mercury MF-1102

Phonogram sleeve, early '70s

Chess 6145 019 (large centre hole)

Chess 6145 019 (small centre hole)

Chess 6145 019 (moulded label)

Atlantic K-11354

Flashbacks FBS-18

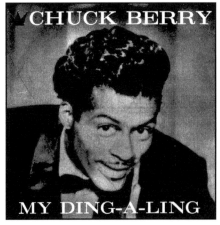

Chess GCHN-01

Chess GCHN-01

Old Gold OG-9845

Old Gold OG-9847

Dino 7CHUCK1

Dino 7CHUCK1

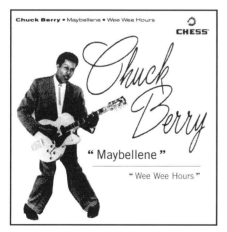

Chess 9830034

Chess 9830034

EPs

Tri-centre with gold print

Tri-centre with silver print

Round centre with silver print

RHYTHM AND BLUES WITH CHUCK BERRY
London RE-U-1053 ● June 1956
Maybellene / Wee Wee Hours / Thirty Days / Together (We Will Always Be)

This came out just one month after the 'Down Bound Train' single [London HLU-8275] and consisted of the first two original US Chess singles. The original pressing carried a maroon label with gold print and is the most rare and expensive one. Later pressings (1957) with a maroon label, silver print and top, and a tri-centre are worth a little less, while those with a round push-out centre are around half the price. They all came with the same art cover.

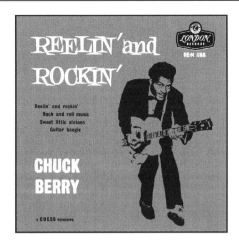

| Tri-centre with silver print | Round centre with silver print |

REELIN' AND ROCKIN'
London RE-M-1188 ● February 1959
Reelin' And Rockin' / Rock And Roll Music / Sweet Little Sixteen / Guitar Boogie *(instr)*

The original release came with a maroon label, silver print and a tri-centre. Later pressings (which appeared during the same year) had maroon label with a silver top and round push-out centres. Picture of Berry on the cover.

CHUCK & BO
Pye International NEP-44009 ● September 1963
See *Various Artists EPs.*

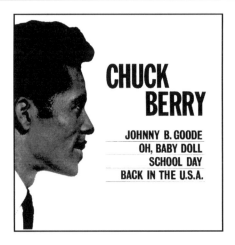

CHUCK BERRY
Pye International NEP-44011 ● October 1963
Johnny B. Goode / Oh Baby Doll / School Day / Back In The USA

By this time, the British music papers had already started writing about the Chuck Berry phenomenon – a black rhythm & blues singer/guitarist/songwriter who seemed to have exerted a great influence on the music of several English groups and solo artists. The cover includes liner-notes to that effect.

CHUCK & BO (VOLUME 2)
Pye International NEP-44012 ● November 1963
See *Various Artists EPs*.

THIS IS CHUCK BERRY
Pye International NEP-44013 ● December 1963
Bye Bye Johnny / Rock And Roll Music / Childhood Sweetheart / Broken Arrow

The liner-note starts: *'Chuck Berry has now become an almost legendary figure to many people in this country'*. However, he was still a few months away from touring England for the first time.

CHUCK & BO (VOLUME 3)
Pye International NEP-44017 ● February 1964
     See *Various Artists EPs.*

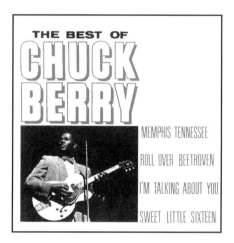

THE BEST OF CHUCK BERRY
Pye International NEP-44018 ● April 1964
Memphis, Tennessee / Roll Over Beethoven / I'm Talking About You / Sweet Little Sixteen

     This carried the same liner-notes as NEP-44013. It was almost time to welcome the 'King of Rhythm & Blues', as they liked to call him back then, so it was important to cash in on his visit with singles, EPs and albums. This EP had a stage picture of Berry on the front, almost as if to confirm that he was coming. 'I'm Talking About You' was a favourite of many UK groups at that time – and the three other songs, well, they were already classics.

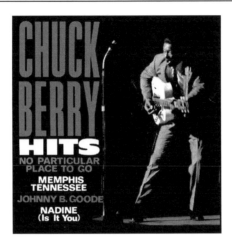

Standard red and yellow label   Pink label

CHUCK BERRY HITS
Pye International NEP-44028 ● October 1964
Johnny B. Goode / Nadine / No Particular Place To Go / Memphis, Tennessee

Here were two of Berry's more recent hits, and it seemed appropriate to include these, but why include 'Memphis' again so soon? This has a great picture of Berry on the front cover, probably taken in England just a few months before.

I have two copies of this Pye International release: one with the standard red and yellow label, the other on a pink label. It's the only one I have ever seen with this unusual combination. Maybe it's a later issue. Were there any others, I wonder?

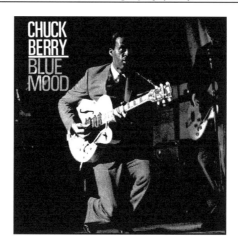

BLUE MOOD
Pye International NEP-44033 ● December 1964
Driftin' Blues+ / Lonely All The Time [Crazy Arms]+ / The Things I Used To Do+ / Fraulein+

    Here Berry was credited with composing both 'Lonely All The Time' and 'Things I Used To Do', however we all know better. Anyway, it was a strange selection of songs even though the title indicates 'blue' tunes, and there is even a mention of three other EPs (all blues) on the reverse of the cover. This also has a great picture of Berry taken in England at the same concert as the one on NEP-44028.

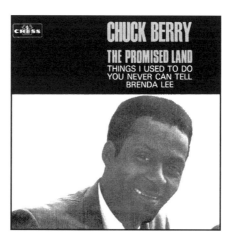

THE PROMISED LAND
Chess [Pye] CRE-6002 ● March 1965
You Never Can Tell / Brenda Lee / Promised Land / The Things I Used To Do+

    Two original singles on one EP. 'The Things I Used To Do' was again erroneously credited to Berry.

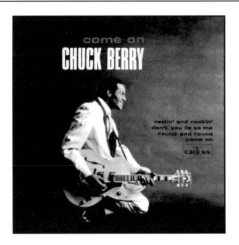

COME ON
Chess [Pye] CRE-6005 ● October 1965
Reelin' And Rockin' / Don't You Lie To Me+ / Around And Around / Come On

'Don't You Lie To Me' was credited to Berry.

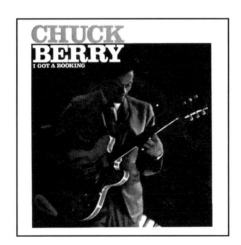

I GOT A BOOKING
Chess [Pye] CRE-6012 ● February 1966
I Want To Be Your Driver / St. Louis Blues+ / Dear Dad / I Got A Booking

Tracks from the 1965 LP, CHUCK BERRY IN LONDON [Chess CRL-4005].

YOU CAME A LONG WAY FROM ST. LOUIS
Chess [Pye] CRE-6016 ● May 1966
You Came A Long Way from St. Louis+ / His Daughter Caroline / My Little Love-Light / Jamaica Farewell+

More tracks from the 1965 LP, CHUCK BERRY IN LONDON [Chess CRL-4005]. UK Chess must have had great faith in the album since they released two EPs containing songs from it.

CHUCK BERRY [33⅓ rpm]
Hammer [Pye] HB-604 ● September 1979
Roll Over Beethoven / Johnny B. Goode / Sweet Little Sixteen / Maybellene / Carol / Memphis, Tennessee

CHUCK BERRY (VOLUME 2) [33⅓ rpm]
Hammer [Pye] HB-610 ● September 1979
School Day / Rock And Roll Music / Sweet Little Rock And Roller / Reelin' And Rockin' / Back In The USA / Thirty Days

Even though it was Pye who distributed the Hammer EPs, they contained Mercury recordings and ran at 33⅓ rpm. They both carry the legend '*The Big Six – Super Single*'.

 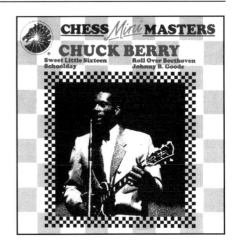

CHESS MINI MASTERS: CHUCK BERRY
Chess [PRT] CHES-4000 ● April 1983
Sweet Little Sixteen / School Day / Roll Over Beethoven / Johnny B. Goode

    Tracks taken from the 1983 2-LP, CHESS MASTERS: CHUCK BERRY [Chess CXMD- 4016].

CHUCK BERRY
SMP [PRT] SKM-4 ● June 1984
My Ding-A-Ling *(live)* / Maybellene *(live)* / Reelin' And Rockin' *(live)*

    The 1969 *Toronto Rock & Roll Revival* again. Art cover.

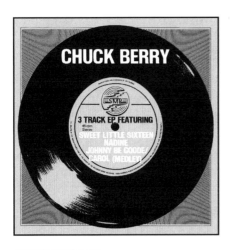 

CHUCK BERRY
SMP [PRT] SKM-5 ● June 1984
Sweet Little Sixteen *(live)* / Nadine *(live)* / *Medley:* Johnny B. Goode – Carol – Promised Land *(live)*

    The 1969 *Toronto Rock & Roll Revival* again. Art cover.

MY DING-A-LING [12" EP]
Chess [Green Line/Charly] GCHX-101 • 1988
My Ding-A-Ling *(live, single edit)* / No Particular Place To Go / School Day / Johnny B. Goode

Italian pressing distributed in the UK by Charly. This was released to tie in with the 1987 2-LP, HAIL! HAIL! ROCK'N'ROLL [Chess DETD-207] (not the movie soundtrack) and came in a picture sleeve. See also the 1988 single, Chess GCHN-01. Both releases have the same sleeve art.

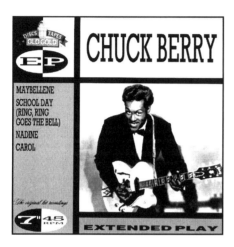 

CHUCK BERRY
Old Gold OG-7703 • 1990
Maybellene / School Day / Nadine / Carol

Nice EP containing Chess tracks and extensive liner notes.

LPs

ONE DOZEN BERRYS
London HA-M-2132 ● November 1958
  Same tracks and cover as the 1958 US LP [Chess LP-1432].

JUKE BOX HITS
Pye International NPL-28019 ● June 1962
  Same tracks and front cover as the 1961 US LP, NEW JUKE BOX HITS [Chess LP-1456]. However, the title is slightly different: no *'NEW'*, just 'JUKE BOX HITS'.

CHUCK BERRY
Pye International NPL-28024 ● May 1963
Maybellene / Down The Road A Piece+* / Mad Lad+ *(instr)* / School Day / Sweet Little Sixteen / Confessin' The Blues+* / Back In The USA / Johnny B. Goode / Oh Baby Doll / Come On / I Got To Find My Baby+* / Betty Jean* / Around And Around / Almost Grown

  This is a good compilation of both classics and rare (at the time) Berry tracks from the Chess vaults. But why couldn't Pye have made a better front cover instead of the insignificant portrait of Berry (the same as the one used on the 1960 US LP, ROCKIN' AT THE HOPS [Chess LP-1448]. The cover should reflect the music, and this album cover did not! The exciting HEY! BO DIDDLEY album cover [Pye International NPL-28025] with Bo Diddley which came out at the same time was much better. This LP was reissued in 1966 on Golden Guinea GGL-0352, and then again the same year as Marble Arch MAL-611, but this time without the four tracks marked *.

ON STAGE
Pye International NPL-28027 ● October 1963
  Same tracks and same front cover as the 1963 US LP [Chess LP-1480], but 'How High The Moon' is faded earlier. The liner note on the back cover says *'If you've got a weak heart, this is not the record for you!'*

MORE CHUCK BERRY
Pye International NPL-28028 ● December 1963

Sweet Little Rock And Roller / Anthony Boy / Little Queenie / Worried Life Blues+ / Carol / Reelin' And Rockin' / Thirty Days / Brown Eyed Handsome Man / Too Much Monkey Business / Wee Wee Hours / Jo Jo Gunne / Beautiful Delilah

Different tracks, but the same front cover as the 1963 US LP, MORE CHUCK BERRY [Chess LP-1465].

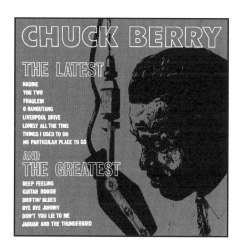

THE LATEST AND THE GREATEST
Pye International NPL-28031 ● May 1964

Nadine / Fraulein+ / Guitar Boogie *(instr)* / The Things I Used To Do+ / Driftin' Blues+ / Liverpool Drive *(instr)* / No Particular Place To Go / Lonely All The Time [Crazy Arms]+ / Jaguar And The Thunderbird / O'Rangutang *(instr)* / You Two / Deep Feeling *(instr)* / Bye Bye Johnny

This contained eight entirely new recordings and six tracks that were not that well known to British fans at the time, but still great songs given that unmistakable Berry touch.   Four of the tracks were taken from the 1964 US LP, ST. LOUIS TO LIVERPOOL [Chess LP-1488] which, together with the next LP, is one of the reasons that that particular album did not see a UK release.

173

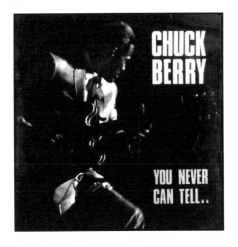 

YOU NEVER CAN TELL
Pye International NPL-28039 • October 1964
You Never Can Tell / Diploma For Two / The Little Girl From Central* / The Way It Was Before /
Around And Around / Big Ben Blues* / Promised Land / Back In The USA / Run Around / Brenda
Lee / Reelin' And Rockin' / Come On

Like THE LATEST AND THE GREATEST above, this album consists of both new
recordings and older tracks from the Chess vaults. Three of the tracks were taken
from the previously-mentioned 1964 US LP, ST. LOUIS TO LIVERPOOL [Chess
LP-1488], and the two songs marked * were previously unissued in the USA at the
time. YOU NEVER CAN TELL was reissued in December 1967 at a budget price on
Marble Arch MAL-702 with the same cover, but minus 'Around And Around' and 'Come
On'. It was also issued in stereo in two versions, both numbered Marble Arch
MALS-702. One of these had the same ten tracks as MAL-702; the other had twelve
tracks – some of them in true stereo – including alternative versions of 'Around And
Around' and 'Come On'. See MALS-702 below for further details.

Chuck Berry & Bo Diddley
TWO GREAT GUITARS
Pye International NPL-28047 • December 1964
Same tracks and cover as the 1964 US LP [Checker LP-2991]. No UK stereo
release.

CHUCK BERRY IN LONDON
Chess [Pye] CRL-4005 • March 1965
Same tracks and cover as the 1965 US LP [Chess LP-1495], except that 'Jamaica
Farewell' is slightly different (without guitar overdub) and faded after 1:44. See US
discography for more information. No UK stereo release. It seems that this album
came out one month ahead of the US release.

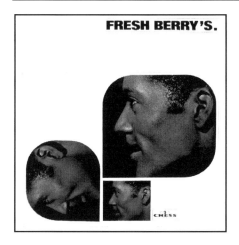

FRESH BERRY'S
Chess [Pye] CRL-4506 ● December 1965
   Same tracks as the 1965 US LP [Chess LP-1498], except 'Sad Day, Long Night' replaces 'Welcome Back Pretty Baby'. The two songs are actually more-or-less the same. On 'Welcome Back Pretty Baby', Berry sings; on the instrumental 'Sad Day, Long Night', a harmonica plays the melody. Otherwise, the cuts have exactly the same backing. The US and UK albums also have different covers. No UK stereo release.

CHUCK BERRY
Golden Guinea [Pye] GGL-0352 ● February 1966
   Same tracks and cover as the 1963 LP [Pye International NPL-28024].

CHUCK BERRY
Marble Arch [Pye] MAL-611 *(mono)* **MALS-611** *(stereo)* **● September 1966**
Maybellene / Mad Lad+ *(instr)* / School Day / Sweet Little Sixteen / Back In The USA / Johnny B. Goode / Oh Baby Doll / Come On / I Around And Around / Almost Grown

   Same tracks as Pye International NPL-28024 and Golden Guinea GGL-0352, minus four ('Down The Road A Piece', 'Confessin' The Blues', 'Got To Find My Baby' and 'Betty Jean'). Different front cover. This picture (probably taken in England in

175

1964) shows Berry on stage in a blue suit playing his yellow Gibson ES-350. On the stereo version, the label bore the legend *'Stereophonic'* and the words *'STEREO MALS'* were rubber-stamped on the back cover. The version of 'Come On' is an alternative stereo take (the same one used later on Marble Arch MALS-702).

CHUCK BERRY'S GREATEST HITS
Marble Arch [Pye] MAL-660 ● January 1967
　　Same tracks as the 1964 US LP [Chess LP-1485] minus two tracks ('Oh Baby Doll' and 'Brown Eyed Handsome Man'). Different front cover.

GOLDEN HITS
Mercury MCL-20102 *(mono)* **SMCL-20102** *(stereo)* ● **March 1967**
　　Same tracks and cover as the 1967 US LP [Mercury MG-21103/SR-61103]. Reissued in 1973 as BACK IN THE USA [Philips International 6336 216] with a different cover.

CHUCK BERRY IN MEMPHIS
Mercury MCL-20110 *(mono)* **SMCL-20110** *(stereo)* ● **December 1967**
　　Same tracks and cover as the 1967 US LP [Mercury MG-21123/SR-61123].

YOU NEVER CAN TELL [10-track version]
Marble Arch [Pye] MAL-702 *(mono)* **MALS-702** *(stereo)* ● **December 1967**
   Same tracks and front cover as the 1965 LP [Pye International NPL-28039], but minus 'Around And Around' and 'Come On'. Also see MALS-702 [12-track version] below.

YOU NEVER CAN TELL [12-track version]
Marble Arch [Pye] MALS-702 *(stereo)* ● **December 1967**
You Never Can Tell *(stereo)* / Diploma For Two *(stereo)* / The Little Girl From Central *(stereo)* / The Way It Was Before / Around And Around *(alt. take)* / Big Ben Blues *(stereo)* / Promised Land *(stereo)* / Back In The USA / Run Around *(stereo)* / Brenda Lee / Reelin' And Rockin' / Come On *(stereo, alt. take)*

   This is a strange and rare one. It has exactly the same cover as MAL-702 above, but the word *'Stereophonic'* appears on the label, and it has a sticker on the back cover saying *'Stereo MALS'*. This LP includes the same 12 songs as on Pye International NPL-28039, but the versions of 'Around And Around' and 'Come On' are different takes, and the version of 'Around And Around' was not available anywhere else, until the release of the US 4-CD set, JOHNNY B. GOODE – HIS COMPLETE '50S RECORDINGS [Hip-O Select (Geffen) B0009473-02] in December 2007. It has a different, more varied lead guitar which gives the song the vitality it needs. Neither song is mentioned anywhere on the cover or label. 'The Little Girl From Central' is a little bit shorter on this stereo issue because of earlier fading.
   This 12-track MALS-702 is the rarest UK Berry album because of the inclusion of 'Around And Around', and also the stereo cuts of 'Diploma For Two' and 'Run Around', which are not available in that form on any other release apart from the 10-track stereo version above. Although it has never been listed in any price guides to my knowledge, I would value it at around double what the 10-track stereo version is worth.

LIVE AT THE FILLMORE AUDITORIUM, SAN FRANCISCO
Mercury 20112-MCL *(mono)* **20112-SMCL** *(stereo)* ● **April 1968**
   Same tracks and cover as the 1967 US LP [Mercury MG-21138/SR-61138].

CHUCK BERRY MEDLEY
Mercury 6851 002 • late 1968/early 1969
  Side 1 is the same as Side 1 on the 1967 US LP, LIVE AT THE FILLMORE AUDITORIUM [Mercury SR-61138]. Side 2 is the same as Side 1 of the 1967 US LP, CHUCK BERRY IN MEMPHIS [Mercury SR-61123]. The cover is also similar to that of CHUCK BERRY IN MEMPHIS. This album appeared both with black and blue labels.

FROM ST. LOUIE TO FRISCO [tape]
Mercury CMP-7029 • January 1969?
  Same tracks as the 1968 US LP [Mercury SR-61176], but only issued in tape format in UK. Who came up with *that* idea? (And, by the way, I have never seen a copy.)

CHUCK BERRY'S GREATEST HITS
Chess [Pye] CRL-4548 • April 1969
No Particular Place To Go / It Wasn't Me* /Thirty Days / My Mustang Ford* / Too Much Monkey Business / Sweet Little Rock And Roller / Go, Go, Go / Johnny B. Goode / Maybellene / Brown Eyed Handsome Man / Memphis, Tennessee / Sweet Little Sixteen / Bye Bye Johnny / Reelin And Rockin' / You Came A Long Way from St. Louis+* / Nadine

178

The three tracks marked * wouldn't normally fit into the Berry 'greatest hits' pattern. This is actually quite a rare UK LP and very seldom turns up on record lists, or on eBay for that matter.

CONCERTO IN B GOODE
Mercury 20162-SMCL • November 1969
Same tracks and cover as the 1969 US LP [Mercury SR-61223]. The promo issue of this has a white Mercury label with a big red '1' and '2' on each side with titles. I have never seen any promo issues of the earlier Mercury albums.

BACK HOME
Chess [Phonogram] 6310 113 • October 1971
Same tracks and cover as the 1970 US LP [Chess LPS-1550]. Reissued in 1975 on Contour 6870 638, and in 1979 on Contour CN-2019, on both occasions with the title *I'm A Rocker*, but with different covers.

SAN FRANCISCO DUES
Chess [Phonogram] 6310 115 • March 1972
Same tracks and cover as the 1971 US LP [Chess CH-50008].

CHUCK BERRY'S GOLDEN DECADE [2-LP]
Chess [Phonogram] 6641 018 • June 1972
Same tracks and gatefold cover with titles on the front as the 1967 US 2-LP [Chess LPS-1514D].

THE LONDON CHUCK BERRY SESSIONS
Chess [Phonogram] 6310 122 • July 1972
Same tracks and gatefold cover as the 1972 US LP [Chess CH-60020]. Later issues of the album came with a round sticker which read: *'Including the full 12 Minute version of The Smash Hit 'My Ding-A-Ling' '*. Can you imagine that this album never made it into the UK charts!

ST. LOUIE TO FRISCO TO MEMPHIS [2-LP]
Philips [Phonogram] 6619 008 ● October 1972
Same tracks and gatefold cover as the 1972 US 2-LP [Mercury SRM-2-6501].

CHUCK BERRY'S GOLDEN DECADE (VOLUME 2) [2-LP]
Chess [Phonogram] 6641 058 ● January 1973
Same tracks as the 1973 US 2-LP [Chess 2CH-60023], but a different gatefold cover.

BIO
Chess [Phonogram] 6499 650 ● October 1973
Same tracks and gatefold cover as the 1973 US LP [Chess CH-50043].

ALL-TIME ROCK'N'ROLL PARTY HITS
Chess [Phonogram] 6310 130 ● October 1973
Johnny B. Goode / Rock And Roll Music / No Particular Place To Go / Memphis, Tennessee / Nadine / Sweet Little Sixteen / Run Rudolph Run+ / Reelin' And Rockin' / Maybellene / Carol / Little Queenie / School Day / Brown Eyed Handsome Man / Roll Over Beethoven / Almost Grown / Bye Bye Johnny

Not the best sound quality, but it's a good compilation of tracks. This album also came out with the number ACB-00208 which could indicate a record club issue. I have also seen this as an 8-track tape.

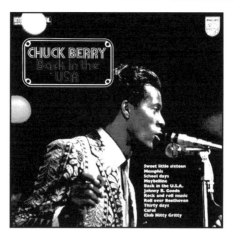

BACK IN THE USA
Philips [Phonogram] 6336 216 ● 1973
Same tracks as the 1967 US LP, GOLDEN HITS [Mercury SR-61103], but different cover. This reissue appeared in many European countries with substantially the same cover but different titles. It was released in 1972 in the Netherlands as ROCK HITS [Fontana International 6430 022], in West Germany as ATTENTION! [Fontana 6430 022], in Norway and Spain as ROCK AND ROLL MUSIC [Fontana Special 6430 022 and Fontana 6430 022 respectively]. (However, the record label inside the Spanish issue actually says GOLDEN HITS.) In 1973 it was released in Italy as ROCK HITS [Fontana Special 6430 022], in France as ROCK AND ROLL MUSIC [Fontana 6430 022] and in the UK – with a different catalogue number from all the other variations – as BACK IN THE USA [Philips 6336 216].

CHUCK BERRY'S GOLDEN DECADE (VOLUME 3) [2-LP]
Chess [Phonogram] 6641 177 ● June 1974
Same tracks and gatefold cover as the 1974 US 2-LP [Chess 2CH-60028], with two exceptions: the UK release has the unreleased alternative track 'Do You Love Me' instead of 'Time Was', and the instrumental 'Berry Pickin' ' replaces 'Viva Rock & Roll'. (NB The label is incorrect on the song sequence and you have to refer to the correct track listing on the sleeve.) See US discography for more information.

CHUCK BERRY '75
Chess [Phonogram] 9109 101 ● April 1975
 Same tracks as the 1975 US LP, CHUCK BERRY [Chess CH-60032]. Same cover, apart from the addition of *'75'*, which actually looks more correct.

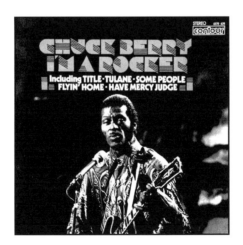

I'M A ROCKER
Contour [Phonogram] 6870 638 ● May 1975
 Reissue of the 1971 LP, BACK HOME [Chess 6310 113]. Same tracks as the 1971 US LP [Chess LPS-1550], but different cover. Reissued in 1979 as Contour CN-2019, again with a different cover.

SWEET LITTLE 16 ROCK'N'ROLL HITS
Philips [Phonogram] SON-006 ● 1976
 Same tracks and almost identical cover to the 1973 LP, ALL-TIME ROCK'N'ROLL PARTY HITS [Chess 6310 130].

MOTORVATIN'
Chess [Phonogram] 9286 690 • January 1977
Johnny B. Goode / Roll Over Beethoven / School Day / Maybellene / Rock And Roll Music / Oh
Baby Doll / Too Much Monkey Business / Carol / Let It Rock / Sweet Little Rock And Roller / Bye
Bye Johnny / Reelin' And Rockin' / No Particular Place To Go / Thirty Days / Sweet Little Sixteen /
Little Queenie / Memphis, Tennessee / You Never Can Tell / Brown Eyed Handsome Man /
Nadine / Promised Land / Back In The USA

22 rock'n'roll classics. 'Let It Rock' is the version without Berry's solo guitar. This
album was in the UK Top Ten in 1977, reaching No. 7 and staying in the charts for
nine weeks. Unfortunately most tracks are in dreadful electronic stereo.

AMERICAN HOT WAX [2-LP]
A&M AMLM-66500 • 1977
See *Various Artists LPs.*

ROCKIN' WITH CHUCK BERRY
Philips Success Series SUC-114 • 1977
Sweet Little Sixteen / Memphis, Tennessee / Roll Over Beethoven / Thirty Days / Carol / Nadine /
Johnny B. Goode / Rock And Roll Music / School Day / Maybellene / Back In The USA / No
Particular Place To Go

Chess recordings in electronic stereo. Same tracks, title and cover as the 1977
Dutch LP [Philips 9279 540].

BEST SELLERS
Hammer HMS-6005 • 1978
Roll Over Beethoven / Johnny B. Goode / Sweet Little Sixteen / School Day / Maybellene / Rock
And Roll Music / Ramblin' Rose+ / Carol / C.C. Rider+ *(live)* / Memphis, Tennessee / Sweet Little
Rock And Roller / Goodnight, Well It's Time To Go [It's Time To Go] / Oh, Baby Doll / Back To
Memphis / Reelin' And Rockin' / Back In The USA / I Do Really Love You / My Heart Will Always
Belong To You+ / Good Lookin' Woman / Thirty Days

All Mercury tracks. See also 1979 LP, 20 GOLDEN GREATS [Hammer HMR-9003].
Best sellers?

ROCKIT
Atlantic K.50648 • October 1979
Same tracks and cover as the 1979 US LP [Atco SD38-118]. As pointed out in the US discography, this remains Berry's last studio album to date. It was reissued in 1988 on LP and CD [Magnum Force MFLP-065 and CDMF-065].

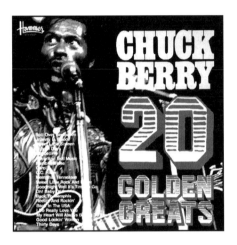

20 GOLDEN GREATS
Hammer HMR-9003 • 1979
Same tracks as the 1978 LP, BEST SELLERS [Hammer HMS-6005]. Different cover, though. Golden greats?

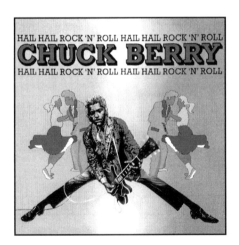

HAIL! HAIL! ROCK'N'ROLL
St. Michael 2102/0102 • 1979
Roll Over Beethoven / School Day / Around And Around / Reelin' And Rockin' / Johnny B. Goode / Down The Road A Piece+ / Jaguar And The Thunderbird / I Got To Find My Baby+ / Go, Go, Go / No Particular Place To Go / Nadine / You Never Can Tell / St. Louis Blues+

This album never shows up in any Berry discographies (except in this one of course). It was released by chain store Marks & Spencer Ltd under licence from

Phonogram and must therefore qualify as a rare album for Berry collectors. Unfortunately, the music is again destroyed by electronic stereo.

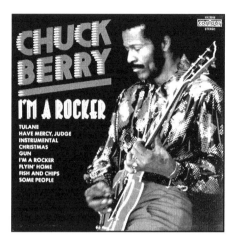

I'M A ROCKER
Contour CN-2019 ● 1979
Second reissue of the 1971 LP, BACK HOME [Chess 6310 113]. Same tracks as the 1971 US LP [Chess LPS-1550], but different cover. Originally reissued in 1975 as Contour 6870 638 again different cover. CN-2019 appeared with two different label colours: one white with a blue top, the other orange with a black top. Same graphics.

PORTRAIT OF CHUCK BERRY
Chess Jazz Masters Series SUC-132 ● 1979
My Ding-A-Ling (Toy Bell) *(live, single edit)* / Little Queenie / Let It Rock / Too Pooped To Pop+ / Bye Bye Johnny / Oh Baby Doll / Reelin' And Rockin' / Sweet Little Rock And Roller / Jo Jo Gunne / Run Rudolph Run+ / Almost Grown / Thirty Days

Same tracks, title and cover as the 1979 Dutch LP [Chess Success Series 9279 541]. 'My Ding-A-Ling' credited to Bartholomew and Berry. 'Too Pooped To Pop' credited to Berry, and 'Run Rudolph Run' credited to *'Marks & Brodie'*. 'Let It Rock' is the version without Berry's solo guitar. Dreadful electronic stereo.

SPOTLIGHT ON CHUCK BERRY [2-LP]
Chess [PRT] SPOT-1003 ● October 1980
❶ School Day / Sweet Little Sixteen / Carol / Route 66+ / Back In The USA / Rock And Roll Music / Promised Land / Let It Rock / Brown Eyed Handsome Man / Maybellene / Around And Around / Run Rudolph Run+
❷ No Particular Place To Go / You Never Can Tell / Nadine / Roll Over Beethoven / Too Much Monkey Business / Go, Go, Go / Reelin' And Rockin' / Memphis, Tennessee / Johnny B. Goode / Tulane / Come On / My Ding-A-Ling *(live, single edit)*

Two LPs in a single cover. Nothing fancy, but a good compilation of songs mostly in mono, except for 'Promised Land', 'Tulane' and 'My Ding-A-Ling', which are in stereo. 'Route 66' is ruined by electronic stereo. 'Run Rudolph Run' is credited to Berry. Promo copies came with plain white labels with no printing on them at all.

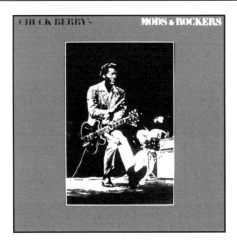

MODS & ROCKERS
Mercury 6336 635 • 1980
Roll Over Beethoven / Everyday I Have The Blues+ *(live)* / Back In The USA / Club Nitty Gritty / Hoochie Coochie Man+ *(live)* / Check Me Out / Johnny B. Goode / It Hurts Me Too+ *(live duet with Steve Miller)* / Misery / Carol / Wee Baby Blues+ *(live)* / Back To Memphis

    I've said it before, the original Mercury albums (and singles) have lousy sound quality, and this album is even worse. I wonder what really happened the first time the tracks were mastered back in the mid- and late '60s in the US. Promo copies of this LP carried a plain white label with just a big *'1'* and *'2'* on either side, but no label name, catalogue number or titles.

CHUCK BERRY LIVE
Everest CBR-1007 • July 1982
School Day / Wee Wee Hours / *Medley:* Johnny B. Goode – Carol – Promised Land / Hoochie Coochie Man+ / Sweet Little Sixteen / Memphis, Tennessee / My Ding-A-Ling

    The 1969 *Toronto Rock & Roll Revival* again, here issued for the first time in the UK. You can actually hear Berry talking between the songs, which is less common. Good sound quality, so it's a pity they didn't release the whole concert. Believe it or not, 'School Day' is titled 'No Particular Place To Go Hail, Hail Rock And Roll'. How do they come up with such nonsense? Reissued in 1984 as Premier CBR-1007.

THE GREATEST HITS – CHUCK BERRY LIVE
Spot SPR-8512 • February 1983
Johnny B. Goode / Sweet Little Sixteen / Nadine / Wee Wee Hours / Rock And Roll Music / Maybellene / Too Much Monkey Business / School Day / My Ding-A-Ling

    The 1969 *Toronto Rock & Roll Revival* again. Here we get the version of 'Johnny B. Goode' with which Berry ended the show (on most Toronto reissues they include the version of 'Johnny B. Goode' from the medley).

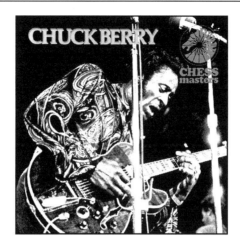

CHESS MASTERS: AMERICA'S HOTTEST WAX
Chess [PRT] CXMP-2011 ● April 1983
Rock And Roll Music *(prev. unissued demo)* / Childhood Sweetheart *(alt. take)* / 21 *(prev. unissued)* / Let Me Sleep Woman *(Ecuadors)* / Do You Love Me *(prev. unissued)* / 21 Blues *(prev. unissued)* / One O'Clock Jump+ *(prev. unissued instr)* / Reelin' And Rockin' *(prev. unissued alt. take)* / Sweet Little Sixteen *(prev unissued alt. take)* / Brown Eyed Handsome Man *(1961 version)* / Say You'll Be Mine *(Ecuadors)* / I've Changed *(prev. unissued)* / Thirteen Question Method *(prev. unissued alt. take)* / How High The Moon+ *(instr)*

This is something else! Same tracks as the 1980 bootleg LP, AMERICA'S HOTTEST WAX [Reelin' 001]. However, this was a legal issue and was a collectors' find when it came out. Actually, it still is, although the bootleg cover was better! You get all the necessary information on each song and the sound quality is excellent. 'Brown Eyed Handsome Man' is the same take as that on Chess LP-1480, ON STAGE, but appears here without the overdubbed audience. The same goes for 'How High The Moon', which is also included here in its entirety. See the US singles discography for more information on the Ecuadors.

CHESS MASTERS: CHUCK BERRY [2-LP]
Chess [PRT] CXMD-4016 ● April 1983
❶ Maybellene / Wee Wee Hours / Thirty Days / You Can't Catch Me / Down Bound Train / No Money Down / Brown Eyed Handsome Man / Roll Over Beethoven / Too Much Monkey Business / Havana Moon / School Day / La Jaunda
❷ Rock And Roll Music / Oh Baby Doll / Sweet Little Sixteen / Reelin' And Rockin' / Johnny B. Goode / Around And Around / Beautiful Delilah / The House Of Blue Lights+ / Carol / Jo Jo Gunne / Memphis, Tennessee / Sweet Little Rock And Roller

Two LPs in a single cover, and it's a very dull one overall with no information.

DUCKWALKING [10" LP]
Chess [PRT] DOW-14 ● July 1983
School Day / No Particular Place To Go / Promised Land / Reelin' And Rockin' / Sweet Little Sixteen / Memphis, Tennessee / Nadine / You Never Can Tell

This was kind-of a collectors' album when it was released because of its size. The front cover picture is another of those great on-stage-with-blue-suit ones from England in 1964 and is worth the price of the album alone. As far as I know this is the only 10" Chuck Berry LP ever made.

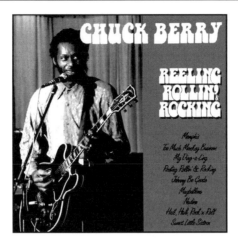

REELING, ROLLIN' AND ROCKING
Bulldog BDL-1051 • November 1983
Memphis, Tennessee / Too Much Monkey Business / My Ding-A-Ling / Reelin' And Rockin' /
Johnny B. Goode / Maybellene / Nadine / School Day / Sweet Little Sixteen

The 1969 *Toronto Rock & Roll Revival* again. Once more we get the version of
'Johnny B. Goode' with which Berry ended the show.

TORONTO ROCK & ROLL (VOLUME 2)
Breakaway BWY-69 • 1983
The 1969 *Toronto Rock & Roll Revival* again. Same tracks and cover as the 1982
US LP [Accord SN-7171]. The only difference is that this particular LP has very good
sound quality in mono.

REELIN' AND ROCKIN'
Magnum Force MFM-017 • April 1984
Reelin' And Rockin' / School Day / My Ding-A-Ling / Too Much Monkey Business / Memphis,
Tennessee / Maybellene / Nadine

The 1969 *Toronto Rock & Roll Revival* again. With just seven songs this album
is a rip-off. Then again, I have never liked any of the Magnum Force releases, period.
They try to convince you that you're buying a top-quality product, but you're not.

20 HITS
Phoenix 20 P20-630 • 1984
This is an English issue of the dreadful US album from 1983 with the same title
and number, even the same cover, containing bits and pieces from the 1969 *Toronto
Rock & Roll Revival*, and sampled together and making it 20 tracks. See the US
discography under 1983 for further info about this LP.

CHUCK BERRY LIVE
Premier CBR-1007 • 1984
The 1969 *Toronto Rock & Roll Revival* again. Same as the 1982 release on
Everest Records CBR-1007. Same cover, same tracks.

REELIN' AND ROCKIN'
Topline TOP-117 • 1984
Rock And Roll Music / Nadine / School Day / Sweet Little Sixteen / Johnny B. Goode / Maybellene / Memphis, Tennessee / Too Much Monkey Business / My Ding-A-Ling

The 1969 *Toronto Rock & Roll Revival* again. How much can you take of this concert? I remember that, back in the '80s when all these Toronto compilation albums came out, I had a hard time listening to them. I have never liked the concert, and, like the Mercury recordings, they don't show Berry at his best and are not good examples of his work or music. However, these albums at least kept his name in the spotlight. Great cover of Berry on the front cover taken in England in 1964.

CHUCK
Revival MEVLP-010 • 1985
Reelin' And Rockin' / Maybellene / Too Much Monkey Business / My Ding-A-Ling / Memphis, Tennessee

The 1969 *Toronto Rock & Roll Revival* again and again… This is actually the first time ever that only his first name – *CHUCK* – was printed on a front cover. You have to read the liner notes or look at the label to find the name Chuck Berry. Plus, a mere five songs on an album qualifies as more than a rip-off!

GREATEST HITS
Showcase SHLP-136 • 1985
Sweet Little Sixteen / Carol / Route 66+ / Back In The USA / No Particular Place To Go / Nadine / Roll Over Beethoven / Too Much Monkey Business / Sweet Little Rock And Roller / Reelin' And Rockin' / Johnny B. Goode / Promised Land / Maybellene / Rock And Roll Music / School Day / Little Queenie

Just one of so many albums that have turned up the last 25 years with the title GREATEST HITS. This is a cheap one and has a lot of incorrect information against each song: 'Sweet Little 16' first published in 1964! 'Back In The USA' first published in 1962! 'No Particular Place To Go' and 'Nadine' first published in 1954! Okay, there are a few correct ones too, but there's no excuse for such misinformation. 'Route 66' is in electronic stereo, 'Promised Land' is in true stereo, and the rest of the tracks are in mono.

ROCK & ROLL RARITIES –
20 MAGIC TRACKS FROM THE GOLDEN ERA OF CHESS RECORDS [2-LP]
Chess 254 200 • Mid-to-late 1986
Same cover and tracks as US 2-LP [Chess CH2-92521].

ST. LOUIS TO LIVERPOOL
Chess [Green Line/Charly] GCH-8007 • 1986
Italian pressing distributed in the UK by Charly. Same tracks and cover as the 1964 US LP [Chess LPS-1488].

NEW JUKE BOX HITS
Chess [Green Line/Charly] GCH-8008 • 1986
Italian pressing distributed in the UK by Charly. Same tracks and cover as the 1961 US LP [Chess LP-1456].

ROCKIN' AT THE HOPS
Chess [Green Line/Charly] GCH-8041 • 1986
Italian pressing distributed in the UK by Charly. Same tracks and cover as the 1960 UK LP [Chess LP-1448].

BERRY IS ON TOP
Chess [Green Line/Charly] GCH-8043 ● 1986
Italian pressing distributed in the UK by Charly. Same tracks and cover as the 1959 US LP [Chess LP-1435].

BIO
Chess [Green Line/Charly] GCH-8046 ● 1986
Italian pressing distributed in the UK by Charly. Same tracks and cover art as the 1973 US LP [Chess CH-50043], but green and no gatefold.

ROCK & ROLL RARITIES [2-LP]
Chess [Green Line/Charly] DETD-206 ● September 1987
❶ Rock And Roll Music *(demo)* / Rock And Roll Music *(unreleased alt. take)* / Sweet Little Sixteen *(demo)* / Sweet Little Sixteen *(unreleased alt. take)* / Reelin' And Rockin' *(unreleased alt. take)* / Johnny B. Goode *(unreleased alt. take)* / Beautiful Delilah *(unreleased alt. take)* / Oh Yeah / The House Of Blue Lights+ / Time Was+ *(1958)* / Sweet Little Rock And Roller *(unreleased alt. take)* / Run Rudolph Run+ / Little Queenie *(unreleased alt. take)* / Betty Jean / County Line
❷ Bye Bye Johnny *(stereo)* / I Got To Find My Baby+ *(stereo)* / Down The Road A Piece+ *(stereo)* / Route 66+ *(alt. take, stereo)* / I'm Talking About You *(stereo)* / Come On *(alt. take, stereo)* / Go, Go, Go *(stereo)* / Brown Eyed Handsome Man *(stereo, 1961)* / Nadine / You Never Can Tell / Promised Land / No Particular Place To Go / I Want To Be Your Driver / Little Marie / My Mustang Ford / Ain't That Just Like A Woman+ / It Wasn't Me

Italian pressing distributed in the UK by Charly. This is a double album release containing all 32 tracks off the 1986 US 2-LP, ROCK'N'ROLL RARITIES [Chess CH2-92521] and the 1986 LP, MORE ROCK'N'ROLL RARITIES [Chess CH-9190]. All the songs from 'Nadine' onwards are in stereo and so-called remixes. 'It Wasn't Me' is without the overdubs by Paul Butterfield and Mike Bloomfield. Also see the US discography under 1986 and the two 'RARITIES' albums for more information. Also released on CD in 1989 [Chess CDCHESS-1005] with only 27 tracks (the five last songs are missing).

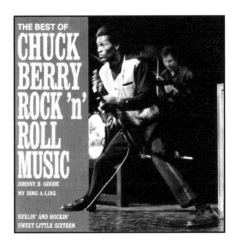

THE BEST OF CHUCK BERRY – ROCK'N'ROLL MUSIC
K-Tel NE-1395 ● 1987
Sweet Little Sixteen / Johnny B. Goode / Back In The USA / Maybellene / Too Much Monkey Business / Rock And Roll Music / Reelin' And Rockin' / No Particular Place To Go / You Never Can Tell / Nadine / Carol / School Day / My Ding-A-Ling *(live, single edit)*

Good sound quality, except that 'You Never Can Tell' and 'My Ding-A-Ling' are in mono. This has a great black and white picture of Berry on the front cover, probably from around 1964-65. Also issued on CD [K-Tel NCD-5155].

MOTORVATIN' (TWENTY CLASSIC TRACKS / GREATEST HITS – LIVE)
Starburst [Magnum Force] SMT-009 • 1987
Maybellene *(Chess)* / Carol *(Toronto)* / Johnny B. Goode *(Toronto)* / Roll Over Beethoven *(Chess)* / Hoochie Coochie Man+ *(Toronto)* / Brown Eyed Handsome Man *(Chess)* / Oh Baby Doll *(Chess)* / Around And Around *(Chess)* / School Day *(Toronto)* / Thirty Days *(Chess)* / Sweet Little Sixteen *(Toronto)* / Memphis, Tennessee *(Toronto)* / Reelin And Rockin' *(Chess)* / Too Much Monkey Business *(Chess)* / You Can't Catch Me *(Chess)* / Wee Wee Hours *(Toronto)* / Rock And Roll Music *(Chess)* / Havana Moon *(Chess)* / No Particular Place To Go *(Chess)* / Little Queenie *(Chess)*

What do we have here? A mess of songs. Magnum really confirmed its lousy policy by this release. They even overdubbed a live audience onto the Chess tracks. One thing that bothers me is that Chris Woodford from the fab mag *Now Dig This* wrote the liner notes. I trust he was unaware of Magnum's plans when he did so. This album is, together with the 1987 LP ROCK & ROLL MUSIC – 16 RARE PERFORMANCES [Warwick WW-2046], the worst ever released in UK and therefore another one to stay well away from.

REELIN' AND ROCKIN'
The Collection OR-0016 • 1987
Another bunch of those awful-sounding *Toronto Rock & Roll Revival* live recordings from '1969. Here 'School Day' is mistitled 'No Particular Place To Go'. The great thing here is the cover: a nice picture of Berry from 1965 holding what looks like a white Gretsch guitar. You'll find an even better copy of this photo on a 1990 UK CD titled GREATEST HITS [No label, ONN-31].

ROCK & ROLL MUSIC – 16 RARE PERFORMANCES
Warwick WW-2046 • 1987
Maybellene *(Chess)* / Brown Eyed Handsome Man *(Chess, 1956)* / School Day *(Toronto)* / One O'Clock Jump+ *(instr, Chess)* / Childhood Sweetheart *(alt. take, Chess)* / 21 *(Chess)* / Wee Wee Hours *(Toronto)* / Rock And Roll Music *(Toronto)* / Roll Over Beethoven *(live, 1956 Alan Freed radio show)* / How High The Moon+ *(instr, Chess)* / Sweet Little Sixteen *(Toronto)* / Nadine *(Toronto)* / Reelin' And Rockin' *(alt. take, Chess)* / Medley: Johnny B. Goode – Carol – Promised Land *(Toronto)*

For the Berry fan who must have everything, this is one of those releases you don't play but just listen to by moving the pick-up quickly from track to track. This is sooo bad I don't know how to approach it. I actually wish I could leave it out of this discography, but I can't. Absolutely everything here is crap, from the left-handed picture of Berry with guitar to the worst sound quality you would ever hear. This is a mixture of Chess recordings (including some alt. takes), live cuts from the 1969 *Toronto Rock & Roll Revival*, and a live recording from a 1956 Alan Freed radio show (see the 1978 Various Artists bootleg LP, ROCK'N'ROLL RADIO [Radiola MR-1087] for more information). The old Chess studio tracks even have live audience dubbed on! The short liner notes tell us that Chuck Berry was born 15 January 1931 in San Jose, and that, thanks to the million-selling title track, he became as popular as Bill Haley and Little Richard. 'School Day' is credited to *'Edwards-Cobbs'*, 'How High The Moon' is credited to Berry, 'Carol' says *'Copyright Control'* and... where's the chainsaw?

HAIL! HAIL! ROCK'N'ROLL
MCA MCF-3411 • February 1988
    Original soundtrack.   Same tracks and cover as the 1987 US LP [MCA MCA-6217]. Also issued on CD [MCA DMCF-3411].

CHUCK BERRY – THE COLLECTION [2-LP]
The Collector Series CCSLP-194 • October 1988
❶ Sweet Little Sixteen / Johnny B. Goode / Back In The USA / Maybellene / Too Much Monkey Business / Rock And Roll Music / Reelin' And Rockin' / No Particular Place To Go / Roll Over Beethoven / You Never Can Tell / Nadine / Carol
❷ School Day / My Ding-A-Ling *(live, single edit)* / Almost Grown / Let It Rock / Little Queenie / Promised Land / Memphis, Tennessee / Sweet Little Rock And Roller / Thirty Days / Brown Eyed Handsome Man / Run Rudolph Run+ / Merry Christmas Baby+

    Another 'greatest hits' album set of Chess tracks, however, what's interesting here are the six great colour pictures of Chuck inside the gatefold cover. 'Merry Christmas Baby' is the album version (from ST. LOUIS TO LIVERPOOL [Chess LP-1488]) and the song is even credited to Berry! 'Run Rudolph Run' is also credited to Berry. The whole package contains mono recordings, except for 'Promised Land' and 'My Ding-A-Ling'. Also issued on CD [The Collector Series CCSCD-194].

CHESS MASTERS: CHUCK BERRY
Stylus SMR-848 • 1988
No Particular Place To Go / Maybellene / You Can't Catch Me / School Day / Roll Over Beethoven / Sweet Little Sixteen / Around And Around / Sweet Little Rock And Roller / Nadine / Rock And Roll Music / Oh Baby Doll / Johnny B. Goode / Reelin' And Rockin' / Memphis, Tennessee / Carol / Come On *(stereo)*

    Another greatest hits album, but I haven't seen the picture on the front cover before, so in this instance it's interesting. There are a couple of titling errors ('Old Baby Doll' and 'Reel And A Rockin' '). 'Come On' is the alternative stereo version. Also issued on CD [Stylus SMD-848].

DECADE '55-'65
Platinum Music [Prism Leisure] PLAT-24 ● 1988
School Day / Maybellene / Sweet Little Sixteen / Roll Over Beethoven / Too Much Monkey Business / Memphis, Tennessee / Let It Rock / Little Queenie / Carol / Almost Grown / Nadine / Johnny B. Goode / No Particular Place To Go / Promised Land / Back In The USA / Rock And Roll Music

16 Chess cuts in good old mono, although three should have been in stereo. First issued on CD [Platinum Music PLATCD-24] in 1987. The LP and CD covers both say *'Made In Germany'*, however, I believe it's a UK release.

HAIL! HAIL! ROCK'N'ROLL [2-LP]
Chess [Green Line/Charly] DETD-207 ● 1988
❶ Maybellene / Thirty Days / No Money Down / Roll Over Beethoven / Brown Eyed Handsome Man / Too Much Monkey Business / You Can't Catch Me / School Day / Rock And Roll Music / Sweet Little Sixteen / Reelin' And Rockin' / Johnny B. Goode / Around And Around / Beautiful Delilah / Carol / Sweet Little Rock And Roller.
❷ Almost Grown / Little Queenie / Back In The USA / Memphis, Tennessee / Too Pooped To Pop+ / Let It Rock / Bye Bye Johnny / I'm Talking About You / Come On / Nadine / No Particular Place To Go / You Never Can Tell / Little Marie / Promised Land / Tulane / My Ding-A-Ling *(live, single edit)*

Italian pressing distributed in the UK by Charly. Not the soundtrack of the film, but a good compilation of 32 tracks very similar to the 1986 US 2-LP, THE GREAT 28 [Chess CHD-92500]. Each song has a reference to the US Billboard charts, the gatefold cover has pictures of the original US Chess albums (except for FRESH BERRY'S, which is the UK issue, and one UK compilation) and a survey of Berry's US Chess single releases (albeit incomplete). This 2-LP was edited down to 28 tracks and reissued on CD in 1989 [Chess CDCHESS-1003], 1990 [Instant CDINS-5035] and 1993 [Charly CPCD-8006].

ROCKIT
Magnum Force MFLP-065 ● 1988
Reissue of the 1979 LP [Atlantic K-50648]. Same tracks and cover. Also issued on CD [Magnum Force CDMF-065].

THE CLASSIC CHUCK BERRY
Ocean OCNWL-2033 ● 1989
Maybellene / Roll Over Beethoven / School Day / Rock And Roll Music / Sweet Little Sixteen / Johnny B. Goode / Carol / Almost Grown / Back In The USA / Go, Go, Go *(stereo)* / Let It Rock / Memphis, Tennessee / Run Rudolph Run+ / Nadine / No Particular Place To Go / You Never Can Tell / Promised Land / My Ding-A-Ling *(live, single edit)*

If you notice that 'Go, Go, Go' often pops up on the various UK album issues it is because it was a single hit there in 1963. Why do they so often include the mono recordings of the mid '60s tracks instead of the stereo ones? Perhaps it is easier to license the mono masters? I believe they should release the songs the way they were originally recorded, not the way they were originally issued.

ROCK AND ROLL MUSIC
Instant [Charly] INS-5002 ● 1989
Maybellene / School Day / Rock And Roll Music / Sweet Little Sixteen / Johnny B. Goode / Memphis, Tennessee / Come On / Let It Rock / Reelin' And Rockin' / Nadine / No Particular Place To Go / You Never Can Tell / Promised Land / My Ding-A-Ling *(live, single edit)*

This is almost the same as the one above on Ocean Records. 14 tracks instead of 18 on the above and only two that are different: 'Come On' and 'Reelin' And Rockin' '. Maybe Charly Records didn't tell Ocean that they were going to release almost the same album at the same time. Different cover though. Also issued on CD [Instant CDINS-5002].

CHARLY BOX SET

In November 1989, Charly released Chess GCH-8008, GCH-8043, GCH-8046 and DETD-206 as a box set. They came in a black cardboard box with a Chuck Berry picture-sticker on the front. It was one of several bundles of albums packaged in generic boxes for the Christmas market. Although it was advertised with the catalogue number BOX-256, this was not stated on the box itself. However, there was a sticker showing the EAN code, 8233350061.

HAIL! HAIL! ROCK'N'ROLL [2-LP]
Instant [Charly] INSD-5035 ● 1990
Not the soundtrack. Same as the 1988 2-LP [Chess DETD-207], but reduced to 28 tracks: 'Little Marie', 'Tulane' and 'My Ding-A-Ling' are missing. Also issued on CD [Instant CDINS-5035].

THE EP COLLECTION
See For Miles SEE-320 ● 1991
Reelin' And Rockin' / Johnny B. Goode / Nadine *(stereo)* / Don't You Lie To Me+ / Around And Around / No Particular Place To Go *(stereo)* / Childhood Sweetheart / My Little Love-Light / Maybellene / I'm Talking About You / Roll Over Beethoven / Sweet Little Sixteen / You Can't Catch Me / Memphis, Tennessee / I Got A Booking / You Never Can Tell *(stereo)* / The Things I Used To Do+ *(stereo)* / Jamaica Farewell+ / Thirty Days / Oh Baby Doll / School Day / Bye Bye Johnny

This was one of a series of albums covering the EP releases in the UK of various artists. The first was by Billy Fury. So many EPs were issued of Chuck Berry that See For Miles would have needed to release a second volume to include everything. Nevertheless, this is a good compilation of tracks with informative and accurate liner notes from Bob Naylor, except that the original title of 'Maybellene' was 'Ida May' not 'Ida Red'. The version of 'Sweet Little Sixteen' included here is the one at the original speed, and 'Jamaica Farewell' is the 'UK' version without the extra guitar. 'Don't You Lie To Me' is credited to Berry. Also issued on CD [See For Miles SEECD-320] with two additional tracks, 'Back In The USA' and 'Rock And Roll Music'.

3" CD Singles

CHUCK BERRY
Old Gold OG-6143 • 1989
Roll Over Beethoven / Johnny B. Goode / Rock And Roll Music

Chess recordings. A rare black and white shot of Berry on the front. Also some liner notes. This came with an adapter for use in CD players that only play 5" disks.

5" CD Singles

THE CHARLY ORIGINALS: CHUCK BERRY
Charly CDS-6 • 1989
No Particular Place To Go / Johnny B. Goode / You Never Can Tell / Memphis, Tennessee

In 1989 this was really a special record (mono versions, though) – not least because it has a colour picture of Berry on the front which I have never seen before or since, probably taken in the UK in '64 or '65.

HAIL, HAIL, ROCK'N'ROLL – THE MIX
Dino CDCHUCK-1 • November 1991
This contains the same medley as the 12" single [Dino 12CHUCK1] plus the complete Chess recording of 'School Day'.

CHUCK BERRY
Master Tone CP-6281 ● 1996
School Day / Johnny B. Goode / Rock And Roll Music / Maybellene

    Chess recordings. CD shaped like a hamburger, and probably made for a fast food chain. No picture of Berry. This was also sold in France.

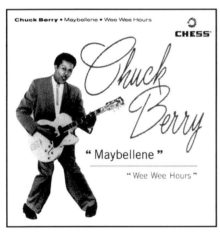

| Cover | Inner sleeve |

Maybellene / Wee Wee Hours
Chess [Universal] 9830035 ● July 2005
    Same cover as the vinyl single, however, there are additional liner notes on the inner cover: a short history with correct birthplace and date of birth(!), and what led to the two songs being recorded. Also, another picture is featured on the other side of the inner sleeve.

CD Albums

A great many cheap CDs were issued in the UK from the late '80s and through the '90s, and most of them are of little interest to Berry fans. The only positive thing is that they kept the Chuck Berry's name and music alive, but unfortunately many have poor sound quality. I have therefore omitted the worst, and have mentioned only those with either good sound quality, a good selection of songs or, once in a while, a nice and rare picture of Berry on the front cover.

ROCK, ROCK, ROCK
Chess [Green Line/Charly] CDCHESS-1016 ● 1989
Same tracks as the 1956 US LP [Chess LP-1425], but the cover is the one used for the 1986 US LP reissue with the 1965 picture of Berry [Chess CH-9254].

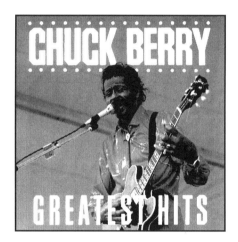

GREATEST HITS
Chess [Green Line/Charly] CDCHESS-21 ● 1986
Maybellene / Thirty Days / Brown Eyed Handsome Man / Roll Over Beethoven / Too Much Monkey Business / School Day / Rock And Roll Music / Sweet Little Sixteen / Reelin' And Rockin' / Johnny B. Goode / Around And Around / Carol / Memphis, Tennessee / Sweet Little Rock And Roller / Little Queenie / Back In The USA / Let It Rock / Nadine / You Never Can Tell / Promised Land / No Particular Place To Go / Beautiful Delilah / Bye Bye Johnny

Italian pressing distributed in the UK by Charly. 23 Chess tracks, all in straight-ahead mono. Great cover! Although this was not released on LP in the UK, one was issued in Poland in 1987 (see Polish discography).

THE BEST OF CHUCK BERRY – ROCK'N'ROLL MUSIC
K-Tel NCD-5155 ● 1987
Sweet Little Sixteen / Johnny B. Goode / Back In The USA / Maybellene / Too Much Monkey Business / Rock And Roll Music / Reelin' And Rockin' / No Particular Place To Go / You Never Can Tell / Nadine / Carol / School Day / My Ding-A-Ling *(live, single edit)*

Good sound quality, except that 'You Never Can Tell' and 'My Ding-A-Ling' are in mono. This has a great black and white picture of Berry on the front cover, probably from around 1964-65. Also issued on LP [K-Tel NE-1395].

HAIL! HAIL! ROCK'N'ROLL
MCA DMCF-3411 ● February 1988
Original soundtrack. Same tracks and cover as the 1987 US LP [MCA MCA-6217]. Also issued on LP [MCA MCF-3411].

CHUCK BERRY – THE COLLECTION
The Collector Series CCSCD-194 ● October 1988
Sweet Little Sixteen / Johnny B. Goode / Back In The USA / Maybellene / Too Much Monkey Business / Rock And Roll Music / Reelin' And Rockin' / No Particular Place To Go / Roll Over Beethoven / You Never Can Tell / Nadine / Carol / School Day / My Ding-A-Ling *(live, single edit)* / Almost Grown / Let It Rock / Little Queenie / Promised Land / Memphis, Tennessee / Sweet Little Rock And Roller / Thirty Days / Brown Eyed Handsome Man / Run Rudolph Run+ / Merry Christmas Baby+

Another 'greatest hits' album set of Chess tracks, however, what's interesting here are the six great colour pictures of Chuck inside the gatefold cover. 'Merry Christmas Baby' is the album version (from ST. LOUIS TO LIVERPOOL [Chess LP-1488]) and the song is even credited to Berry! 'Run Rudolph Run' is also credited to Berry. The whole package contains mono recordings, except for 'Promised Land' and 'My Ding-A-Ling'. Also issued on 2-LP [The Collector Series CCSLP-194].

CHESS MASTERS: CHUCK BERRY
Stylus SMD-848 ● 1988
No Particular Place To Go / Maybellene / You Can't Catch Me / School Day / Roll Over Beethoven / Sweet Little Sixteen / Around And Around / Sweet Little Rock And Roller / Nadine / Rock And Roll Music / Oh Baby Doll / Johnny B. Goode / Reelin' And Rockin' / Memphis, Tennessee / Carol / Come On *(stereo)*

Another greatest hits album, but I haven't seen the picture on the front cover before, so in this instance it's interesting. There are a couple of titling errors (eg 'Old Baby Doll' and 'Reel And A Rockin' '). 'Come On' is the alternative stereo version. Also issued on LP [Stylus SMR-848].

DECADE '55-'65
Platinum Music [Prism Leisure] PLATCD-24 ● 1988
School Day / Maybellene / Sweet Little Sixteen / Roll Over Beethoven / Too Much Monkey Business / Memphis, Tennessee / Let It Rock / Little Queenie / Carol / Almost Grown / Nadine / Johnny B. Goode / No Particular Place To Go / Promised Land / Back In The USA / Rock And Roll Music

16 Chess cuts in good old mono, although three should have been in stereo. Also issued on LP [Platinum Music PLAT-24] in 1988. The LP and CD covers both say *'Made In Germany'*, however, I believe it's a UK release.

ROCKIT
Magnum Force CDMF-065 ● 1988
Reissue of the 1979 LP [Atlantic K-50648]. Same tracks and cover. Also issued on LP [Magnum Force MFLP-065].

ROCK AND ROLL MUSIC
Instant [Charly] CDINS-5002 ● 1989
Maybellene / School Day / Rock And Roll Music / Sweet Little Sixteen / Johnny B. Goode / Memphis, Tennessee / Come On / Let It Rock / Reelin' And Rockin' / Nadine / No Particular Place To Go / You Never Can Tell / Promised Land / My Ding-A-Ling *(live, single edit)*

Compilation also released on LP [Instant INS-5002].

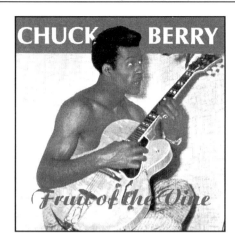

FRUIT OF THE VINE
Chess [Charly] CDRED-19 • 1990
Down Bound Train / Wee Wee Hours / No Money Down / Drifting Heart / Brown Eyed Handsome Man / Havana Moon / Oh Baby Doll / Anthony Boy / Merry Christmas Baby+ *(single version)* / Jo Jo Gunne / Childhood Sweetheart / I Got To Find My Baby+ *(stereo)* / Worried Life Blues+ / Jaguar And The Thunderbird / Confessin' The Blues+ / Thirteen Question Method / The Things I Used To Do+ *(stereo)* / You Two *(stereo)* / Little Marie *(stereo)* / Dear Dad *(stereo)* / It Wasn't Me *(stereo)* / Ramona Say Yes *(stereo)* / Tulane *(stereo)* / Have Mercy Judge *(stereo)*

This is really something! My favourite Berry CD of mostly non-hits. The songs are in chronological order of recording. If you want to hear Berry from a different musical point of view, this is it! Superb sound quality. 'Ramona Say Yes' is the version without the saxophone.

GREATEST HITS
No label, ONN-31 • 1990
21 Mercury tracks, the usual stuff from 'C.C. Rider' to 'Maybellene' with the lack of bass. This album was only available on compact disc. The great thing here is the cover: a nice picture of Berry from 1965 holding what looks like a white Gretsch guitar.

HAIL! HAIL! ROCK'N'ROLL
Instant [Charly] CDINS-5035 • 1990
Not the soundtrack. Same as the 1988 2-LP [Chess DETD-207], but reduced to 28 tracks: 'Little Marie', 'Tulane' and 'My Ding-A-Ling' are missing. Also issued on 2-LP [Instant INSD-5035].

THE LONDON SESSIONS
Chess [Charly] CDRED-20 • 1990
Same tracks as the 1972 LP, THE CHUCK BERRY LONDON SESSIONS [Chess 6310 122]. It has a different front cover, though. The copy I have has a *'A Free Bonus CD'* sticker, which meant you got *'The Incredible Chess CD'* featuring 20 Chess artists from Chuck Berry to Etta James and Otis Spann as a gift when purchasing the above Berry CD.

THE BEST OF CHUCK BERRY
Music Club MCCD-019 • 1991
Roll Over Beethoven / No Particular Place To Go / Memphis, Tennessee / Tulane *(stereo)* / Havana Moon / Wee Wee Hours / Nadine / Let It Rock / Sweet Little Sixteen / Maybellene / Back In The USA / Little Queenie / Almost Grown / Johnny B. Goode / School Day / Oh Baby Doll /

Sweet Little Rock And Roller / Reelin' And Rockin' / Promised Land / Rock And Roll Music / Down Bound Train / Brown Eyed Handsome Man / Merry Christmas Baby+ *(single version)* / Bye Bye Johnny / Around And Around / No Money Down

26 tracks and almost 70 minutes of playing time – that's good value for money even though only 'Tulane' is in stereo. Good sound quality.

THE CHESS MASTERS (VOLUME 1: 1955-58)
Magnum Force CDMF-076 ● 1991
Maybellene / Wee Wee Hours / Thirty Days / You Can't Catch Me / No Money Down / Brown Eyed Handsome Man / Roll Over Beethoven / Too Much Monkey Business / School Day / Rock And Roll Music / Oh Baby Doll / Sweet Little Sixteen / Rock At The Philharmonic *(instr)* / Guitar Boogie *(instr)* / Reelin' And Rockin' / Johnny B. Goode

THE CHESS MASTERS (VOLUME 2: 1958-65)
Magnum Force CDMF-080 ● 1991
Around And Around / Beautiful Delilah / Carol / Memphis, Tennessee / Sweet Little Rock And Roller / Little Queenie / Almost Grown / Back In The USA / Let It Rock / Bye Bye Johnny / Come On / Nadine *(stereo)* / You Never Can Tell *(stereo)* / Promised Land *(stereo)* / No Particular Place To Go *(stereo)* / It Wasn't Me *(stereo)*

Just once it's good to notice that Magnum released two serious compilations of Berry tracks. The sound quality is good too. The sleevenotes on both volumes include comments from Berry on some of the songs, the quotes being taken from *Chuck Berry – The Autobiography* (1987).

CHUCK BERRY – THE CHESS YEARS [9-CD]
Chess [Charly] CDRED BOX-3 ● 1991
❶ Maybellene / Wee Wee Hours / Thirty Days / Together (We Will Always Be) / You Can't Catch Me / Roly Poly *(instr)* / Berry Pickin' *(instr)* / Down Bound Train / No Money Down / Drifting Heart / Brown Eyed Handsome Man / Roll Over Beethoven / Too Much Monkey Business / Havana Moon / Rock And Roll Music *(demo)* / Deep Feeling *(instr)* / School Day / La Jaunda / Blue Feeling *(instr)* / Low Feeling *(instr)* / Wee Wee Hours / How You've Changed / Rock And Roll Music / Oh Baby Doll / Sweet Little Sixteen *(demo)*
❷ Thirteen Question Method / How High The Moon+ *(instr)* / I've Changed / Sweet Little Sixteen / Rock At The Philharmonic *(instr)* / Guitar Boogie *(instr)* / Night Beat *(instr)* / Time Was+ *(slow version)* / Reelin And Rockin' / Johnny B. Goode / Around And Around / In-Go *(instr)* / It Don't Take But A Few Minutes / Blues For Hawaiians *(instr)* / Beautiful Delilah / Vacation Time / 21 / 21 Blues / Carol / Oh Yeah / Hey Pedro / Time Was+ *(fast version)* / House of Blue Lights+ / Anthony Boy / Jo Jo Gunne / Sweet Little Rock & Roller / Memphis Tennessee / Merry Christmas Baby+ *(single version)* / Run Rudolph Run+ / Little Queenie
❸ That's My Desire+ / Little Queenie *(alt. take)* / Do You Love Me *(alt. take)* / Almost Grown / Back In The USA / Blue On Blue *(instr)* / Betty Jean / County Line / Childhood Sweetheart / One O'Clock Jump+ *(instr)* / I Just Want To Make Love To You+ *(with overdubbed audience)* / Broken Arrow / Let It Rock / Too Pooped To Pop+ / Say You'll Be Mine+ / Let Me Sleep Woman+ / Childhood Sweetheart *(alt. take)* / Driftin' Blues+ / I Got To Find My Baby+ / Don't You Lie To Me+ / Worried Life Blues+ / Our Little Rendezvous / Bye Bye Johnny / Run Around / Jaguar And Thunderbird / Diploma For Two / Little Star / The Way It Was Before / Away From You / Down The Road A Piece+
❹ Confessin' The Blues+ / Sweet Sixteen+ / Thirteen Question Method / Stop And Listen / Still Got The Blues *(with overdubbed audience)* / Lucky So And So+ / Mad Lad+ *(instr)* / Cryin' Steel *(instr)* / Surfin' Steel *(instr) (with overdubbed audience)* / Route 66+ / I'm Talking About You / Rip It Up+ / Come On / The Man And The Donkey *(with overdubbed audience)* / Go, Go, Go *(with overdubbed audience)* / Trick Or Treat *(with overdubbed audience)* / Brown Eyed Handsome Man *(with overdubbed audience)* / All Aboard *(with overdubbed audience)* / How High The Moon+ *(instr) (with overdubbed audience)* / Nadine / You Never Can Tell / The Girl From Central High / The Things I Used To Do+ / Fraulein+ / Lonely All The Time [Crazy Arms]+ / O'Rangutang *(instr)* / Big Ben Blues / Promised Land / Brenda Lee

❺ No Particular Place To Go / Liverpool Drive *(instr)* / You Two / Chuck's Beat *(instr) (with Bo Diddley, edited – 6:30)* / Bo's Beat+ *(instr) (with Bo Diddley, single edit)* / Little Marie / Go, Bobby Soxer / Lonely Schooldays *(slow version)* / His Daughter Caroline / Dear Dad / I Want To Be Your Driver / The Song Of My Love / Butterscotch *(instr)* / After It's Over *(instr)* / Why Should We End This Way / You Came A Long Way From St. Louis+ / She Once Was Mine / Jamaica Farewell+ / My Little Lovelight / I Got A Booking / St. Louis Blues+ / Run Joe+ / It's My Own Business / One For My Baby (And One More For The Road)+ / Everyday We Rock & Roll

❻ My Mustang Ford / Merrily We Rock & Roll / Vaya Con Dios+ / Wee Hour Blues / It Wasn't Me / Ain't That Just Like A Woman+ / Right Off Rampart Street / Welcome Back Pretty Baby / Sad Day Long Night *(instr)* / Ramona, Say Yes / Viva, Viva Rock & Roll / Lonely Schooldays *(fast version)* / Tulane / Have Mercy Judge / Instrumental *(instr)* / Christmas / Gun *(instr)* / I'm A Rocker / Flyin' Home *(instr)* / Fish & Chips / Some People / Oh Louisiana / Festival / Let's Do Our Thing Together / Your Lick *(instr)* / Bound To Lose / Bordeaux In My Pirough

❼ San Francisco Dues / My Dream / My Ding-A-Ling *(live, album version)* / Johnny B. Goode *(live)* / Reelin' And Rockin' *(live)* / Let's Boogie / Mean Old World+ / I Love You / I Will Not Let You Go / London Berry Blues *(instr)* / Rain Eyes / Sue Answer [Sue Ann? Sir] / Got It And Gone / A Deuce

❽ Talkin' About My Buddy / Hello Little Girl, Goodbye / Aimlessly Driftin' / Woodpecker *(instr)* / Bio / I'm Just A Name / Too Late+ / Hi-Heel Sneakers+ / South Of The Border+ / Swannee River+ / You Are My Sunshine+ / Don't You Lie To Me+ / My Babe+ / I Just Want To Make Love To You+ / Shake Rattle & Roll+ / Baby What You Want Me To Do+

❾ Rock'n'Roll Music *(alt. take)* / Sweet Little Sixteen *(alt. take)* / Reelin' And Rockin' *(alt. take)* / Johnny B. Goode *(alt. take)* / Beautiful Delilah *(alt. take)* / Sweet Little Rock & Roller *(alt. take)* / Betty Jean *(alt. take)* / I Got To Find My Baby+ *(stereo)* / Bye Bye Johnny *(stereo)* / Down The Road A Piece+ *(stereo)* / Route 66+ *(alt. take)* / I'm Talking About You *(stereo)* / Come On *(stereo, alt. take)* / Go, Go, Go *(stereo)* / Brown Eyed Handsome Man *(stereo)* / Nadine *(stereo)* / You Never Can Tell *(stereo)* / Promised Land *(stereo)* / No Particular Place To Go *(stereo)* / Little Marie *(stereo)* / I Want To Be Your Driver *(stereo)* / My Mustang Ford *(stereo)* / It Wasn't Me *(stereo)* / Ain't That Just Like A Woman+ *(stereo)*

220 tracks in all, more-or-less chronologically arranged, and according to the notes on the box it should represent Berry's complete output for the Chess label. Well, it doesn't. Several songs are missing, and the sound quality is not that good on any tracks either, and too many are in mono where they could have been stereo.

Disc 1 contains 25 tracks, from 'Maybellene' (May 1955) to the demo version of 'Sweet Little Sixteen' (December 1957). 'Wee Wee Hours' is included twice. In the booklet they try to convince us that the second version was recorded in 1957, but it wasn't. It is exactly the same tune that Berry recorded on 21 May 1955 along with 'Maybellene'. Two songs are missing: The single version of 'La Jaunda' and the 'Untitled Instrumental' (recorded 15 December 1956) which appeared on the 1990 US LP/CD MISSING BERRIES – RARITIES (VOLUME 3) [Chess CH-/CHD-9318].

Disc 2 contains 30 tracks, from 'Thirteen Question Method' (May 1957) to 'Little Queenie' (November 1958). The following songs are missing here: the original speeded-up version of 'Sweet Little Sixteen'; the alternative version of 'Around And Around' with the different overdubbed lead guitar (first available on the stereo version of the 1967 UK LP, YOU NEVER CAN TELL [Marble Arch MALS-702]) and later on the 2007 US 4-CD set, JOHNNY B. GOODE – HIS COMPLETE '50S RECORDINGS [Hip-O Select B0009473-02]); and the slightly different album version of 'Merry Christmas Baby'.

Disc 3 also contains 30 tracks, from 'That's My Desire' (November 1958) to 'Down The Road A Piece' (February 1960). The following songs are missing: the original version of 'Do You Love Me', recorded February 1959, which was first issued on the 1973 UK 2-LP, CHUCK BERRY'S GOLDEN DECADE (VOLUME 3) [Chess 6641 177] (the version included here is the alternative version first made available in 1993 on the UK LP, CHESS MASTERS: AMERICA'S HOTTEST WAX [Chess CXMP-2011]); 'I Just Want To Make Love To You', which has the overdubbed live audience (well, they could be excused because the version without the live audience didn't appear until 1993, on the UK CD, ON THE BLUES SIDE [Ace CDCH-397]); 'Bye Bye Johnny' is in stereo, and that is a mistake because you get the same stereo version on Disc 9; and

'Run Around' and 'Diploma For Two' are in mono, which means they haven't included the stereo versions from the 1967 UK LP, YOU NEVER CAN TELL [Marble Arch MALS-702]). 'That's My Desire' and 'Blue On Blue' were both dubbed from disc, with audible crackles, etc.

Disc 4 contains 29 tracks, from 'Confessin' The Blues' (February 1960) to 'Brenda Lee' (February 1964). The problem here is that they have included almost the entire ON STAGE album with the fake live audience. Even 'How High The Moon' is faded out exactly as it is on the LP (you'll find the complete take without the audience noise on Disc 2). Moreover, the instrumental 'Cryin' Steel' (which was first titled 'Surfin' Steel' on that particular album) you get twice, with and without the fake live audience! 'Stop And Listen' suffers from terrible(!) electronic stereo. And the following songs are missing: 'I Still Got The Blues', 'All Aboard' and 'Man And The Donkey' all without overdubbed audience noise; and stereo versions of 'Big Ben Blues' and 'The Little Girl From Central' in stereo first released on the 1967 UK LP, YOU NEVER CAN TELL [Marble Arch MALS-702]).

Disc 5 contains 25 tracks from 'No Particular Place To Go' (March 1964) to 'Everyday We Rock And Roll' (September 1965). Most tracks are not in stereo, even though all of them could have been. It seems they have stuck with the old mono masters they used in the UK back in 1964-65. 'Chuck's Beat' is edited down to 6:30 and 'Bo's Beat' is the 3:15 single edit (and would you believe they are both in mono!); 'Jamaica Farewell' is actually the full-length version, but also in mono. The stereo versions from 'His Daughter Caroline' to 'St. Louis Blues' originally on the 1965 US LP [Chess LP-1495] – except 'Dear Dad' which *is* in stereo – are missing here (only mono versions are included), the stereo version of 'Lonely School Days' *(slow version)* is missing, and 'Run Joe' in stereo is also missing. Good grief !

Disc 6 contains 27 tracks from 'My Mustang Ford' (September 1965) to 'Bordeaux In My Pirough' (January 1971). 'Right Off Rampart Street' is not in stereo, and 'Wee Hour Blues' is ruined by some heavy surface noise. 'Ramona Say Yes' is the stereo version, and therefore without the saxophone.

Disc 7 contains 14 tracks from 'San Francisco Dues' (January 1971) to 'A Deuce' (March 1973), and includes the whole 1972 LONDON SESSIONS album with the 12-minute long version of 'My Ding-A-Ling'. But where is 'Roll 'Em Pete'? This live cut from the *Lanchester Arts Festival* was originally issued in 1973 as the 'B' side of the US and German 'Bio' singles, but is not included on this set. Complete?

Disc 8 contains 16 tracks from 'Talkin' About My Buddy' (June 1973) to 'Baby What You Want Me To Do' (August 1974). There is some surface noise on several songs, with 'Talkin' About My Buddy' being the worst. 'South Of the Border' from the 1972 BBC2 TV show, *Sounds For Saturday* (initially bootlegged on the SIX TWO FIVE LP) is missing. The song was officially released in the UK in 1974 as a single with 'Bio' on the 'B' side.

Disc 9 has 24 tracks and contains various rare tracks and the stereo remixes from the 1986 ROCK'N'ROLL RARITIES and MORE ROCK'N;ROLL RARITIES albums – although the RARITIES albums together contained 32 tracks The box set includes a great booklet (a few mistakes occur) with many pictures I haven't seen before, most of them taken in England by Bill Millar. The liner notes are by Adam Komorowski, however, the session discography is unreliable. Again, I suggest you stick to Fred Rothwell's book, *Long Distance Information*.

In summary, this so called 'complete' survey of Chuck Berry's Chess years doesn't include the following tracks (excluding all the missing stereo versions): 'La Jaunda' *(single version)*, 'Untitled Instrumental' (15 December 1956), 'Sweet Little Sixteen' *(original speeded up version)*, 'Around And Around' *(alt. version)*, 'Merry Christmas Baby' *(album version),* 'Do You Love Me' *(alt. version)*, 'Chuck's Beat' *(complete version)*, 'Bo's Beat' *(complete version)*, 'Ramona Say Yes' *(single version)*, 'Roll 'Em Pete' *(live)* and 'South Of The Border' *(live)*.

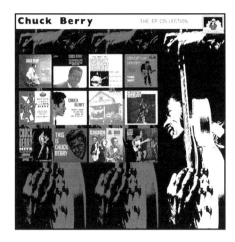

THE EP COLLECTION
See For Miles SEECD-320 ● 1991
Reelin' And Rockin' / Johnny B. Goode / Nadine *(stereo)* / Don't You Lie To Me**+** / Around And Around / No Particular Place To Go *(stereo)* / Childhood Sweetheart / My Little Love-Light / Maybellene / I'm Talking About You / Roll Over Beethoven / Sweet Little Sixteen / You Can't Catch Me / Memphis, Tennessee / I Got A Booking / You Never Can Tell *(stereo)* / The Things I Used To Do**+** *(stereo)* / Jamaica Farewell**+** / Thirty Days / Oh Baby Doll / School Day / Bye Bye Johnny / Back In The USA / Rock And Roll Music

This was one of a series of albums covering the EP releases in the UK of various artists. The first was by Billy Fury. So many EPs were issued of Chuck Berry that See For Miles would have needed to release a second volume to include everything. Nevertheless, this is a good compilation of tracks with informative and accurate liner notes from Bob Naylor, except that the original title of 'Maybellene' was 'Ida May' not 'Ida Red'. The version of 'Sweet Little Sixteen' included here is the one at the original speed, and 'Jamaica Farewell' is the 'UK' version without the extra guitar. 'Don't You Lie To Me' is credited to Berry. Also issued on LP [See For Miles SEE-320] minus the last two cuts.

20 GREAT TRACKS
Music For Pleasure [EMI] CDMFP-5936 ● 1992
Maybellene / Roll Over Beethoven / Reelin' And Rockin' / Rock And Roll Music / Sweet Little Sixteen *(original speed)* / Johnny B. Goode / No Particular Place To Go *(stereo)* / Memphis, Tennessee / Wee Wee Hours / You Never Can Tell *(stereo)* / Go, Go, Go / Down Bound Train / No Money Down / Havana Moon / House Of Blue Lights**+** / Crying Steel *(instr)* / I'm Just A Lucky So And So**+** / Promised Land *(stereo)* / My Mustang Ford *(stereo)* / Drifting Heart

I have listed this CD just because of the unusual inclusion of songs like 'Crying Steel' and 'I'm Just A Lucky So And So'. 'House Of Blue Lights' is also a welcome change, and 'My Mustang Ford' is likewise a rare Berry track. Unfortunately, 'Go, Go, Go' is the version with the overdubbed live audience from the 1963 ON STAGE album.

BLUES BERRY
Orbis BLU NC-003 • 1993
Memphis, Tennessee / Almost Grown / Maybellene / Johnny B. Goode / No Particular Place To Go / No Money Down / Thirty Days / Too Much Monkey Business / You Can't Catch Me / School Day / Sweet Little Sixteen / Around And Around / Carol / Little Queenie / Back In The USA / Nadine / You Never Can Tell / Promised Land

This album was a coverdisc given away with a magazine called *The Blues Collection*, and was not sold separately. The series showcased a different artist each week and was originally published in France in 1992 (see French discography for details), albeit in a different order. This release reminds me of the 1960 US LP, ROCKIN' AT THE HOPS [Chess LP-1448], which did not include much rock'n'roll. It depends a little on what you call blues, but if you want to use a title like BLUES BERRY then you really ought to include more than just one tune in that genre in addition to 'No Money Down'.

HAIL! HAIL! ROCK'N'ROLL
Charly CPCD-8006 • 1993
Not the soundtrack. Same tracks and cover as the 1990 CD [Instant CDINS-5035].

ON THE BLUES SIDE
Ace CDCH-397 • 1993
Confessin' The Blues+ / Run Around / Worried Life Blues+ / The Things I Used To Do+ / Blues For Hawaiians *(instr)* / Wee Wee Hours / I Still Got The Blues / Down The Road A Piece+ / No Money Down / Stop And Listen / Blue On Blue *(instr)* / Sweet Sixteen+ / I Got To Find My Baby+ *(stereo)* / I Just Want To Make Love To You+ / Merry Christmas Baby+ / Deep Feeling *(instr)* / Wee Hour Blues *(stereo)* / Don't You Lie To Me+ / Ain't That Just Like A Woman+ *(stereo)* / Driftin' Blues+ / Blue Feeling *(instr)*

This, on the other hand, is a very good blues collection by Berry: 21 tracks and all very much in the blues genre. A little info on some of the tracks is included. The sound is fairly okay on most tracks. However, there's a strange background noise on 'Blues For Hawaiians'. 'I Still Got The Blues' and 'I Just Want To Make Love To You' are both referred to as being *'unissued'*, but they were of course first made available on the 1963 US LP, ON STAGE [Chess LP-1480]. However, they appear here for the first time without the overdubbed live audience, albeit in mono. 'Down The Road A Piece' is faded out like in the old days, and 'Blue On Blue' is faded as well! 'Merry

Christmas Baby' is the single version. All tracks are mono versions except were noted. Why must there always be something wrong with almost every release? At this stage, I really was hoping that Bear Family Records would do something.

BERRY IS ON TOP
Chess [MCA] CHLD-19250 ● 1994
Originally released in Germany and France in 1993 [MCA MCD-30487] with a different cover, this CD contains the same twelve tracks as the original 1959 US LP [Chess LP-1435], but with eight bonus cuts: 'Down The Road A Piece', 'No Money Down', 'Down Bound Train', 'Jaguar And The Thunderbird', 'Things I Used To Do' *(stereo),* 'No Particular Place To Go', 'Fraulein' *(stereo)* and 'Nadine'.

THE BEST OF CHUCK BERRY
MCA MCBD-19510 ● 1994
No Particular Place To Go *(stereo)* / School Day / Sweet Little Sixteen / Let It Rock / Memphis, Tennessee / Nadine *(stereo)* / You Never Can Tell *(stereo)* / Promised Land / Reelin' And Rockin' / My Ding-A-Ling *(live, single edit)* / Maybellene / Roll Over Beethoven / Johnny B. Goode / Carol / Almost Grown / Back In The USA / Little Queenie / Brown Eyed Handsome Man / Sweet Little Rock And Roller / Rock And Roll Music

Yes, it is – 20 greatest hits! Good liner notes including a run-down of each track. There's a great picture of Berry from England 1965, but why is he left-handed? This compilation was reissued in 1997 on Universal MCBD-19536.

CHUCK BERRY IN CONCERT
Prestige Rock'n'Roll Greats Series CDSGP-0155 ● 1994
Reelin' And Rockin' / School Day / My Ding-A-Ling / Too Much Monkey Business / Memphis, Tennessee / Maybellene / Nadine

The 1969 *Toronto Rock & Roll Revival* again.

LET IT ROCK
Charly (Classic Rock'n'Roll) CDCD-1192 ● 1994
Let It Rock / You Never Can Tell / Route 66+ / Come On / Nadine / Thirty Days / Confessin' The Blues+ / You Can't Catch Me / County Line / Tulane / Wee Wee Hours / Sweet Little Rock And Roller / Beautiful Delilah / High Heel Sneakers+ / Go, Go, Go / Bye Bye Johnny

An interesting combination of Berry tracks, with at least four that rarely make an appearance on compilation albums – most notably 'Tulane' and 'High Heel Sneakers'.

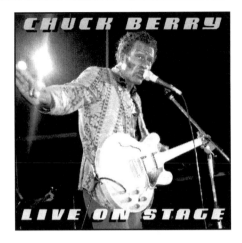

LIVE ON STAGE
Magnum Force CDMF-092 • 1994
School Day / Sweet Little Sixteen / Roll Over Beethoven / Everyday I Have The Blues+ / Bio / *Medley:* Maybellene – Mountain Dew+ / Let It Rock / *Medley:* Carol – Little Queenie / Key To The Highway+ / Got My Mojo Working+ / Reelin' And Rockin' / Johnny B. Goode

Recorded at the Peterborough *Rock'n'Roll Spectacular* on Saturday, 3 September 1983. 'Key To The Highway' and 'Got My Mojo Working' feature Ingrid Berry on vocals. As is so often the case with Berry concerts, it's better to be there than to just listen to the show afterwards: you need the visual effects. The sound is not too good, and it would have been interesting to know from what source it was recorded. But that's Magnum Force in a nutshell. The spectacular also featured Billy J. Kramer & The Dakotas, Screamin' Lord Sutch, Tommy Bruce, the Glitter Band and Billie Davis.

THE LONDON CHUCK BERRY SESSIONS
Chess [MCA] CHLD-19181 • 1994
Same tracks and cover as the 1989 US CD reissue [Chess CHD-9295], with the liner notes by Andy McKaie.

POET OF ROCK'N'ROLL [4-CD]
Charly Rock'n'Roll CDDIG-1 • 1994
❶ *Rockin' Rollin' Blues Man:* Johnny B. Goode / Maybellene / Roll Over Beethoven / Rock And Roll Music / School Day / Sweet Little Sixteen *(alt. version)* / Carol / Almost Grown / Back In The USA / Nadine *(stereo w/ longer fading)* / Too Much Monkey Business / Brown Eyed Handsome Man / Oh Baby Doll / Promised Land *(stereo)* / The Things I Used To Do+ *(stereo)* / Worried Life Blues+ / Run Around / Childhood Sweetheart *(alt. version)* / Ingo *(instr)* / Driftin' Blues+ / Confessin' The Blues+ / Sweet Sixteen+ / Deep Feeling *(instr)* / Bio / I'm Just A Lucky So And So+ / Wee Wee Hours / After It's Over *(instr)*
❷ *Still Rockin':* No Particular Place To Go *(stereo)* / Reelin' And Rockin' / You Never Can Tell *(stereo)* / Thirty Days / No Money Down / Little Queenie / Memphis, Tennessee / Sweet Little Rock And Roller / Let It Rock / Come On / Go, Bobby Soxer *(stereo)* / Go, Go, Go / Beautiful Delilah / Hello Little Girl, Goodbye / Blue Feeling *(instr)* / Why Should We End This Way / Welcome Back Pretty Baby / I've Changed / Blue On Blue *(instr)* / She Once Was Mine *(mono)* / Right Off Rampart Street *(mono)* / Mean Old World+ / Instrumental *(instr)* / I Got A Booking (*mono)* / San Francisco Dues / I Want To be Your Driver *(mono)* / Merry Christmas Baby+ *(single version)*

YOU'VE NEVER SEEN ANYTHING LIKE THIS!

The definitive Chuck Berry collection—over 100 tracks chronicling the life and times of the Poet of Rock'n'Roll. Four picture CDs, more than four and a half hours of music and a sixty-page book lavishly illustrated in full colour.

Cat. No. CDDIG 1
Bar Code 082333223929

❸ *Still Rollin':* You Can't Catch Me / I Got To Find My Baby+ *(stereo)* / Jo Jo Gunne / Betty Jean / Butterscotch *(instr)* / Rip It Up+ / Bye Bye Johnny / Don't You Lie To Me+ / Roly Poly *(instr)* / Jaguar And The Thunderbird / Down The Road A Piece+ *(stereo)* / Ain't That Just Like A Woman+ / Around And Around / It Wasn't Me / Ramona Say Yes *(stereo)* / My Mustang Ford / O'Rangutang *(instr)* / Sue Answer [Sue Ann? Sir] / Tulane / Have Mercy Judge / Gun *(instr)* / I Love You / I'm Talking About You / Oh Yeah / Liverpool Drive *(instr)* / Little Marie

❹ *All American Boy:* Berry Pickin' *(instr)* / Havana Moon / La Jaunda / Vaya Con Dios+ / I'm Just A Name / Lonely All The Time [Crazy Arms]+ *(stereo)* / You Two *(stereo)* / Fraulein+ *(stereo)* / Too Late+ / Bound To Lose / Lonely School Days *(slow version)* / Bordeaux In My Pirough / Oh Louisiana / Got It And Gone / Guitar Boogie *(instr)* / Down Bound Train / Route 66+ *(alt. version)* / Rock At The Philharmonic *(instr)* / One For My Baby (And One More For The Road)+ / Away from You / Do You Love Me / My Dream *(poem)* / Wee Hours Blues / Anthony Boy / Too Pooped To Pop+

If you should want to own just one Chuck Berry record set, this is it. It actually has 'everything': the greatest hits, the best of the best (not 'Rip It Up'), rock'n'roll, blues, instrumentals, ballads – you name it.

The set claims to contain *'105 titles from the genius whose lyrics and music inspired the world of Rock'n'Roll'* and features great extensive liner notes, many great pictures, a detailed song by song analysis from Clive Anderson, recording dates and US chart positions.

Disc 1 is divided into 14 rock'n'roll songs and 13 blues tunes. The same goes for Disc 2. Disc 3 is rock'n'roll almost all the way through, mostly non-hits, interrupted only by the occasional blues. Finally, Disc 4 is a celebration of the ethnic diversity of the USA and the many musical strands that make up Chuck Berry's work: Hispanic and Cuban influences, country music, jazz and a little bit of Louisiana.

The sound quality is very good too!

I just can't praise this set highly enough. Unfortunately it's been deleted for some years, and because Charly lost its rights to license and release the Chess catalogue in court, it will never turn up again. You will have to search for it in used record stores or, better still, on the Internet. If you should happen to find it, buy it !

This set was also made available to shops for display in windows etc. All four CDs have a warning printed in big letters: *'This CD will damage your CD player'*.

VOLUME 12 – CHUCK BERRY: OH YEAH!
Charly R&B Masters CDRB-12 • 1994
No Money Down / 21 Blues / Oh Yeah! / Do You Love Me *(1959)* / Childhood Sweetheart / Driftin' Blues+ / I Got To Find My Baby+ / Jaguar And The Thunderbird / Down The Road A Piece+ / Confessin' The Blues+ / The Things I Used To Do+ / I Want To Be Your Driver / She Once Was Mine / I Got A Booking / Lonely Schooldays *(slow version)* / Let's Do Our Thing Together / Your Lick *(instr)* / San Francisco Dues / Let's Boogie / Bio

Nice compilation of mostly bluesy tracks. Stereo masters are used from 'Things I Used To Do' onwards. 'Down The Road A Piccc' is faded out early.

Shabba Ranks
A MI SHABBA
Epic 477482-2 • 1995
See French discography.

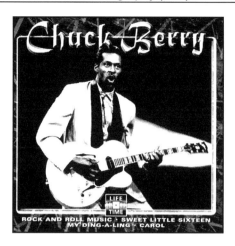

JOHNNY B. GOODE
Life/Time LT-5076 • 1995
Maybellene / Rock And Roll Music / Nadine / School Day / Bonsoir Cherie [Hoochie Coochie Man+] / *Medley:* Carol – Promised Land / Johnny B. Goode / Reelin' And Rockin' / Memphis, Tennessee / Sweet Little Sixteen / Wee Wee Hours / My Ding-A-Ling [Chess] *(live, single edit)*

Toronto Festival again, except for 'My Ding-A-Ling'. The most interesting thing about this CD is the picture on the front cover, which was probably taken in 1958.

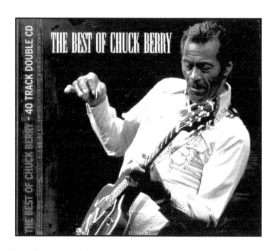

THE BEST OF CHUCK BERRY [2-CD]
MCA MCD-11560 • 1996
❶ Roll Over Beethoven / Sweet Little Sixteen / Johnny B. Goode / You Never Can Tell *(stereo)* / You Can't Catch Me / Down Bound Train / Too Much Monkey Business / Havana Moon / School Day / Oh Baby Doll / Beautiful Delilah / Sweet Little Rock And Roller / Anthony Boy / Little Queenie / Almost Grown / Let It Rock / Back In The USA / Reelin' And Rockin' *(live, album version)* / Around And Around / Brown Eyed Handsome Man
❷ Maybellene / No Particular Place To Go *(stereo)* / Rock And Roll Music / Run Rudolph Run+ / Jo Jo Gunne / Carol / Confessin' The Blues+ / Jaguar And The Thunderbird / Down The Road A Piece+ / Thirty Days / Merry Christmas Baby+ / My Ding-A-Ling *(live, single edit)* / I'm Talking About You / Too Pooped To Pop+ / Bye Bye Johnny / Promised Land *(stereo)* / Tulane *(stereo)* / Come On / Nadine *(stereo)* / Memphis, Tennessee

209

Very good value for money, 40 tracks. 'Sweet Little Sixteen' is the one at normal speed. 'Reelin' And Rockin'' is the live version from the 1972 LONDON SESSIONS album, running for approx. 7 minutes. 'Down The Road A Piece' is the faded mono version. 'Nadine' has an unusual stereo effect with the drums way up in the middle, but it sounds great. My only complaint is that I feel it should have been at least one instrumental featured.

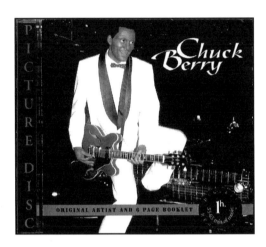

CHUCK BERRY – MEMBERS' EDITION
United Audio Entertainment UAE-30022 • 1996

This has a nice picture of the waxwork of Berry from Madame Tussaud's Rock Circus – pity then that the songs are not up to par. It contains the same mess of Chess and Toronto tracks as the one on the 1995 Various Artists CD, THE ESSENTIAL COLLECTION [Wisepack LECDD-625]. The liner notes tell us that Berry was born in San Jose, California, in 1926 (it was St. Louis, Missouri) and that the Beach Boys stole 'Sweet Little Sixteen' note for note for their 'Fun, Fun, Fun', (it was 'Surfin' USA'), and further that he celebrated his 60th birthday in 1987! Hey, you already told us he was born on 18 October 1926! Keep the front cover and throw the rest in the garbage can.

REELIN AND ROCKIN'
Razamataz RZ-4005 • 1996

14 Mercury tracks in an awful sound quality. The only interesting thing is the picture of Berry's head wearing a cap, which is quite new, probably from the mid-'90s.

TWO GREAT GUITARS
Chuck Berry & Bo Diddley

THE SUPER SUPER BLUES BAND
Howlin' Wolf, Muddy Waters & Bo Diddley

Chuck Berry & Bo Diddley / Howlin' Wolf, Muddy Waters & Bo Diddley
TWO GREAT GUITARS / THE SUPER SUPER BLUES BAND
Beat Goes On BGOCD-334 • 1996
Liverpool Drive *(instr)* / Chuck's Beat *(instr)* / When The Saints Go Marching In *(Bo Diddley)* / Bo's Beat *(instr)*

Two LPs on one CD., including a reissue of the original TWO GREAT GUITARS album from 1964. Good new liner notes from Neil Slaven. In the years that followed, we were treated to many excellent BGO '2 on 1' reissues of Berry's original UK Pye and Chess albums.

The following four CDs came out in 1996 and 1997 and featured various live versions of Berry songs from the 1969 *Toronto Rock & Roll Revival*, the 1982 *Live At The Roxy* TV show (released on video), and one even contains the 1972 BBC2 TV show, *Sounds For Saturday*, previously only available on the 1972 SIX TWO FIVE bootleg LP [Driving Wheel LP-1001]. I have listed them in the UK discography, but one of them was made in Ireland and one doesn't say. They could be bootlegs themselves, but who can tell these days?

CHUCK BERRY
Master Tone CP-6204 • 1996
School Day / Wee Wee Hours / *Medley:* Johnny B. Goode – Carol – Promised Land / Hoochie Coochie Man+ / Sweet Little Sixteen / Rock And Roll Music [Chess] / My Ding-A-Ling [Chess] *(live, single edit)* / Maybellene [Chess] / Too Much Monkey Business / Nadine / Reelin' And Rockin' / Johnny B. Goode / Bonsoir Cherie [Hoochie Coochie Man+]

When I started listening to this I thought, hey this is goode, sound quality and kind-of stereo, not bad, *Toronto Festival* and everything. The songs are not even faded between tracks. However, by the time he got to 'Sweet Little Sixteen', the engineer or mastermind must have had too much Gordon's Gin or something, because the next three tracks are original Chess recordings, and when we get back to Toronto the sound quality has gone downhill. Not only that, we get 'Hoochie Coochie Man' for a second time, mistitled 'Bonsoir Cherie'. Licence to kill!

The cover proclaims 'picture disc', which is true, but just happens to be the same photo as is used on the front, inside and back.

CHUCK BERRY [2-CD]
Newsound – Penny PYCD-260 • 1996
❶ Roll Over Beethoven / Sweet Little Sixteen / Memphis, Tennessee / South Of The Border+ / Beer Drinkin' Woman+ / Let It Rock / Mean Old World+ / Carol / Liverpool Drive *(instr)* / Nadine / Bye Bye Johnny / Bonsoir Cherie [It's Time To Go] – Johnny B. Goode
❷ Rock And Roll Music / School Day / *Medley:* Johnny B. Goode – Carol – Promised Land / Hoochie Coochie Man+ / Maybellene / Too Much Monkey Business / Reelin' And Rockin' / Sweet Little Sixteen / Wee Wee Hours / Promised Land* / School Day* / Brown Eyed Handsome Man*

Disc 1 contains the 1972 BBC2 TV show, *Sounds For Saturday*, previously only available on the 1972 SIX TWO FIVE bootleg LP [Driving Wheel LP-1001]. Disc 2 contains 10 songs from the 1969 *Toronto Rock & Roll Revival* and three from the *Live At the Roxy* TV show in 1982 (*). Reissued in 1998 on CD ROCK'N'ROLL MUSIC [Newsound 2000 NSTD-208] with a different cover.

CHUCK BERRY – ORIGINAL LEGENDS VERSIONS
Mandarim MR-03978 • 1996
School Day / Maybellene / Reelin' And Rockin' / Wee Wee Hours / Sweet Little Sixteen* / Nadine* / Promised Land* / Memphis, Tennessee* / Rock And Roll Music / Too Much Monkey Business / Roll Over Beethoven* / Let It Rock*

This CD comes packaged in a round metal box and contains six songs from the 1969 *Toronto Rock & Roll Revival* and six from the 1982 *Live At The Roxy* TV show (*). It is refreshing to hear the Roxy tracks, but it feels strange mixing them with the Toronto material since the former has much better sound quality in stereo. Made in Ireland.

FOREVER CLASSIC – CHUCK BERRY
Master Tone MCPS-0301 ● 1997
School Day / Maybellene / Reelin' And Rockin' / Wee Wee Hours / Sweet Little Sixteen* / Nadine* / Promised Land* / Johnny B. Goode* / *Medley:* Carol – Little Queenie* / Rock And Roll Music / Hoochie Coochie Man+ / Too Much Monkey Business / Roll Over Beethoven* / Let It Rock* / Memphis, Tennessee* / Brown Eyed Handsome Man* / Mean Old World+**

17 tracks including seven songs from the 1969 *Toronto Rock & Roll Revival*, nine from the 1982 *Live At The Roxy* TV show (*) and one from the 1972 BBC2 TV show, *Sounds For Saturday* (**). The cover proclaims *'Original Hits'*, which they most definitely are not.

LIVE
Columbia River Entertainment Group VMK-1154 ● 1997
Roll Over Beethoven / School Day / Sweet Little Sixteen / Nadine / Let It Rock / Promised Land / Memphis, Tennessee / Johnny B. Goode / Brown Eyed Handsome Man / Too Much Monkey Business / *Medley:* Carol-Little Queenie / Rock And Roll Music *(with Tina Turner)* / Reelin' And Rockin'

Finally we get the complete 1982 *Live At The Roxy* TV show on CD! Recorded in Hollywood, California in 1982 and originally released on video. The sleeve and label both only list 10 titles, however, all 13 songs from the show are included. I have never understood why Berry always ends his shows with the dreadful version of 'Reelin' And Rockin' ' and 'House Lights' (*'Do you want us to quit? Do you want us to play?'*) Give me a break! 'Johnny B. Goode' is pseudonymous with Chuck Berry, and would therefore be a more appropriate song to end every concert with. Listen to the Japanese live LP, TOKYO SESSION [East World WTP-90072] from 1981 and you'll see what I mean.

HIS BEST (VOLUME 1)
Chess [Universal] MCD-09371 ● July 1997
Part of the *'Chess 50th Anniversary'* series, this comes in a 'digipak' card cover. Same tracks as the 1997 US CD [Chess CHD-9371]. It says on the cover that there was to be a VOLUME 2 released in UK, but I haven't seen it.

THE BEST OF CHUCK BERRY
Universal MCBD-19536 ● 1997
Same 20 tracks as the 1994 CD [MCA MCBD-19510], but a different front cover.

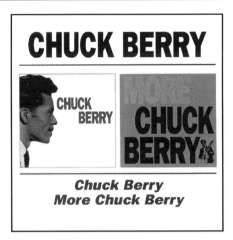

CHUCK BERRY / MORE CHUCK BERRY
Beat Goes On BGOCD-394 ● 1997
Two LPs on one CD. Same tracks as the two 1963 LPs [Pye International NPL-28024 and NPL-28026]. Additional sleevenotes. Digipak versions of this CD (very professionally done) also appeared on the market in 2007, but they seem to be counterfeits emanating from Russia. See below for more interesting releases from BGO.

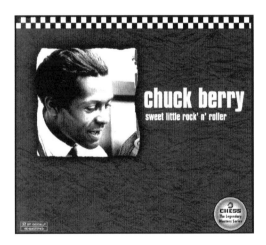

SWEET LITTLE ROCK'N'ROLLER
Chess [Universal] MCD-80245 ● 1997
Carol / Back In The USA / Sweet Little Rock And Roller / Little Queenie / School Day / Promised Land *(stereo)* / Maybellene / Nadine / Blues For Hawaiians *(instr)* / No Money Down / Fraulein+ *(stereo)* / Roll Over Beethoven / Memphis, Tennessee / Sweet Little Sixteen / Johnny B. Goode / No Particular Place To Go / Down The Road A Piece+ / Let It Rock / You Never Can Tell *(stereo)* / My Ding-A-Ling *(live, single edit)*

Part of the *'Chess 50th Anniversary'* series, this comes in a 'digipak' card cover. At first glance this looks quite interesting, but there is too much electronic stereo! It's almost unbelievable in 1997. *'32-bit digitally remastered'*, my foot. These so-called 'masters' might turn up again in the future, and that makes it even worse. You'll get burned by just touching this crap. See also 1999 CD MCA 112 172-2.

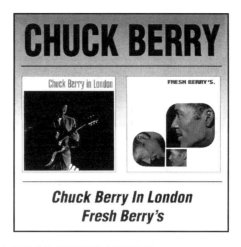

Chuck Berry In London
Fresh Berry's

CHUCK BERRY IN LONDON / FRESH BERRY'S
Beat Goes On BGOCD-395 • 1998
   Two LPs on one CD. Same tracks as the 1965 UK LPs [Chess CRL-4005 and CRL-4506], except that this time they used mostly stereo masters (although 'I Want To Be Your Driver' is in mono! The instrumental 'Sad Day – Long Night' is in stereo, which was so far only available in that form on the 1988 US CHESS BOX 6-LP/3-CD set [Chess CH6-/CHD3-80001]. 'Jamaica Farewell' is in stereo and is therefore the US version with the extra guitar added. Additional sleevenotes. Digipak versions of this CD (very professionally done) also appeared on the market in 2007, but they seems to be counterfeits emanating from Russia, or somewhere.

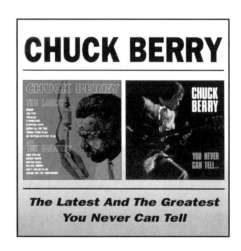

The Latest And The Greatest
You Never Can Tell

THE LATEST AND THE GREATEST / YOU NEVER CAN TELL
Beat Goes On BGOCD-428 • 1998
   Two LPs on one CD. Another nice compilation of two great albums from 1964 [Pye International NPL-28031 and NPL-28039]. From NPL-28031 we get stereo versions of 'Nadine', 'Fraulein', 'Things I Used To Do', 'Liverpool Drive', 'No Particular Place To Go', 'Lonely All The Time' ['Crazy Arms'] and 'You Two'. From NPL-28039 we get stereo versions of 'You Never Can Tell', 'The Little Girl From Central', 'Big Ben

Blues' and 'Promised Land'. Better still, 'O'Rangutang' is not faded and runs for a full 3 minutes! However, 'Drifting Heart' (not mentioned on the cover) is accidentally included instead of 'Driftin' Blues' from NPL-28031. Additional sleevenotes. Digipak versions of this CD (very professionally done) also appeared on the market in 2007, but they seems to be counterfeits emanating from Russia, or somewhere.

ROCK'N'ROLL MUSIC [2-CD]
Newsound 2000 NSTD-208 • 1998
      Same tracks as the 1996 2-CD, CHUCK BERRY [Essential Collection PYCD-260], but with a different cover.

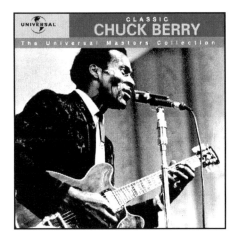

CLASSIC CHUCK BERRY
MCA [Universal] 112 172-2 • 1999
      This has the same layout and cover as the 1999 US CD, THE BEST OF CHUCK BERRY [MCA MCAD-1944] with eleven tracks. However, this one contains twenty tracks, but can you believe hearing electronic stereo in 1999? That is what you get on at least 5 of the tracks. Hey, give somebody back their school money and find something else to do in life. This is so bad, it's not even worthwhile listing the additional songs. You are hereby warned. I hate these kind of releases that indicate *'Made in the EU'*. What country are we talking about? This could be UK or Germany or anywhere.

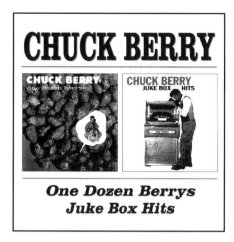

ONE DOZEN BERRYS / JUKE BOX HITS
Beat Goes On BGOCD-458 • 1999

Two LPs on one CD. Same tracks as the 1958 LP London HA-M-2132 and Pye International NPL-28019 from 1962. But what's going on? All the songs from the London album are in electronic stereo! If you press the 'mono' button, everything is OK again. The Pye LP tracks are all in mono. Additional liner notes by Fred Rothwell and, for the first time on a Berry BGO release, we get a session discography (compiled by Fred of course, based on his book *Long Distance Information*). Digipak versions of this CD (very professionally done) also appeared on the market in 2007, but they seems to be counterfeits emanating from Russia, or somewhere.

ROCK'N'ROLL HITS
Dressed To Kill METRO-260 • 1999

Reelin' And Rockin' / School Day / My Ding-A-Ling *(live, single edit)* / Too Much Monkey Business / Memphis, Tennessee / Maybellene / Nadine

Seven tracks clocking in at just 33:47! And the cover is sooo dull with a Berry picture in the middle surrounded by several sunshine labels which look like the original Sun label. Artwork by George & Pete. Distributed by BMG. I'll rest my case.

CHUCK BERRY LIVE!
Columbia River Entertainment Group 100012 • 2000

Same tracks as the 1994 CD, LIVE ON STAGE [Magnum Force CDMF-092], recorded at the Peterborough *Rock'n'Roll Spectacular* on Saturday, 3 September 1983.

CHUCK BERRY TV SPECIAL 1972
Newsound 2000 NST-058 • 2000

This is the 1972 *Sounds For Saturday* BBC2 TV show again, originally bootlegged on LP as SIX TWO FIVE [Driving Wheel LP-1001]. It's probably the best TV show ever by Chuck Berry – and it's in colour! The CD inlay card contains Berry's life story and the sleeve features a couple of photos of him from Germany in 1973. See *Section 8 (Chuck Berry on TV)* for more information.

GOLDEN COLLECTION 2000
Lighthouse [EMI] CD8-289906 • 2000
Containing 30 Chess tracks in the 'greatest hits' or 'best of' tradition. I haven't seen the CD or heard the songs, but from the track listing and timing it seems to contain the usual Chess versions.

ULTIMATE LEGENDS – CHUCK BERRY
Ultimate Music Collection [TKO] ULT-40422 • 2000
Roll Over Beethoven / Sweet Little Rock And Roller / No Particular Place To Go / Brown-Eyed Handsome Man / School Day / Rock And Roll Music / Maybellene / Memphis, Tennessee / Reelin' And Rockin' / Hoochie Coochie Man+ / Nadine / Sweet Little Sixteen / Wee Wee Hours / *Medley:* Carol – Promised Land / My Ding-A-Ling / Johnny B. Goode

I just hate to include such issues. The first four tracks are the original Chess recordings, the rest are from the *Toronto Festival* in '69. The cover is okay and makes the CD look interesting – which it's *not*! Unfortunately, this was also issued in Australia in 2001, titled THE BERRY BEST, which it's *absolutely not*!

JAZZ ON A SUMMER'S DAY
Charly SDVD-001 • November 2001
Sweet Little Sixteen

Original soundtrack. This is actually a bonus audio CD issued with the DVD of the movie. It is listed here because this CD often turns up in used record stores and on the Internet.

THE LONDON ROCK AND ROLL SHOW
TKO/Magnum Force CDMF-105 • 2001
See *Various Artists CD Albums.*

ROCK'N'ROLL MUSIC
Musicbank APWCD-1168 • 2001
Roll Over Beethoven / Sweet Little Sixteen / Memphis, Tennessee / South Of The Border+ / Beer Drinkin' Woman+ / Let It Rock / Mean Old World+ / Carol / Liverpool Drive *(instr)* / Nadine / Promised Land / *Medley:* Bonsoir Cherie [It's Time To Go] – Johnny B. Goode

Other than 'Promised Land', the tracks on this album are from the 1972 *Sounds for Saturday* BBC2 TV show (again), originally bootlegged on LP in 1972 as SIX TWO FIVE [Driving Wheel LP-1001]. The orphan is from the 1982 *Live At The Roxy* show, which has a much fuller sound. Speaking of sound, the 1972 concert here appears to have been dubbed from a poor source (ie LP). I bought this CD as the seller pointed out it was from Czechoslovakia. However, although the CD was manufactured in that country, it is actually a UK release. There's a good '50s picture of Berry on the cover.

ROCK AND ROLL MUSIC
Fabulous FABCD-157 • 2003
You know what? I don't intend to list any of the 15 tracks on this one. It's a combination of Toronto 1969, one live recording from a 1956 Alan Freed radio show (see the 1978 Various Artists bootleg LP, ROCK'N'ROLL RADIO [Radiola MR-1087] for more information), five Chess tracks with overdubbed audience and finally the 1972 hit single, 'My Ding-A-Ling'. The cover and liner notes are not interesting either. At the end it says: '*This collection features a typical Chuck Berry show.*' You could actually kill for less!

FATHER OF ROCK AND ROLL
American Legends 192022 ● October 2005
Roll Over Beethoven / School Day / Sweet Little Sixteen / Nadine / Promised Land / Johnny B. Goode / *Medley:* Carol – Little Queenie / Rock And Roll Music / Reelin' And Rockin'

Part of the 1982 *Live At The Roxy* show. Seek out the 1997 CD, LIVE [Columbia River Entertainment Group VMK-1154] instead. It contains the complete show.

GOLD [2-CD]
Geffen [Universal] 06024 98805589 ● 2005
Tracks are identical to the 2000 US 2-CD, THE ANTHOLOGY [MCA 088 112 304-2]. Different cover and pictures in the booklet; same liner-notes, though. Goode stuff!

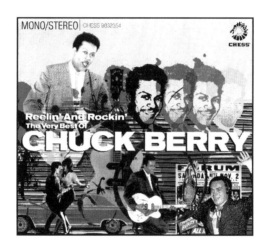

REELIN' AND ROCKIN' – THE VERY BEST OF CHUCK BERRY [2-CD]
Universal 9832354 ● 2006
❶ Guitar Boogie *(instr)* / Johnny B. Goode / Bye, Bye Johnny *(mono)* / Go, Go, Go *(mono)* / Bio / Maybellene / You Can't Catch Me / Beautiful Delilah / School Day / I'm Talking About You *(mono)* / I Got To Find My Baby+ *(mono)* / Memphis, Tennessee / No Money Down / Jaguar And The Thunderbird / Down The Road A Piece+ *(mono, faded)* / Run Rudolph Run+ / I Want To Be Your Driver *(stereo)* / Promised Land *(stereo)* / Back In The USA / Thirty Days / Havana Moon / Rock And Roll Music / Too Pooped To Pop+ / Come On / Viva, Viva Rock & Roll *(stereo)* / I'm A Rocker *(stereo)* / *Back To Memphis *(mono)* / *Check Me Out *(mono)* / Deep Feeling *(instr)*
❷ Liverpool Drive *(instr, stereo)* / Roll Over Beethoven / Let It Rock / Sweet Little Sixteen / Nadine / It Wasn't Me *(stereo)* / Confessin' The Blues+ / Too Much Monkey Business / Around And Around / Almost Grown / Brown Eyed Handsome Man / You Never Can Tell *(stereo)* / Wee Wee Hours / Little Marie *(stereo)* / Little Queenie / Carol / Oh Baby Doll / Jo Jo Gunne / No Particular Place To Go *(stereo)* / Dear Dad *(stereo)* / *Sweet Little Rock And Roller / Ramona, Say Yes *(album version, stereo)* / Tulane *(stereo)* / Festival *(stereo)* / Flyin' Home *(instr, stereo)* / Reelin' And Rockin' *(live, album version)* / My Ding-A-Ling *(live, single edit)*

Nice double digipak with a few really good pictures and great liner notes by Peter Doggett. Again there are a few things I need to point out. The usual and most obvious stereo versions are included. 'Down The Road A Piece' is faded and is not in stereo. Three Mercury tracks (*) are included, which surprisingly are in *mono* on this compilation. 'Sweet Little Sixteen' is normal speed. 'Flyin' Home' is Berry's own composition from the 1970 BACK HOME album, and *not* the Goodman-Hampton tune as indicated in the booklet. And 'Ramona, Say Yes' appears without the essential saxophone.

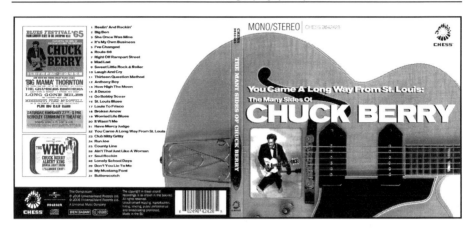

YOU CAME A LONG WAY FROM ST. LOUIS: THE MANY SIDES OF CHUCK BERRY
Universal 9842428 ● 2006
Reelin' And Rockin' / Big Ben *(stereo)* / She Once Was Mine *(mono)* / It's My Own Business *(stereo)* / I've Changed / Route 66+ / Right Off Rampart Street *(mono)* / Mad Lad+ *(instr)* / Sweet Little Rock And Roller / Laugh And Cry* / Thirteen Question Method / Anthony Boy / How High The Moon+ *(instr)* / A Deuce *(stereo)* / Go Bobby Soxer / St. Louis Blues+ *(mono)* / Louie To Frisco* *(mono)* / Broken Arrow / Worried Life Blues+ / It Wasn't Me *(no overdub, stereo)* / Have Mercy Judge *(stereo)* / You Came A Long Way from St. Louis+ *(mono)* / Club Nitty Gritty* / Run Joe+ *(mono)* / County Line / Ain't That Just Like A Woman+ *(stereo remix)* / Soul Rockin' * / Lonely School Days *(stereo, fast version)* / Don't You Lie To Me+ / My Mustang Ford *(complete stereo remix)* / Butterscotch *(instr, stereo)*

During the years, UK have come up with some strange compilations of Berry tracks. And this is another one in the 'series'. Intended as a companion to the above REELIN' AND ROCKIN' 2-CD set. Here they have also included Mercury tracks (*), four of them, but unfortunately did not use the superior remastered recordings with a full bass sound that were made available in 1989 on the US CD reissues of the original albums.

Trackwise it's an interesting release, with some really obscure Berry tracks, and also includes a great cover with some interesting pictures in the booklet. Many of the songs are not your everyday choice when you pick up a Chuck Berry CD, and it therefore may attract a wider audience. Liner notes once again are by Peter Doggett. But why on earth can't they track down the correct masters? Stereo masters where stereo masters are available (although they did manage a few). And why does 'Louie To Frisco' run a little too slow? From a Berry fan's point of view it's all irritating, and I am fed up with albums that are not up to par. Call me next time.

THE ULTIMATE COLLECTION [3-CD]
Spectrum [Universal] 982 8919 ● 30 April 2007
❶ **982 8920:** Maybellene / Wee Wee Hours / Thirty Days / No Money Down / Down Bound Train / Roll Over Beethoven / Too Much Monkey Business / Brown Eyed Handsome Man / You Can't Catch Me / Havana Moon / School Day / Oh Baby Doll / Rock And Roll Music / Sweet Little Sixteen / Reelin' And Rockin' / House Of Blue Lights+ / Johnny B. Goode / Around And Around / Beautiful Delilah / Carol
❷ **982 8921:** Sweet Little Rock And Roller* / Jo Jo Gunne / Merry Christmas Baby+ *(single version)* / Run Rudolph Run+ / Anthony Boy / Little Queenie / Almost Grown / Memphis, Tennessee / Back In The USA / Childhood Sweetheart / Too Pooped To Pop+ / Let It Rock / Bye Bye Johnny / Mad Lad+ *(instr)* / Betty Jean / Down The Road A Piece+ / Jaguar And The Thunderbird / I'm Talking About You / Route 66+

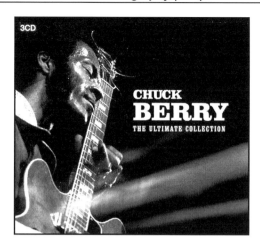

❸ **982 8922:** Go, Go, Go / Come On / Nadine / No Particular Place To Go / You Never Can Tell / Go, Bobby Soxer / Little Marie / Promised Land / The Things I Used To Do+ / Dear Dad / Lonely School Days *(fast version)* / It Wasn't Me / Tulane / *Club Nitty Gritty / *It Hurts Me Too+ *(studio version)* / My Ding-A-Ling *(live, single edit)* / Reelin' And Rockin' *(live, album version)*

Another 'best of' compilation or whatever. Nice to see that the Berry catalogue gets a new release almost every year in the UK. This one has an attractive front cover, but only contains one (1) instrumental – which is unusual. Each CD features a different goode picture of Berry, none of which I had ever seen before. Unusually, three Mercury tracks (*) are included. Even though this 3-CD set contains 56 tracks, it sells below full price, which might attract more buyers. Again, mono tracks have been included where stereo versions could have been used, like 'Bye Bye Johnny', 'Down The Road A Piece'; some, like 'Go, Go, Go' and 'Things I Used To Do' are even prematurely faded. 'Ultimate'? Well, all the hits are here (except for the wrong version of 'Sweet Little Rock And Roller) and many of the greatest Berry songs are also included, although 'Club Nitty Gritty' should have been left out. There is no accompanying booklet, but the insert to CD1 contains intelligent notes written by Dave McAleer. A goode compilation overall with excellent sound quality.

Many other Berry CDs have been issued in the UK, but I have mostly stuck to the ones that are of interest for the collector and Berry fan – including several with a health warning.

Various Artists Singles

Chuck Berry – Bo Diddley
BIG DADDIES [maxisingle]
Down The Road A Piece+ / Johnny B. Goode *(live, 1972)*
Chess [Phonogram] 6145 012 ● August 1972
    'Johnny B. Goode' is the live version recorded in England in 1972 at the *Lanchester Arts Festival*, and was released before 'My Ding-A-Ling' to promote his new LP, THE LONDON CHUCK BERRY SESSIONS [Chess 6310 122]. Bo Diddley's featured cuts are 'You Can't Judge A Book By The Cover' and 'We're Gonna Get Married'. This 4-track maxisingle did not come with a picture sleeve.

Various Artists EPs

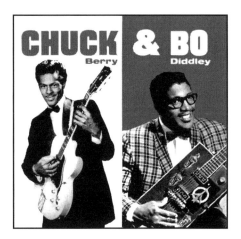

Chuck Berry – Bo Diddley
CHUCK & BO
Pye International NEP-44009 ● September 1963
Roll Over Beethoven / Our Little Rendezvous

This was the first in a series of three volumes featuring Chuck Berry and Bo Diddley. All three carried the same pictures of the two artists on the front cover, but had different coloured backgrounds. Bo Diddley's tracks were 'Pills' and 'The Greatest Lover In The World'.

CHUCK AND BO

Roll Over Beethoven
Our Little Rendezvous
Pills
The Greatest Lover In The World

7" E.P.   NEP 44009

CHUCK BERRY

Johnny B. Goode/Oh, Baby Doll
School Day/Back In The U.S.A.

7" E.P.   NEP 44011

Chuck Berry – Bo Diddley
CHUCK & BO (VOLUME 2)
Pye International NEP-44012 ● November 1963
You Can't Catch Me / No Money Down

    This had liner notes, unlike the first volume. Bo Diddley's tracks were 'She's Fine, She's Mine' and 'Bo Meets The Monster'.

Chuck Berry – Bo Diddley
CHUCK & BO (VOLUME 3)
Pye International NEP-44017 ● February 1964
Too Pooped To Pop / It Don't Take But A Few Minutes

    This had new liner notes. Bo Diddley's tracks were 'Deed And Deed I Do' and 'Diana'.

THE BLUES (VOLUME 2 – PART 1)
Chess [Pye] CRE-6011 ● January 1965
Wee Wee Hours

Includes songs by John Lee Hooker, Little Walter and Otis Rush. Picture of Berry and Little Walter on the front cover.

THE HITMAKERS
Pye NEP-24215 ● 1965
No Particular Place To Go

Includes songs by Sandie Shaw, The Rockin' Berries and Julie Grant. Only Sandie Shaw is pictured on the cover.

London Rainbow, 7 September 1973.

HITMAKERS
Pye NEP-24242 • 1965
Promised Land

Includes songs by the Kinks, Sue Thompson and the Shangri-Las. Picture of each artist on the front cover. Berry picture on sleeve.

NEW ALBUMS [promo]
Phonogram DJ-004 • 1973
Carol

A 4-track maxi 45 to promote new releases. The Berry track was to make people aware of the new double album, GOLDEN DECADE (VOLUME 2) [Chess 6641 058]. The other artists on this record were Rod Stewart, Dianne Davidson and the Stylistics. The record came in a plain cover.

ORIGINAL OLDIES FROM THE 50's (VOLUME 6) [33⅓ rpm]
Audiofidelity Mini Disc Series MD-506 • 1984
(Sweet Little Sixteen)

I don't know if this was common to all the pressings of this disc, but a live version of Fats Domino's 'Hello Josephine' appears on the copy I have instead of the Berry classic. Also includes songs by the Moonglows, the Drifters, Frankie Avalon, the Falcons and Skip & Flip. No pictures of any artists.

ORIGINAL OLDIES FROM THE 50's (VOLUME 10) [33⅓ rpm]
Audiofidelity Mini Disc Series MD-510 • 1984
Maybellene

Chess recording. Also includes songs by the Olympics, Brook Benton, Paul Evans, the Fireflies and Jerry Butler. No pictures of any artists.

Various Artists LPs

I have not collected UK compilation albums in a comprehensive way. However, there have been some interesting releases. The following is just a sample of what's been released and far from complete in any sense.

THE BLUES (VOLUME 1)
Pye International NPL-28030 ● 1964
Worried Life Blues+

THE BLUES (VOLUME 2)
Pye International NPL-28035 ● 1964
Thirty Days / Wee Wee Hours

These two albums feature the same artists and tracks as the two 1963 US LPs [Argo LP-4026 and LP-4027]. The only difference is that only the name 'Chuck Berry' appears in large lettering on VOLUME 1, while on VOLUME 2 both 'Chuck Berry' and 'Bo Diddley' are prominent.

THE HIT MAKERS
Pye NPL-18108 ● 1964
No Particular Place To Go

Picture of Berry on the cover. Other artists include the Searchers, Sandie Shaw, the Honeycombs, the Dixie Cups, the Shangri-Las, Julie Grant, the Kinks, Dionne Warwick, the Rockin' Berries, Kenny Ball and Tony Jackson.

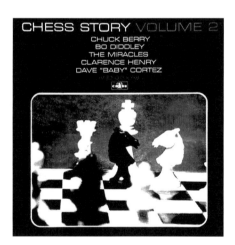

CHESS STORY (VOLUME 2)
Chess [Pye] CRL-4516 ● 1965
Maybellene

Other artists include Clarence 'Frogman' Henry, the Moonglows, Dave 'Baby' Cortez, the Miracles, the Vibrations, Bo Diddley, the Tuneweavers, the Students, Lee Andrews & The Hearts, the Monotones and the Flamingos.

THE HIT MAKERS (VOLUME 2)
Pye NPL-18115 • 1965
Promised Land

Picture of Berry on the cover. Other artists include the Kinks (2), the Shangri-Las, Sounds Orchestral, the Lancastrians, Tommy Quickly, the Ivy League, Sandie Shaw, the Searchers, the Rockin' Berries and Sue Thompson.

THE BLUES
Marble Arch [Pye] MAL-804 • 1968
Worried Life Blues**+**

10 songs by Washboard Sam, Willie Dixon, Little Milton, Muddy Waters, Howlin' Wolf, Jimmy Witherspoon, Elmore James, Jimmy Rogers, and Little Walter. This is not the same as the 1964 LP, THE BLUES (VOLUME 1) [Pye International NPL-28030].

Fats Domino – Jerry Lee Lewis – Chuck Berry
ROCK'N'ROLL
Fontana Special SFL-13120 • 1969
Rock And Roll Music / Sweet Little Rock And Roller / Sweet Little Sixteen / Roll Over Beethoven / Check Me Out

Mercury recordings with overdubbed live audience and a picture of Berry on the cover. Jerry Lee is represented by three live songs from the LIVE AT STAR-CLUB, HAMBURG LP, and there are four live songs by Fats Domino. This particular LP was also released in several other European countries. It was reissued in 1975 as Contour 6870 536 with the same title and cover, and again in 1976 as ROCK'N'ROLL GREATS (VOLUME 1) [Contour CN-2014] with a different cover.

AMERICAN GRAFFITI [2-LP]
MCA MCF-2531 • November 1973
Original soundtrack. Same tracks and gatefold sleeve as the 1973 US LP [MCA MCA2-8001]. I have a newspaper clipping reporting that three tracks ('Surfin' Safari' and 'All Summer Long' by the Beach Boys and 'Teen Angel' by Mark Dinning) were to be omitted from this release for contractual reasons. This is not true, as the original UK release I possess has all the 41 tracks.

CHESS GOLDEN DECADE (VOLUME 2: 1956 – TAKE IT EASY GREASY)
Checker 6445 151 ● 1973
Roll Over Beethoven

Berry picture on the sleeve. This album was released at the end of 1973. For some reason it was later renumbered 6445 206. This was a very good series consisting of eight volumes, and was only issued in the UK. All the LPs have gatefold sleeves and great liner notes. The mono recordings are in mono and the stereo ones in stereo, which was very unusual in the '70s. This is one of the best compilation series of Chess' history I have come across.

CHESS GOLDEN DECADE
  (VOLUME 5: 1959-61 – GOOD MORNING LITTLE SCHOOLGIRL)
Chess 6445 201 ● 1974
Let It Rock

Berry picture on the sleeve.

ROCK REVIVAL!!!!!!
Fontana Special 6430 002 ● 1974
Memphis, Tennessee

Mercury cut. None of these cheapo labels like Fontana and Contour had good sound quality. Electronic stereo is the worst thing ever invented. What's even worse is that they continued until way up in the '80s with this destruction of good music. It appears that in the UK and Germany they almost always use the 'electronic stereo' masters. Even as late as the 1990s they were still serving up these dreadful versions. Also on the album are Gary 'US' Bonds, the Contours, the Sensations, the Champs, the Drifters, Jerry Lee Lewis (2, including 'Johnny B. Goode'), Dicky Doo & The Don'ts, Fats Domino (3) and James Brown.

CHESS GOLDEN DECADE (VOLUME 8: 1965-66 – THE 'IN' CROWD)
Chess 6445 204 ● 1975
You Came A Long Way From St. Louis+

CRAZY ROCK
Contour 6870 527 • 1975
Carol / Club Nitty Gritty

Mercury recordings with electronic stereo! Other artists include Billy Lee Riley, Jerry Lee Lewis (2, including 'Roll Over Beethoven'), Clyde McPhatter (2), Charlie Rich (2), Marty Wilde (2) and Little Richard.

FANTASTIC ROCK
Contour 6870 528 • 1975
Johnny B. Goode / Thirty Days

Mercury recordings. Picture of Berry on the cover. Other artists include Billy Lee Riley (2), Clyde McPhatter, the Platters, Jerry Lee Lewis (2), Fats Domino, Screamin' Jay Hawkins, Marty Wilde(!) and Charlie Rich.

Fats Domino – Jerry Lee Lewis – Chuck Berry
ROCK'N'ROLL
Contour 6870 536 • 1975
Same tracks and cover as the 1969 LP [Fontana SFL-13120]. Picture of Berry on the cover.

Fats Domino – Jerry Lee Lewis – Chuck Berry
ROCK'N'ROLL GREATS
Contour CN-2014 • 1976
Same tracks as the 1969 LP, ROCK'N'ROLL [Fontana SFL-13120] and Contour 6870 536 above, but different cover with no pictures of the artists.

SCHOOL DAYS
J&B JB-377 • 1976
School Day / Maybellene

Chess recordings. Other artists include Jerry Lee Lewis (2), Dion (2), the Crystals, Roy Orbison (2), Del Shannon (2), Bo Diddley, Little Richard (2), Frankie Valli & The 4 Seasons (2), Carl Perkins, Bill Haley, the Chiffons and Gene Vincent.

AMERICAN HOT WAX [2-LP]
A&M AMLM-66500 • 1978
Original soundtrack. Same tracks and gatefold cover as the 1978 US 2-LP [A&M SP-6500].

Chuck Berry – Fats Domino
GIANTS OF ROCK & ROLL
Hammer HMR-9007 • 1980
Side 1 contains 10 Fats Domino tracks – live and studio. Side 2 features Berry with the same ten Mercury tracks as on the 1976 US LP, CHUCK BERRY'S GREATEST HITS [Everest FS-321]. Picture of both artists' heads on the front cover.

GOLDEN GREATS OF THE 50s & 60s [9-LP]
Reader's Digest N82001-ND1/9 • 1980
Maybellene / School Day / Rock And Roll Music / You Never Can Tell / Let It Rock / Memphis, Tennessee / No Particular Place To Go / My Ding-A-Ling *(live, single edit)*

It's ridiculous to issue a compilation of Berry tracks such as this and not include 'Johnny B. Goode', the classic of all classics. Nevertheless, it was a great box set at the time containing 16 rock'n'roll artists with one side each. The ninth LP is titled JUKEBOX JIVE and includes artists like Jack Scott, the Olympics, Carl Perkins and many more. Unfortunately, most songs on the set are destroyed by electronic stereo. Other artists with one side each include Bill Haley, Fats Domino, Sam Cooke, the Platters, Pat Boone, Eddie Cochran, the Everly Brothers, Lonnie Donegan, Buddy Holly, Jerry Lee Lewis, Connie Francis, Duane Eddy, Brenda Lee, Bobby Vee and Roy Orbison.

BEST OF CHESS / CHECKER / CADET – RHYTHM & ROCK
Chess [PRT] CXMP-2002 • 1981
School Day

Other artists include Tommy Tucker (2), Clarence 'Frogman' Henry, Dale Hawkins, Bo Diddley (2), Jackie Brenston, Koko Taylor, Dave 'Baby' Cortez, Jimmy McCracklin, Eddie Fontaine, Rusty York and Little Walter.

SPOTLIGHT ON THE '60s [2-LP]
PRT SPOT-1015 • 1981
No Particular Place To Go

24-track double album in a single cover with mostly English artists and groups. Terrible cover design with no pictures of anyone.

SPOTLIGHT ON ROCK'N'ROLL [2-LP]
PRT SPOT-1019 • 1981
Sweet Little Sixteen

Another 24-track double album in a single cover, again with no pictures of any artists. Good selection of songs, but some are re-recordings by the original artists. The interesting thing about these two PRT albums is that Berry is the only artists featured on both issues.

THE HISTORY OF ROCK (VOLUME 4) [2-LP]
The History of Rock HRL-004 • 1982
School Day / Sweet Little Sixteen / Johnny B. Goode / Rock And Roll Music / Memphis, Tennessee / Come On / No Particular Place To Go / You Never Can Tell / Roll Over Beethoven / Maybellene

Part of a series of 31 double-albums of rock music. Berry picture on the cover. Most artists have one side each. Other artists on VOLUME 4 are Gene Vincent, the Everly Brothers and Sam Cooke. A very good compilation with liner notes and many great pictures. This series was also distributed in several other European countries including Norway in 1983.

CHESS MASTERS SAMPLER
Chess [PRT] CXSP-7250 ● 1984
Brown Eyed Handsome Man

The album contains a small selection from the Chess roster of artists and was sold to whet the customer's appetite for the huge catalogue available at the time in the UK. A list of the 15 single and 21 double album releases in the *Chess Masters* series was printed on the cover. Other artists include Little Walter, Sonny Boy Williamson, Howlin' Wolf, Muddy Waters, John Lee Hooker, Elmore James, Jimmy Rogers, Bo Diddley, Koko Taylor, Little Milton, Tommy Tucker, Sugar Pie DeSanto and Etta James. Berry picture on the cover.

STARBURST – 20 CLASSIC ROCK'N'ROLL TRACKS
Meteor [Magnum Music Group] MRB-001 ● 1984
Reelin' And Rockin' / Maybellene

Berry's tracks are from the 1969 *Toronto Rock & Roll Revival*, and 'Reelin' And Rockin'' is even edited! Some of the songs are classics all right, but they are not the original recordings, and the content is also a little unusual, including some numbers from the late '60s and '70s. Other artists include Gene Vincent (2), Ronnie Hawkins (2), Link Wray (2), Billy Fury (2), Shakin' Stevens & The Sunsets (2), Roy Brown, Little Richard (2), the Blue Caps (2), Carl Perkins (2) and the Jets. Drawings of Berry, Little Richard and Gene Vincent on the cover.

THEN CAME ROCK'N'ROLL [2-LP]
EMI THEN-1 ● 1984
Sweet Little Sixteen / Memphis, Tennessee / Johnny B. Goode

36 original rock'n'roll classics. Gatefold cover with pictures (including one of Berry) and extensive liner notes. The profile is on the big names like Berry, Jerry Lee Lewis (2), Eddie Cochran (4), Buddy Holly (3), Fats Domino (4), Little Richard (2), Gene Vincent (4), Bill Haley (1) and the Everly Brothers (2). Of the major rockers, only Elvis Presley, Carl Perkins and Bo Diddley are missing. Other artists include Bobby Vee (2), the Ventures, Frankie Lymon (2), the (post-Holly) Crickets, Johnny Burnette (2), Johnny Otis, Johnny & The Hurricanes and Danny & The Juniors. I don't know why they included Bobby Vee instead of Ricky Nelson. That's surely a big mistake, and as for the Crickets without Holly – give me a break!

RIP IT UP – ROCK'N'ROLL
K-Tel ONE-1301 ● 1985
Memphis, Tennessee / Johnny B. Goode / Sweet Little Sixteen / Nadine

The 1969 *Toronto Rock & Roll Revival* again. Berry picture on the cover. Also tracks by Bill Haley (4), Little Richard (4) and the Jodimars (4). Reissued on CD in 1987 [K-Tel ONCD-5115].

THE BEST OF CHESS ROCK'N'ROLL [2-LP]
Chess [Green Line/Charly] GCH2-6024 ● 1988
Italian pressing distributed in the UK by Charly. Same tracks and gatefold sleeve as the US 2-LP [Chess CH2-6024].

CHESS – THE RHYTHM AND THE BLUES
Chess [Green Line/Charly] SAM-500 ● 1988
Maybellene / Johnny B. Goode

Italian pressing distributed in the UK by Charly. Sampler. The cover is worth the price of the album alone! Berry is so prominent that at first sight you could mistake this for a Berry album. The US sheet music of 'Roll Over Beethoven' and '30 Days', and the blue Chess single issue (second pressing) of 'Maybellene' are on the front cover, while the NEW JUKE BOX HITS and THE BLUES (VOLUME 1) LPs are depicted on the back, together with small pictures of Bo Diddley, Little Walter and Sonny Boy Williamson. Other artists include Bo Diddley, John Lee Hooker, Sonny Boy Williamson, Elmore James, Little Walter, Etta James, Howlin' Wolf, Buddy Guy, B.B. King, Muddy Waters, Jimmy Rogers and Albert King.

THE CHESS STORY 1954-69 [2-LP]
Connoisseur Collection VSOPLP-130 ● 1989
Bye Bye Johnny

Nice release with a gatefold cover, liner notes and many pictures. Other artists include Bo Diddley, Dale Hawkins, Little Walter, Tommy Tucker, Dave 'Baby' Cortez, Muddy Waters, John Lee Hooker, Howlin' Wolf, Jimmy Rogers, Elmore James, Buddy Guy, the Ramsey Lewis Trio, Bobby Charles, Clarence 'Frogman' Henry, the Hawketts, the Marathons, the Moonglows, Etta James, Little Milton, Joe Tex, the Dells, Fontella Bass and Jackie Ross. Also released on CD [Connoisseur Collection VSOPCD-130].

THE GOLDEN YEARS OF THE FIFTIES
Hallmark SHM-3289 ● 1989
Maybellene / Sweet Little Sixteen / School Day

Chess recordings. Presented by English radio deejay Simon Bates. This is in a series covering pop music from the '50s right up to present day. Other artists include Buddy Holly (3), Bo Diddley (2), Bill Haley (2), the Poni-Tails, Danny & The Juniors, Billy Williams and Lloyd Price. Berry picture on the cover.

STONED ALCHEMY – 30 ORIGINAL BLUES AND R&B HITS
THAT INSPIRED THE ROLLING STONES [2-LP]
Instant [Charly] INSD-5016 ● 1989
Come On / Down The Road A Piece**+** / Around And Around / You Can't Catch Me / Route 66**+** *(alt. version)* / Carol

This is not as good as it looks. There are a few tracks with bad sound quality, and the alternative version of 'Route 66' could not have inspired the Stones as it was first issued in 1986. Other artists include Howlin' Wolf (3), Benny Spellman, Muddy Waters (5), Bo Diddley (5), Alvin Robinson, Jimmy Reed (2), Irma Thomas, Buster Brown, Betty Harris, Tommy Tucker, Gene Allison, Dale Hawkins and Bobby Womack. Also issued on CD [Instant CDINS-5016] minus three tracks. Berry picture on the cover.

Jive Bunny & The Mastermixers
JIVE BUNNY – THE ALBUM
Telstar STAR-2390 ● 1989
Rock And Roll Party Mix [includes excerpt from 'Roll Over Beethoven'] / *That's What I Like* [includes part of guitar solo from 'Johnny B. Goode']

Original concept and production: John Pickles. Mixed by Andy Pickles. This was the first in a string of mixes using various musical styles, usually famous rock'n'roll and pop songs, and it became very popular thanks to media exposure. Actually it was a great dance concept. The album spent 22 weeks on the UK charts in the early months of 1990, reaching No.2. The two Berry tracks are the original Chess recordings, mixed into the medleys, no complete tracks.

See also 1994 UK Various Artists CD, PARTY MEGAMIX 2 [Prism Leisure PLATCD-3933].

ROCK GUITAR LEGENDS [4-LP]
Knight RGLLP-47001 ● 1990
Johnny B. Goode

48 tracks including Berry's Chess classic. '*To start this series there was only one logical choice, Chuck Berry's 'Johnny B. Goode' (1958 – Chess). Berry was the first Guitar Hero of the Rock and Roll era* (true!) *and the catalyst for thousands of '60s bands who covered his enormous repertoire and plundered his licks. Without Chuck Berry most of what follows would not have happened.*' So begin the liner notes. This box is a nice compilation of famous rock guitarists, either playing solo or in a band setting. Berry is the only one from the '50s! Where are Eddie Cochran, James Burton, Cliff Gallup, Duane Eddy and the others? Most tracks date from the '70s and '80s, with a few from the '60s thrown in. No proper pictures of any artists, although there are shadows of Berry, Clapton and Townshend in the 4-page booklet. Other artists include Fleetwood Mac (2, including 'Albatross'), Cream, T-Rex ('Get It On'), the Shadows (3), Dave Edmunds (2), Jimi Hendrix, Chris Spedding ('Guitar Jamboree'), Jeff Beck, Beck, Bogert & Appice (2), the Manish Boys, Black Sabbath (2), Townshend & Lane, Deep Purple, the Faces ('Memphis'), the Dixie Dregs, the Allman Brothers Band (2), Elvin Bishop, the Band (2), Santana, Albert Lee, the Doobie Brothers, Toto, Boston (2), Billy Squier, Pat Travers, Todd Rundgren, Little Feat, Bonnie Raitt, Les Dudek, Derek & The Dominos, Roy Buchanan, Tom Johnston, the Steve Morse Band, J.J. Cale, Ry Cooder, the Gregg Allman Band, Rainbow and Joe Walsh.

WHITE LIGHTNING – 30 ORIGINAL HITS THAT LIT UP THE SIXTIES [2-LP]
Instant [Charly] INSD-5017 ● 1990
Roll Over Beethoven / I'm Talking About You / Too Much Monkey Business

Overall, the Instant albums from 1989,1990 and 1992 featuring original recordings that inspired the English music scene in the '50s and '60s are educational and good value for money. This WHITE LIGHTNING issue has the best cover, with some interesting pictures – especially the reproductions of several posters from the mid '60s, two with Berry. Other artists include John Lee Hooker (2), Bo Diddley (3), Howlin' Wolf (3), Muddy Waters, Little Walter, Billy Boy Arnold (2), Wilbert Harrison, Elmore James (3), Lowell Fulson, Ernie K-Doe, Rosco Gordon, Buddy Guy, Chris Kenner, Bessie Banks, Jimmy Reed, Sonny Boy Williamson, Joe Turner, Etta James and Otis Rush. Also issued on CD [Instant CDINS-5017] minus two tracks. Picture of Berry on the cover.

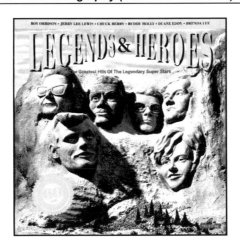

LEGENDS & HEROES [3-LP]
Teledisc TELLY-52 ● 1991
Maybellene / Roll Over Beethoven / School Day / Rock And Roll Music / Sweet Little Sixteen /
Johnny B. Goode / Memphis, Tennessee / Nadine / No Particular Place To Go / You Never Can Tell

Six legends with one side apiece containing ten songs: Roy Orbison, Brenda Lee, Buddy Holly, Duane Eddy, Jerry Lee Lewis and Berry. Nice compilation with gatefold cover and extensive liner notes. However, Berry was born in St. Louis, Missouri and not San Jose, California! I have never seen a CD release of this.

LOVE 'EM DO – 20 HITS THAT INSPIRED THE BEATLES
Instant [Charly] INS-5063 ● 1992
Little Queenie / Rock And Roll Music / Roll Over Beethoven

This is a good compilation, aimed more at Beatles fans than others, and I think it's a good education for all Beatles followers (although I believe they are generally rather better informed than most Elvis fans). Good liner notes by Adam Komorowski. Other artists include Carl Perkins (3), the Shirelles (2), the Isley Brothers, Little Richard (3), Wilbert Harrison, Lee Dorsey, the Teddy Bears, Jimmy Reed, Clarence 'Frogman' Henry, Eddie Fontaine, the Cookies and Bobby Freeman. Picture of Berry on the cover. Also issued on CD [Instant CDINS-5063].

Various Artists CD Albums

RIP IT UP – ROCK'N'ROLL
K-Tel ONCD-5115 ● 1987
Memphis, Tennessee / Johnny B. Goode / Sweet Little Sixteen / Nadine

The 1969 *Toronto Rock & Roll Revival* again. CD reissue of the 1985 LP [K-Tel ONE-1301]. Berry picture on the cover.

Chuck Berry – Fats Domino
ROCK & ROLL LIVE
Magnum Force CDMFD-001 ● 1987
Reelin' And Rockin' / School Day / My Ding-A-Ling / Too Much Monkey Business / Memphis, Tennessee / Maybellene / Nadine

The 1969 *Toronto Rock & Roll Revival* again, plus 10 live songs by Domino. This might also have been released on LP, but I have not seen a copy.

THE CHESS STORY 1954-69
Connoisseur Collection VSOPCD-130 ● 1989
Bye Bye Johnny

Nice release with a gatefold cover, liner notes and many pictures. Other artists include Bo Diddley, Dale Hawkins, Little Walter, Tommy Tucker, Dave 'Baby' Cortez, Muddy Waters, John Lee Hooker, Howlin' Wolf, Jimmy Rogers, Elmore James, Buddy Guy, the Ramsey Lewis Trio, Bobby Charles, Clarence 'Frogman' Henry, the Hawketts, the Marathons, the Moonglows, Etta James, Little Milton, Joe Tex, the Dells, Fontella Bass and Jackie Ross. Also released on 2-LP [Connoisseur Collection VSOPLP-130].

STONED ALCHEMY – 27 ORIGINAL BLUES AND R&B HITS
THAT INSPIRED THE ROLLING STONES
Instant [Charly] CDINS-5016 ● 1989
Come On / Down The Road A Piece+ / Around And Around / You Can't Catch Me / Route 66+ *(alt. version)* / Carol

This is not as good as it looks. There are a few tracks with bad sound quality, and the alternative version of 'Route 66' could not have inspired the Stones as it was first issued in 1986. Other artists include Howlin' Wolf (3), Benny Spellman, Muddy Waters (5), Bo Diddley (5), Alvin Robinson, Jimmy Reed (2), Irma Thomas, Buster Brown, Betty Harris, Tommy Tucker, Gene Allison, Dale Hawkins and Bobby Womack. Also issued on 2-LP [Instant INSD-5016] with three extra tracks. Picture of Berry on the cover.

WHITE LIGHTNING – 28 ORIGINAL HITS THAT LIT UP THE SIXTIES
Instant [Charly] CDINS-5017 ● 1990
Roll Over Beethoven / I'm Talking About You / Too Much Monkey Business

Overall, the Instant albums from 1989,1990 and 1992 featuring original recordings that inspired the English music scene in the '50s and '60s are good value for money and educational. This WHITE LIGHTNING issue has the best cover, with some interesting pictures – especially the reproductions of several posters from the mid '60s, two with Berry. Other artists include John Lee Hooker (2), Bo Diddley (3), Howlin' Wolf (3), Muddy Waters, Little Walter, Billy Boy Arnold (2), Wilbert Harrison, Elmore James (3), Lowell Fulson, Ernie K-Doe, Rosco Gordon, Buddy Guy, Chris Kenner, Bessie Banks, Jimmy Reed, Sonny Boy Williamson, Joe Turner, Etta James and Otis Rush. Also issued on 2-LP [Instant INSD-5017] with two extra tracks. Picture of Berry on the cover.

ROCK AND ROLL DANCE PARTY (ALAN FREED'S ROCK'N'ROLL RADIO)
Magnum Force CDMF-075 • 1991
Maybellene *(live, 1956 Alan Freed radio show)* / Roll Over Beethoven *(live, 1956 Alan Freed radio show)*

This appears to be a legal CD reissue of various live radio recordings including the two Berry songs that first appeared on the 1978 Various Artists US bootleg, ROCK'N'ROLL RADIO [Radiola MR-1087] and ALAN FREED'S ROCK'N'ROLL DANCE PARTY (VOLUME 1) [WINS LP-1010]. Also included are 25 performances by other artists from the '50s including the Drifters, Bill Haley, Gene Vincent, the Johnny Burnette Rock & Roll Trio, Etta James, Frankie Lymon and others. The sound quality is not any better than on the bootlegs. I suggest that you look at the record releases from Japan to get the best issue of this compilation, front cover photo and better sound. As always, the Japanese knew how to deliver the goods.

LOVE 'EM DO – 20 HITS THAT INSPIRED THE BEATLES
Instant [Charly] CDINS-5063 • 1992
Little Queenie / Rock And Roll Music / Roll Over Beethoven

This is a good compilation, aimed more at Beatles fans than others, and I think it's a good education for all Beatles followers (although I believe they are generally rather better informed than most Elvis fans). Good liner notes by Adam Komorowski. Other artists include Carl Perkins (3), the Shirelles (2), the Isley Brothers, Little Richard (3), Wilbert Harrison, Lee Dorsey, the Teddy Bears, Jimmy Reed, Clarence 'Frogman' Henry, Eddie Fontaine, the Cookies and Bobby Freeman. Picture of Berry on the cover. Also issued on LP [Instant INS-5063].

UNDER THE INFLUENCE –
THE ORIGINAL VERSIONS OF THE SONGS THE BEATLES COVERED
Sequel NEXCD-226 • 1992
Roll Over Beethoven / Rock And Roll Music

A good 24-track compilation (better and more comprehensive than the Instant LP), with many pictures and informative liner notes. Why two albums with a similar theme were released almost at the same time is strange. However, both contain a good survey of the type of music that influenced the Beatles, and not too many duplicated songs. Other artists in this collection include Arthur Alexander, the

Cookies, the Shirelles (2), Lenny Welch, the Isley Brothers, Peggy Lee, the Marvelettes, Smokey Robinson & The Miracles, the Donays, Barrett Strong, Little Richard (2), Larry Williams (3), Carl Perkins (3), Dr. Feelgood & The Interns, Buddy Holly and Buck Owens. Picture of Berry on the cover.

GUITAR ROCK – 18 GUITAR LEGENDS
Stardust STACD-045 • 1993
No Particular Place To Go

Other artists include Dave Edmunds, the Stray Cats, Jeff Healey, Glenn Frey, Gary Moore, Lynyrd Skynyrd, Joe Walsh, J.J. Cale, Roy Buchanan, Justin Hayward & John Lodge, U.P. Wilson, Jimi Hendrix, Fleetwood Mac, Toto, Mott The Hoople, REO Speedwagon and Johnny Winter ('Johnny B. Goode').

THE PYE INTERNATIONAL STORY [2-CD]
Sequel NEDCD-239 • 1994
Let It Rock / Memphis, Tennessee / No Particular Place To Go

Nice set containing 50 tracks covering the history of this popular record label, who followed very much in the footsteps of Decca's famous London label, leasing American hits and non-hits and making them available to English buyers. I won't list all the artists included, but it starts with Ritchie Valens (November 1958) and ends with Meri Wilson (August 1977). Berry is the only one to have three songs included! Picture of Berry on the cover.

Chuck Berry – Bo Diddley
TWO ON ONE – CHUCK BERRY / BO DIDDLEY
Charly '2 on 1' CDTT-2 • 1994
Rock And Roll Music / No Particular Place To Go *(stereo)* / Brown Eyed Handsome Man / Roll Over Beethoven / Johnny B. Goode / Carol / Reelin' And Rockin' / Memphis, Tennessee / Back In The USA / My Ding-A-Ling *(live, single edit)*

Chess recordings. This was one of a series of ten volumes featuring different artists. Also contains 10 songs by Diddley, including one of my favourites, 'Crackin' Up'. Liner notes and pictures. Issued in a special cardboard box.

PARTY MEGAMIX 2
Prism Leisure PLATCD-3933 ● 1994
That's What I Like [includes part of guitar solo from 'Johnny B. Goode'] / *Chuck Berry Megamix:*
My Ding-A-Ling – Rock And Roll Music – Sweet Little Sixteen – Reelin' And Rockin' – Johnny B.
Goode – Roll Over Beethoven – My Ding-A-Ling

Over 80 sensationally sequenced songs – so it says, anyway. *Buddy Holly*
Medley, *Frank Sinatra Mix*, *Opera Megamix*, etc. This is interesting, just for the fun of
it... I think. The songs are blended together and extra drums added. The sleeve says
1993, but the label says 1994.

See also 1991 Danish Various Artists LP, ROCK'N'ROLL HALL OF FAME, with
the same Berry mix but a much more interesting album concept, and 1996 US CD,
CAN CAN YOU PARTY [Stardust 26666]. For more info about the concept see 1989
UK Various Artists LP, JIVE BUNNY – THE ALBUM [Telstar STAR-2390].

As a matter of fact, this Jive Bunny (it doesn't say on the record, but it is) craze
really got out of hand after a while. Too many albums came on the market around the
world with various mixes: NON STOP PARTY, BEACH PARTY, IT'S PARTY TIME,
HAVIN' A PARTY... you name it. Also, some might argue that it's a tribute to Berry
and should be listed as such, but I don't see it that way.

CHESS R&B LEGENDS IN LONDON
Charly R&B Masters CDRB-22 ● 1995
After It's Over *(instr)* / St. Louis Blues+ / Why Should We End This Way / Let's Boogie / Mean Old
World+

Songs from two Berry LPs: 1964's CHUCK BERRY IN LONDON (tracks 1-3) and
1972's THE LONDON CHUCK BERRY SESSIONS (tracks 4 and 5). Other artists
include Howlin' Wolf (5), Muddy Waters (5) and Bo Diddley (5). Picture of Berry on the
cover.

Chuck Berry – Gene Vincent
THE ESSENTIAL COLLECTION [2-CD]
Wisepack LECDD-625 ● 1995
Sweet Little Rock And Roller / Roll Over Beethoven / Rock And Roll Music / No Particular Place
To Go / Brown Eyed Handsome Man / Thirty Days / Little Queenie / Carol / Promised Land
(stereo) / Memphis, Tennessee* / Too Much Monkey Business* / My Ding-A-Ling* / Reelin' And
Rockin' / Johnny B. Goode* / Maybellene* / Nadine* / School Day* / Sweet Little Sixteen*

At first sight this seems like good value for money: 18 songs by Berry on one CD
and 20 by Vincent on the other. However, the Berry tracks are a mixture of Chess
cuts and live material from the 1969 *Toronto Rock & Roll Revival* (marked *). This was
one in a series of *'Essential Collections'*, including everyone from Frank Sinatra to Eric
Clapton.

Chuck Berry & Bo Diddley / Howlin' Wolf, Muddy Waters & Bo Diddley
TWO GREAT GUITARS / THE SUPER SUPER BLUES BAND
BGO BGOCD-334 ● 1996
Liverpool Drive *(instr)* / Chuck's Beat *(instr)* / When The Saints Go Marching In *(Bo Diddley)* / Bo's
Beat *(instr)*

Two LPs on one CD., including a reissue of the original TWO GREAT GUITARS
album from 1964. Good new liner notes from Neil Slaven. In the years that followed,
we were treated to many excellent BGO '2 on 1' reissues of Berry's original UK Pye
and Chess albums.

THE CHESS STORY [2-CD]
Charly CD LAB-100 • 1996
Maybellene / Sweet Little Sixteen *(original speed)* / My Ding-A-Ling *(live, single edit)*

This was the first in a series of digipak 'book' sets produced by Charly showcasing different labels and contains 53 tracks tracing the history of Chess. Disk 1 covers *'From The Blues To Doo-Wop'* while Disk 2 picks up the story *'From 'Rock'n'Roll To Soul'*. To quote from the back cover: *'This is the story of Leonard and Phil Chess, two Jewish immigrants from Poland, who created and developed the Chess label into the greatest Blues and R&B record label in the world. Here is a musical history that contains essential classics by Muddy Waters, Chuck Berry, Howlin' Wolf and Buddy Guy, as well as many rockin' rarities here making their CD debuts.'*

Nice booklet with info for each song and artist, and two pictures of Berry. In addition to the many hits, there are quite a few unusual rarities such as Bobby Lewis' 'Mumbles Blues', Carolyn Bradshaw's 'Oh! I Like It' and 'Four O'Clock In The Morning' by Stanley Mitchell & The Tornados. This set is extremely rare as it coincided with Charly losing their long-running court battle with MCA over rights to issue Chess material and was withdrawn shortly before (or possibly shortly after) its release.

CHESS BLUES GUITAR 1949-69 [2-CD]
Chess [Universal] MCD-09393 • 1998
Guitar Boogie *(instr)* / I Still Got The Blues *(mono)*

In the same series as the one below, same layout. 45 tracks.

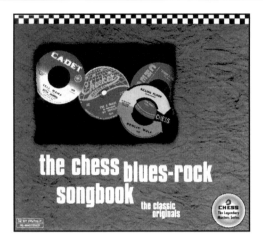

THE CHESS BLUES-ROCK SONGBOOK [2-CD]
Chess [Universal] MCD-09389 • 1998
Roll Over Beethoven / Rock And Roll Music / Johnny B. Goode / Memphis, Tennessee / Back In
The USA

Includes booklet with discographical information. Since Berry has most songs on
the set it's rather strange that they didn't at least include a tiny little picture of him. It's
a good compilation though, 36 tracks, released in connection with the Chess *50th
Anniversary* celebration in 1998.

Chuck Berry – Bo Diddley – Muddy Waters – Howlin' Wolf
THE LONDON BLUES FESTIVAL [2-CD]
ITM CD-960017/18 • 1998
Same Berry tracks as the original 1972 LONDON SESSIONS LP, except they left
out 'My Ding-A-Ling'. The other artists' tracks are likewise lifted from their respective
LONDON SESSIONS albums. BLUES FESTIVAL? Don't let the title fool you. This
kind of release is very close to what must rank as bootleg, but it's been on sale
everywhere.

THE GREATEST ROCK'N'ROLL ALBUM OF ALL TIME [6-CD]
Dressed To Kill 246 • 2000
Reelin' And Rockin' / School Day / My Ding-A-Ling / Too Much Monkey Business / Memphis,
Tennessee / Maybellene / Nadin

77 tracks in total. The Berry cuts are all from the 1969 *Toronto Rock & Roll
Revival*. Also features live recordings by Jerry Lee Lewis (18, including covers of
Roll Over Beethoven, Little Queenie and *Sweet Little Sixteen*), Carl Perkins (10),
Little Richard (16) and Fats Domino (25). I have listed this album primarily because
of its grossly misleading title.

THE BEST AIR GUITAR ALBUM IN THE WORLD... EVER! [2-CD]
EMI Virgin/Universal TV VTDCD-416 ● 2001
Johnny B. Goode

43 tracks on two CDs including Berry's famed Chess recording. Whether you think this is a good album largely depends on who you like or dig. There are several guitarists and songs I would have wanted to include here, however, there's enough guitar music to satisfy most people with an interest in the '70s, '80s and '90s. The '50s are represented only by Berry and Eddie Cochran ('Summertime Blues'). The '60s has Dick Dale, the Surfaris ('Wipe Out'), the Troggs, the Who, Cream, Steppenwolf and Jeff Beck. The '70s (which has most coverage) features people like David Bowie, T. Rex, Free, Santana, Deep Purple, Jimi Hendrix, Queen and Dire Straits. Later material is by the likes of Joe Walsh, Paul McCartney, Motorhead, Iron Maiden, Z.Z. Top etc. A little more information about each track would have been nice, especially for those who don't know who plays guitar in each band. See also Norwegian discography.

THE LONDON ROCK AND ROLL SHOW
TKO/Magnum Force CDMF-105 ● 2001
School Day / Memphis, Tennessee / Sweet Little Sixteen / Mean Old 'Frisco+ / Beer Drinkin' Woman+ / Wee Wee Hours / *Medley:* Let It Rock – Roll 'Em Pete+ – Carol – Little Queenie / Reelin' And Rockin'

Recording of the famed rock'n'roll spectacular on 5 August 1972 at the Wembley Stadium in London. Unfortunately the CD has such bad sound quality you wonder what went on when it was transferred to shiny. The original soundtrack quality of this show was bad in the first place and hardly essential, and when you don't have the visual benefits it is even worse. Not only that, all the songs run at the wrong speed: they are too slow. Magnum have released so many sloppy records over nearly three decades, and this new one must be almost the baddest of the bad. It is very seldom that a record featuring the greats of rock'n'roll gets a bad review in *Now Dig This*, but this one did! Here we get Berry's version of Arthur 'Big Boy' Crudup's 1942 'Mean Ole Frisco' for the first time on record. Chuck should have recorded a proper studio version of this! Other artists include Bo Diddley (2), Jerry Lee Lewis (5, including a cover of 'Sweet Little Sixteen' and a medley of rock'n'roll songs), Bill Haley (2) and Little Richard (5).

243

THE BEST AIR GUITAR ALBUM IN THE WORLD... EVER! (VOLUME 2) [2-CD]
EMI Virgin/Universal TV VTDCD-488 ● 2002
Carol

Chess recording. This also came out in Norway and, although it was not as popular as VOLUME 1, it also sold well. Goode for a Berry!

BEYOND MISSISSIPPI [2-CD]
Manteca MANTDCD-209 ● 2002
Deep Feeling *(instr)*

'The blues that left town... and took a wrong turn down the right road.' A selection of 35 tracks that reveals just how diverse, yet resilient, the whole genre was. Includes the Golden Gate Quartet, Charlie Patton, Dr. John, Memphis Minnie, Muddy Waters, Mahalia Jackson, Bob Dylan, Tom Waits, Bo Diddley, Lightnin' Hopkins, Van Morrison, Nina Simone, Albert King, Reverend Gary Davis and others. A superb compilation combining many musical styles. The liner notes tell us: '*Unfortunately Charles Edward Berry is often seen simply as a pioneer rock'n'roller with a touch of the novelty act about him. He has always seen himself as a bluesman.'* Oh really?

EXPRESS YOURSELF – SOUL IN THE 20TH CENTURY [4-CD]
Universal LC-6583319-2 ● 2002
School Day

Chess recording. 83 tracks spanning nearly sixty years of black music, starting with Louis Jordan back in 1946. Of course I'm glad that Berry is featured, but I think it is really a shame and a musical forgery that the compilers have left out a legend and inspirational source of the stature of Little Richard. No picture of Berry on the cover or in the booklet. This was made in the EU, so you will probably also find the set in various countries including Scandinavia, Germany and the Netherlands.

LOVE THAT LOUIE: THE LOUIE LOUIE FILES
Ace CDCHD-844 ● 2002
Havana Moon

Interesting album tracing the history of the rock'n'roll classic, 'Louie Louie', written by Richard Berry and recorded by him on 16 March 1957. The beat of 'Louie Louie' is from a Latin number, 'El Loco Cha Cha' by Rene Touzet & His Orchestra recorded in 1956, while the lyrical influence is definitely Berry's 'Havana Moon'. Additionally, there are 19 cover versions, soundalikes and rewrites of 'Louie Louie' by artists like the Wailers, the Kingsmen, the Sonics, the Sandpipers, Paul Revere & The Raiders, the Kinks, Toots & The Maytals and others.

THE BEST AIR GUITAR ALBUM IN THE WORLD... EVER! (VOLS. 1 AND 2) [4-CD]
EMI Virgin/Universal TV VTDCDX-526 ● 2003
Carol / Johnny B. Goode

Chess recordings. The two platinum-selling 2-CD albums from 2001 and 2002 combined into a box set.

Fun at Blueberry Hill, St. Louis – August 2002.

MOJO CHESS CLASSICS
Mojo, no number ● August 2005
Night Beat *(instr)*

Coverdisc given away free with *Mojo* magazine. 15 interesting and mostly obscure tracks from the Chess vaults, hand-picked by *Mojo*. Liner notes by editor Phil Alexander.

ELTON JOHN'S CHRISTMAS PARTY
Hear Music CD-70007 ● November 2005
Run Rudolph Run**+**

A compilation of 21 tracks put together by Sir Elton John himself for sale at coffee giant Starbucks' many locations. Apart from two songs by himself, the album consists of seasonal tunes by the likes of Bruce Springsteen, the Ronettes, the Beach Boys, the Crystals, the Eagles, Kate Bush, the Ventures, El Vez, Otis Redding, U2, the Pet Shop Boys, Jimmy Buffett, etc. Quite a varied selection of songs and artists.

CHESS ORIGINALS
Universal-Island 9830156 ● 2005
Come On / Rock And Roll Music *(demo)* / Too Much Monkey Business / Memphis, Tennessee

Other artists include Bo Diddley (6), Muddy Waters (4), Howlin' Wolf (4), Sonny Boy Williamson (2), Little Walter, Tommy Tucker, Dale Hawkins, Etta James and Eddie Fontaine. Great compilation, digipak with booklet, good liner notes and pictures, one of Berry.

245

CHESS PIECES – THE VERY BEST OF CHESS [2-CD]
Universal-Island 9831719 ● 2005
Maybellene / Johnny B. Goode / No Particular Place To Go

48 tracks on two CDs for the price of a single CD – not bad value. A very well laid-out digipak with a booklet containing some extremely nice pictures, including a colour one of Berry I hadn't seen before, probably from England 1965. Actually, the booklet is worth the asking price alone, and includes more interesting Berry stuff.

THE CHESS STORY [2-CD]
Universal-Island 9833298 ● 2006
Maybellene / Rock And Roll Music *(alt)* / No Particular Place To Go

Nice digipak issue with a 24-page booklet containing pictures of Berry, Diddley and others. They're all here, the music and the artists that made history. 50 tracks.

MORE MONKEY BUSINESS CATALOG MARKETING [promo]
Universal 991390949 ● 2006
Too Much Monkey Business

18-track digipak with artists ranging from Pulp, Def Leppard and Cure to Dusty Springfield, Stevie Wonder and Walker Brothers. The reason for listing this particular promo CD is not only because it contains Berry's classic protest song, but also because it has a great old-fashioned Fifties cover. The Berry track was to promote the newly released double UK CD, REELIN' AND ROCKIN' [Universal 9832354].

CAVERN – THE MOST FAMOUS CLUB IN THE WORLD
EMI Catalogue Marketing/Universal Music TV 50999 5 07453 2 6 ● August 2007
No Particular Place To Go

A 3-CD set to celebrate the Cavern Club's 50th anniversary in 2007 (the club first opened its doors on 16 January 1957). Great cover with the Beatles, the Rolling Stones, Queen and the Who most prominent, with special guests like Travis, Berry, Rod Stewart, the Kinks, Stevie Wonder – you name it Very few '50s artists are included. Apart from Berry, there's only one track by Bo Diddley, one by Gene Vincent and one by Lonnie Donegan. I am not quite sure about the title of this record set, as I think the Star-Club in Hamburg is probably just as famous, but anyway...

INTERNATIONAL DISCOGRAPHIES

This section contains details of Chuck Berry releases from all over the world except the USA and UK. I have compiled these discographies from a variety of sources including my own collection, other people's record collections, sale lists, etc. While substantial, they are by no means complete, and further additions and amendments are always welcome.

Chuck Berry backstage at the Paris Olympia with French rock'n'roll legends
Eddy Mitchell *(left)* and Johnny Hallyday – 11 January 2005.

ARGENTINA

Singles

Nadine / School Day
Micsa 9035 • 1976
Colourful label with Pacific motif.

LPs

CHUCK BERRY
Micsa SEL-654 • 1976
Same tracks as the 1964 US LP, CHUCK BERRY'S GREATEST HITS [Chess LP-1485], except 'Carol' replaces 'Memphis, Tennessee'. Different cover.

AUSTRALIA

Way down under! Many Berry records have seen the light of day in Australia since the '50s. However, several of his earliest recordings were not released in Oz at the time.

Berry's first Australian single came out on Columbia (black label with gold lettering). However, Malte Koch has a 45 rpm copy with a dark blue label and gold lettering, a combination I have also seen on 'Carol' *b/w* 'Hey Pedro' [Philips 31700.BF] The other 1950s singles and EP were issued on Philips (dark blue label with silver lettering). From 1964, Berry's records were released on the Chess label. Singles had a dark blue label with silver lettering and silver Chess logo on top, and a small centre hole. To the best of my knowledge, all the Chess singles up to and including CH-065 came in standard Australian Chess company sleeves – no picture sleeves. The Chess EPs also had a dark blue label with silver lettering. The Chess LPs had black labels. I have next to no information about Australian Mercury releases.

Some of the information on early Berry releases in Australia was taken from an article and discography by Paul Simons in the Australian fanzine, *The Big Beat Of The '50s* (the official club magazine of the Australian Rock'n'Roll Appreciation Society).

In later years, many Berry records from Australia were also sold in New Zealand and vice versa. Berry's New Zealand releases are, of course, listed under that country.

Singles

Columbia DO-3867

Philips 31671.BF

School Day / Deep Feeling (instr)
Columbia DO-3867 • 1957
Issued on both 78 rpm and 45 rpm.

Rock And Roll Music / Blue Feeling (instr)
Philips 31671.BF • 1957

Sweet Little Sixteen / Reelin' And Rockin'
Philips 31683.BF • 1958

Johnny B. Goode / Around And Around
Philips 31691.BF • 1958

Beautiful Delilah / Vacation Time
Philips 31697.BF • 1958

Carol / Hey Pedro
Philips 31700.BF • 1958

Nadine / O'Rangutang *(instr)*
Chess CH-023 • 1964

No Particular Place To Go / You Two
Chess CH-026 • 1964

You Never Can Tell / Brenda Lee
Chess CH-027 • 1964

Chuck Berry & Bo Diddley
Chuck's Beat *(instr, single edit)* **/ Bo's Beat+** *(instr, single edit)*
Chess CH-030 • 1964

Little Marie / Go, Bobby Soxer
Chess CH-032 • 1964

Promised Land / The Things I Used To Do+
Chess CH-034 • 1964

Dear Dad / Lonely School Days *(slow version)*
Chess CH-045 • 1965

Ramona Say Yes / Lonely School Days *(fast version)*
Chess CH-065 • 1965

My Ding-A-Ling *(live, single edit)* **/ Johnny B. Goode** *(live)*
Chess CH-106 • 1972

Reelin' And Rockin' *(live, single edit)* **/ Let's Boogie**
Chess CH-107 • 1973

EPs

REELIN' AND ROCKIN' TO THE FABULOUS CHUCK BERRY
Philips 35121.BE ● 1958/59
Reelin' And Rockin' / Sweet Little Sixteen / Rock And Roll Music / Blue Feeling *(instr)*

No Chuck on the cover, just a drawing of a dancing couple.

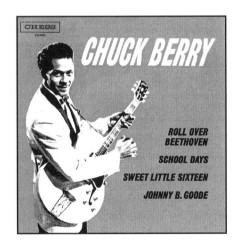

CHUCK BERRY
Chess CHX-001 ● 1964
Roll Over Beethoven / Sweet Little Sixteen / School Day / Johnny B. Goode

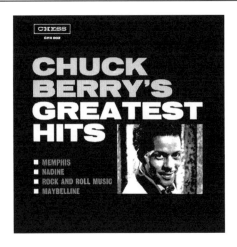

CHUCK BERRY'S GREATEST HITS
Chess CHX-002 • 1964
Memphis, Tennessee / Maybellene / Nadine / Rock And Roll Music

CHUCK BERRY IS ON TOP
Chess CHX-003 • 1964
Little Queenie / Around And Around / Carol / Anthony Boy

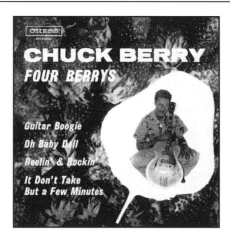

FOUR BERRYS
Chess CHX-004 ● 1964
Reelin' And Rockin' / It Don't Take But A Few Minutes / Guitar Boogie / Oh Baby Doll

The black and white cover is taken from the front of the 1958 US LP, ONE DOZEN BERRYS [Chess LP-1432], with the small picture of Chuck surrounded by strawberries.

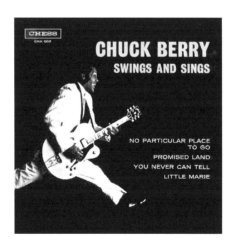

CHUCK BERRY SWINGS AND SINGS
Chess CHX-005 ● 1965
No Particular Place To Go / Promised Land / You Never Can Tell / Little Marie

CHUCK BERRY
Chess CHX-006 • 1973
Too Much Monkey Business / Reelin' And Rockin' / Back In The USA / Oh Baby Doll

I bought this on the Internet in 2005, and frankly had never heard of it before. It's also quite strange that this EP was released in '73!

Just to give you an idea of what nonsense you can find on the Internet: A guy had Chess CHX-001 for sale on eBay in February 2004. He said that Berry had five EPs on the Australian Chess label (wrong), that they all came with the same great picture (wrong) but in different colours (wrong), and that CHX-001 was the first (correct). I wonder where they get this information from! As you can see from the pictures, all the Chess EPs came with different covers (unless there's something I don't know).

CHUCK BERRY
Chess PRA EP-107 • 197?
You Never Can Tell / Johnny B. Goode / Carol / No Particular Place To Go

The liner notes on the EP cover state that Berry had five hits in Australia and that four of them appear on this EP. In actual fact, he had many more than five – see *Section 12 (Achievements & Awards)*.

CHUCK BERRY
RCA-Victor 20664 • 1982
Sweet Little Sixteen / Reelin' And Rockin' / Johnny B. Goode / Memphis, Tennessee

Chess cuts. This was released to promote the 2-LP, THE GREAT 28 [RCA-Victor VAL2-0550]. Art cover.

LPs

ANOTHER DOZEN BERRYS
Philips B-94231L • 1958/59
School Day / Deep Feeling *(instr)* / Too Much Monkey Business / Wee Wee Hours / Roly Poly *(instr)* / No Money Down / Brown Eyed Handsome Man / Berry Pickin' *(instr)* / Together (We Will Always Be) / Havana Moon / Down Bound Train / Drifting Heart

As you can see from the track listing, this was the 1957 US LP, AFTER SCHOOL SESSION [Chess LP-1426] under a different title. The cover is red, with the original US ONE DOZEN BERRYS cover in the background, with additional strawberries in front and one strawberry in a bowl of cream (or ice cream) a little to the right of centre. The title ANOTHER DOZEN BERRYS is printed on the right side underneath the bowl. But why did they use such a title when neither the AFTER SCHOOL SESSION or the ONE DOZEN BERRYS albums were issued in the '50s in Australia? The only reason I can think of is that the original US Chess LP of ONE DOZEN BERRYS might have been sold as an import.

ON STAGE
Chess CHL-211 • 1963
Same tracks as the 1963 US LP [Chess LP-1480] with the song titles 'Memphis' and 'Surfin' USA' printed at the top of the front cover. The back cover is slightly different, with the same liner notes, but with references to *'Side 1'* and *'Side 2'*. However, the song sequence on Side 1 is incorrectly listed: 'Maybellene' is shown as being the first track, but the show actually opens with 'Go, Go, Go'. The label is correct, though. 'How High The Moon' is faded out early.

ONE DOZEN BERRYS
Chess CHL-213 • 1964
Same tracks as the 1958 US LP [Chess LP-1432]. There are references on the back cover to two other Australian Berry albums (Chess CHL-211 and CHL-215) and Bo Diddley's HAVE GUITAR – WILL TRAVEL [Chess CHL-212].

BERRY IS ON TOP
Chess CHL-214 • 1964
Same tracks and cover as the 1959 US LP [Chess LP-1435].

CHUCK BERRY'S GREATEST HITS
Chess CHL-215 • 1964
Same tracks as the 1964 US LP [Chess LP-1485], but without the song titles on the front cover. However, it has liner notes on the back cover. Later reissued in electronic stereo as Chess CHLS-215 with *'Stereo'* printed at the top of the front cover.

Chuck Berry & Bo Diddley
TWO GREAT GUITARS
Chess CHL-216 *(mono)* **CHLS-216** *(stereo)* **• 1964**
Same tracks as the 1964 US LP [Checker LP-/LPS-2991]. Same front cover, but more colourful. On the back cover there are pictures of three other Berry albums and one by Bo Diddley (all on Chess).

NEW JUKE BOX HITS
Chess CHL-217 *(mono)* **• 1964**
Same tracks as the 1961 US LP [Chess LP-1456]. Same front cover, but slightly different back cover with illustrations of four other Australian Berry albums. Same liner notes.

ST. LOUIS TO LIVERPOOL
Chess CHL-219 *(mono)* **CHLS-219** *(stereo)* **• 1964**
Same tracks and cover as the 1964 US LP [Chess LP-/LPS-1488].

AFTER SCHOOL SESSION
Chess CHL-223 *(mono)* **• 1965**
Same tracks as the 1957 US LP [Chess LP-1426]. The front cover is black and white, apart from the title which is in red. The back cover has illustrations of six other Australian Berry albums.

CHUCK BERRY IN LONDON
Chess CHL-225 *(mono)* **CHLS-225** *(stereo)* **• 1965**
Same tracks as the 1965 US LP [Chess LP-/LPS-1495]. Same front cover, different back cover.

GOLDEN HITS
Philips PD-263 *(mono)* **PDS-263** *(stereo)* **• 1967**
Same tracks and cover as the 1967 US LP [Mercury MG-21103/SR-61103].

CONCERTO IN B GOODE
Mercury RS-139 *(stereo)* **• 1969**
Same tracks as the 1969 US LP [Mercury SR-61223]. Same cover, except that – unlike the US version – the back cover has no pictures of the other Mercury albums by Berry. Could it be that the other three albums were not issued in Australia at the time? Red 'knight' label.

BACK HOME
Chess CHLS- ? • 1970
Same tracks and probably same cover as the 1970 US LP [Chess LPS-1550].

SAN FRANCISCO DUES
Chess CHLS-281 • 1971
Same tracks and cover as the 1969 US LP [Chess CH-50008]. Black label.

THE LONDON CHUCK BERRY SESSIONS
Chess CHLS-283 • 1972
Same tracks and gatefold cover as the 1972 US LP [Chess CH-60020].

CHUCK BERRY'S GOLDEN DECADE [2-LP]
Chess 2CHLS-002 • 1972
Same tracks as the 1972 US reissue [Chess 2CH-1514]. Same gatefold cover as the second pressing (pink radio).

ROCK HITS
Summit SRA-295097 • 1972
Same tracks as the US LP, GOLDEN HITS [Mercury SR-61103], and the same cover as the many European pressings of this title: ROCK HITS [Fontana International 6430 022], Netherlands, 1972; ATTENTION! [Fontana 6430 022], West Germany, 1972; ROCK AND ROLL MUSIC [Fontana Special 6430 022], Norway, 1972; ROCK AND ROLL MUSIC [Fontana 6430 022 respectively], Spain, 1972 (however, the record label inside the Spanish issue actually says GOLDEN HITS); ROCK HITS [Fontana Special 6430 022], Italy, 1973; ROCK AND ROLL MUSIC [Fontana 6430 022], France, 1973; and BACK IN THE USA [Philips 6336 216], UK, 1973. However, this has the front cover picture on both sides of the album cover.

ST. LOUIE TO FRISCO TO MEMPHIS [2-LP]
Mercury 6643 005 • 1973
Same tracks and gatefold cover as the 1972 US 2-LP [Mercury SRM2-6501]. Blue-grey label.

CHUCK BERRY'S GOLDEN DECADE (VOLUME 2) [2-LP]
Chess 2CHLS-005 • 1973
Same tracks and gatefold cover as the 1973 US 2-LP [Chess 2CH-60023].

BIO
Chess CHLS-303 • 1973
Same tracks as the 1973 US LP [Chess CH-50043], but no gatefold cover.

CHUCK BERRY'S GOLDEN DECADE (VOLUME 3) [2-LP]
Chess 2CHLS-007 • 1974
Same tracks and gatefold cover as the 1974 US 2-LP [Chess 2CH-60028].

CHUCK BERRY
Chess CHLS-? • 1975
Same tracks and probably the same cover as the 1975 US LP [Chess CH-60032], but no more information available.

CHUCK BERRY'S GREATEST HITS
Chess 9124 202 • 1977
Same tracks, title and cover as the 1977 Dutch LP Chess 9283 004.

ROCKIN' WITH CHUCK BERRY
Rainbow [Philips] RDL-1506 • 1978
Chess recordings. Same tracks, title and cover as the 1977 Dutch LP [Philips 9279 540] and the 1977 UK LP [Philips SUC-114].

ROCKIT
Atlantic SD-38118 • 1979
Same tracks and cover as the 1979 US LP [Atco SD-38.118].

ROCK LEGENDS
Mercury 6870 648 • 1980
Same tracks as the 1967 US LP, GOLDEN HITS [Mercury SR-61103], but a different cover. The liner notes are mostly rubbish. The small print says that the songs were first published in the USA in 1955, 1956, 1957 and 1958. Yeah, but not on Mercury!

THE GREAT 28 [2-LP]
RCA-Victor VAL2-0550 • 1982
Same tracks and cover as the 1982 US Chess 2-LP [Chess CH-8201]. Green label.

CHUCK BERRY LIVE
Axis [EMI] AX-260165 • 1984
Nadine / School Day / Wee Wee Hours / *Medley:* Johnny B. Goode – Carol – Promised Land / Sweet Little Sixteen / Rock And Roll Music / Memphis, Tennessee / Too Much Monkey Business / Reelin' And Rockin' / Maybellene / Johnny B. Goode

Live cuts from the 1969 *Toronto Rock & Roll Revival*. Each track is faded right at the end. Front cover is same as the 1981 US LP [SSS International SSS-36].

THE BIG DADDY OF 'EM ALL
Hammard HAM-143 • 1986
Sweet Little Sixteen / Johnny B. Goode / Maybellene / School Day / Rock And Roll Music / Carol / Reelin' And Rockin' / Memphis, Tennessee / Bring Another Drink+ / Good Lookin' Woman / Roll Over Beethoven / Back In The USA / Sweet Little Rock And Roller / Oh Baby Doll / C.C. Rider+ *(live)* / Thirty Days / Goodnight, Well It's Time To Go [It's Time To Go] / Back To Memphis

Mercury recordings. Great picture of Berry on the cover, however, a sticker proclaiming *'18 Smash Hits'* is a damn lie and taking it too far.

REELIN' AND ROCKIN'
Powderworks [RCA] POW-3059 • 1986
Maybellene / Rock And Roll Music / Reelin' And Rockin' / Sweet Little Sixteen / Johnny B. Goode / School Day / Back In The USA / Sweet Little Rock And Roller / Memphis, Tennessee

Mercury recordings.

CD Albums

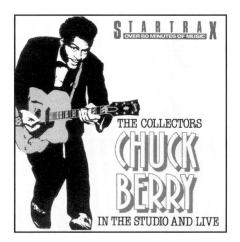

THE COLLECTOR'S CHUCK BERRY – IN THE STUDIO AND LIVE
Mercury 848 405-2 ● 1991
In the Studio: Sweet Little Sixteen / Memphis, Tennessee / School Day / Maybellene / Back In The USA / Around And Around / Brown Eyed Handsome Man / Johnny B. Goode / Rock And Roll Music / Roll Over Beethoven / Thirty Days / Carol / Let It Rock / Reelin' And Rockin' / Club Nitty Gritty
Live on Stage: *Medley:* Rockin' At The Fillmore *(instr)* – Everyday I Have The Blues**+** / C.C. Rider**+** / Hoochie Coochie Man**+** / Good Morning Little Schoolgirl**+** / Bring Another Drink**+** / Worried Life Blues**+** / My Ding-A-Ling

Unusual selection of songs from the 1967 LIVE AT THE FILLMORE set, as six out of the eight are not Berry compositions. Recording dates are shown on the inner sleeve, but overall a very dull cover.

ULTIMATE COLLECTION
Universal 117 751 ● 1997
Maybellene / Roll Over Beethoven / School Day / Sweet Little Rock And Roller / Back In The USA / Little Queenie / Promised Land / My Ding-A-Ling *(live, single edit)* / No Particular Place To Go / You Never Can Tell / Rock And Roll Music / Sweet Little Sixteen / Nadine / Johnny B. Goode / Carol / Memphis, Tennessee

Original Chess recordings in poor sound quality. I don't understand why the big companies released anything like this in the '90s.

ROCKIN' AND ROLLIN'
Master Songs 501492 ● 2000
Maybellene *(live, 1956 Alan Freed radio show?)* / Sweet Little Sixteen / School Day / Rock And Roll Music / Johnny B. Goode / Carol / Memphis, Tennessee / Roll Over Beethoven *(live, 1956 Alan Freed radio show?)* / Back In The USA. / Sweet Little Rock And Roller / Reelin' And Rockin' / C.C. Rider**+** *(live)* / Bring Another Drink**+** / Good Lookin' Woman / Goodnight, Well It's Time To Go [It's Time To Go] / Back To Memphis

I haven't heard this album, but looking at the track selection it must be Mercury recordings. The subtitle is *'16 In-Concert Classics'*, and that is of course untrue, except for 'C.C. Rider' off the 1967 FILLMORE album. 'Maybellene' and 'Roll Over Beethoven' are probably live recordings from a 1956 Alan Freed radio show (see the 1978 Various Artists bootleg LP, ROCK'N'ROLL RADIO [Radiola MR-1087] for more information), as has often been the case with similar releases. Nice, colourful cover.

GREATEST HITS
Mastersound CD-80028 • 2001
Rock And Roll Music / Johnny B. Goode / Roll Over Beethoven / Back In The USA / Maybellene /
Carol / Memphis, Tennessee / Sweet Little Rock And Roller / Sweet Little Sixteen / School Day /
Back To Memphis / Reelin' And Rockin'

I haven't heard this one either, but this is also the Mercury recordings –
unfortunately. Isn't it kinda silly to have two releases so close to each other with
almost identical tracks, and the stupid thing with 'GREATEST HITS' and Mercury
recordings? I hate this!

THE BERRY BEST
Flashback FB-02101 • 2002
If you wanna look at the titles here, please turn to the UK discography and the
2000 CD, ULTIMATE LEGENDS – CHUCK BERRY [The Ultimate Music Collection
ULT-40422]. Although this has a different cover, it's still the same old silly combination
of Chess and Toronto tracks. A complete waste of time and money!

Various Artists LPs

ROCK, ROCK, ROCK
Philips 94230.B • 1957
Same tracks as the 1956 US LP [Chess LP-1425]. I haven't seen this record, so
can't confirm cover or label details.

Chuck Berry – Little Richard – Jerry Lee Lewis
THE WILD MEN OF ROCK [3-LP]
Telmak TMAK-147(B) • 1986
Johnny B. Goode / Reelin' And Rockin' / Rock And Roll Music / Sweet Little Sixteen / Maybellene /
Too Much Monkey Business *(live)* / Nadine *(live)* / School Day *(live)* / My Ding-A-Ling *(live)*

This is Record 2 of a 3-LP set. (The other two records feature Little Richard and
Jerry Lee Lewis). Side 1 consists of five Chess studio tracks. The four live tracks on
Side 2 are from the 1969 *Toronto Rock & Roll Revival.*

Various Artists CD Albums

Barry White – Chuck Berry – Fats Domino
THREE OF A KIND (VOLUME 04) [3-CD]
Universal 5607092 • 2003
The Berry tracks are the ones included on the 20 SUPER HITS LP, originally
issued in West Germany in 1980 [Chess 6.24372AP] and reissued on CD circa 1988
[Chess 8.24372 ZR]. Same cover. Barry White has 13 tracks and Fats Domino 14
live tracks.

AUSTRIA

3" CD Singles

Johnny B. Goode
BASF, unknown number • mid-1990s
Johnny B. Goode / Roll Over Beethoven / Rock And Roll Music / Carol

Part of the BASF *'Maxima Collection'* series.

BELGIUM

Very little Berry material has been released in Belgium. There might be more than you'll find here, but no more information is available. Most – if not all – Berry records that were pressed and issued in the Netherlands were also sold in Belgium.

Singles

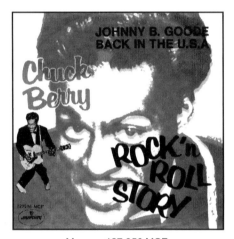

Mercury 127 356.MCF   Mercury 127 356.MCF

Johnny B. Goode / Back In the USA
Mercury Rock'n'Roll Story 127 356.MCF • 196?
   Picture sleeve.

Memphis, Tennessee / Maybellene
Surprise Golden 45's JTU-804 • 197?
   Picture sleeve.

Roll Over Beethoven / Johnny B. Goode
Surprise Golden 45's JTU-812 • 197?
   Picture sleeve.

Rock And Roll Music / Sweet Little Sixteen
Surprise Golden 45's JTU-817 • 197?
   Mercury recordings. Picture sleeve. This is from a series of fifty singles, all with picture sleeves, issued probably in the late 1970s, featuring everyone from Berry and the Beach Boys to Bob Marley and Glenn Miller.

Johnny B. Goode / Sweet Little Sixteen
Philips Golden Oldies 6168 027 • 1978
   Chess recordings. Picture sleeve.

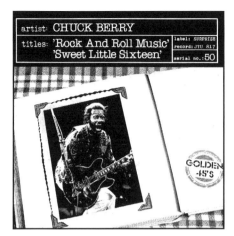

Surprise Golden 45's JTU-817   Philips Golden Oldies 6168 027

My Ding-A-Ling *(live, single edit)* **/ Carol**
Friends [CNR] 190.056 • 1988
This was a plug single for the 1988 2-LP, HAIL! HAIL! ROCK'N'ROLL [Friends 690.014], also released as two separate CDs on the Injection Disco Dance Label [100.181 and 100.182]. Picture sleeve. See also 1988 CD single [Injection Disco Dance Label 100.179]. All these records were also released in Norway and the Netherlands.

LPs

GREATEST HITS
Surprise JTU-AL-39 • 1981
Mercury recordings. Same tracks as the 1976 US LP [Everest FS-321], but a different cover. Once again, a misleading 'greatest hits' package of Mercury recordings. At the end of the liner notes on the back of cover it says: *'On this album you will find a selection of his very greatest hits from the period 1955-1963, and boy, they sound as fresh as ever!'* The songs are inferior re-recordings of course. This selection was also issued in the Netherlands circa 1981 [Rainbow 6064], but with the tracks in a different order and with a better cover.

SWEET LITTLE ROCK AND ROLLER
Surprise JTU-AL-48 • 1981
Same tracks as the 1981 Dutch LP [Rainbow 6063], but in a different order. Different cover, which is great! Also issued in West Germany in 1981 [Time Wind F-50009, Vintage F-50009] and on picture disc in Denmark in 1983 [Unknown label, PD-50009] and 1984 [Unknown label, AR-30026].

CHUCK BERRY [3-LP]
Vogue [MFP] VMFP-521/3 • 1981
This contains the two records from the 1972 US 2-LP, CHUCK BERRY'S GOLDEN DECADE (VOLUME 1) [Chess 2CH-1514] plus a third LP featuring the following Chess recordings: 'Carol', 'You Never Can Tell', 'Run Rudolph Run', 'Let It Rock', 'Sweet Little Rock And Roller', 'Go, Go, Go', 'Guitar Boogie' *(instr)*, 'Rock At The Philharmonic' *(instr)*, 'Come On', 'Roly Poly' *(instr)*, 'Viva, Viva Rock & Roll', 'Oh Yeah'. 'Let It Rock' is the version without Berry's lead guitar. Good sound, but no stereo.

263

CHUCK BERRY – GREATEST HITS [3-LP]
Surprise TRI BOX-07 • 1982
   This 3-LP set consists of the two Surprise albums above, plus one by various rock'n'roll guitar groups [Surprise JTU-AL-12]. This company never fails to surprise me, and they certainly lived up to their name with this one!

THE BEST OF CHUCK BERRY
Vogue [MFP] VMFP-521 • 1982
   Identical to the first record in the Berry box set above, but a different cover.

20 GREATEST HITS
Fun 9012 • 1982
   Mercury recordings. Very similar to the 1982 Dutch LP [Masters MA-0016983], but a different cover.

HAIL! HAIL! ROCK'N'ROLL [2-LP]
Friends [CNR] 690.014/15 • 1988
   Not the movie soundtrack. Same tracks as the 1988 UK 2-LP [Chess DETD-207], but different gatefold cover. Also released as separate CDs [Injection Disco Dance Label 100.181 and 100.182]. There was also a plug single [Friends 690.014 (7" vinyl) and Injection Disco Dance Label 100.179 (CD)]. All these records were also released in Norway and the Netherlands.

CD Singles

MY DING-A-LING
Injection Disco Dance Label [CNR] 100.179 • 1988
My Ding-A-Ling *(live, single edit)* / No Particular Place To Go / Maybellene / Roll Over Beethoven

   This was a plug single for the 1988 2-LP, HAIL! HAIL! ROCK'N'ROLL [Friends 690.014], also released as two separate CDs [Injection Disco Dance Label 100.181 and 100.182]. Same front cover picture. See also 1988 7" plug single [Friends 190.056]. All these records were also released in Norway and the Netherlands.

CD Albums

HAIL! HAIL! ROCK'N'ROLL (1955-58)
Injection Disco Dance Label [CNR] 100.181 • 1988

HAIL! HAIL! ROCK'N'ROLL (1959-72)
Injection Disco Dance Label [CNR] 100.182 • 1988
   Not the movie soundtrack. This is the 1988 2-LP, HAIL! HAIL! ROCK'N'ROLL [Friends 690.014/15] released as two separate CDs, both with the same cover. There was also a plug single [Friends 690.014 (7" vinyl) and Injection Disco Dance Label 100.179 (CD)]. All these records were also released in Norway and the Netherlands.

Various Artists LPs

BY REQUEST: 22 GOLDEN GREATS WE ALL REMEMBER
Rejoice 274 276 • 198?
Lonely School Days *(Chess, slow version)*

This has a great large picture of Berry on the front cover. I'm not certain, but it's possible this is a bootleg. The cover looks a little suspicious, but the label seems genuine enough, so... Other artists include Roy Orbison, Chris Andrews (2 tracks), Crispian St. Peters, Fats Domino, the Royal Showband, Connie Francis, Carl Mann, Eydie Gorme, Eddie Hodges, Cliff Gleaves, Wanda Jackson, Ned Miller, Buzz Clifford, Connie Stevens, Kris Jensen, Teddy Randazzo, Ray Campi, Joe Barry, the Bobby Fuller Four and Jesse James.

BRAZIL

Singles

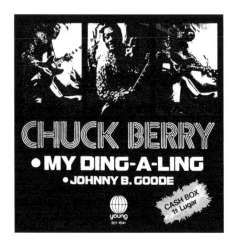

My Ding-A-Ling *(live, single edit)* / **Johnny B. Goode** *(live)*
Young [Importa/Som] 301.1041 • 1972
 Grey label. Picture sleeve. The white label promo issue of this record carries the number 993.0107.

EPs

RHYTHM AND BLUES
London ELA-501 • 1957
Maybellene / Wee Wee Hours / Thirty Days / Together (We Will Always Be)

No picture of Berry on front cover, and no year printed on cover or label. Black label with silver lettering. Round push-out centre. Same tracks as the 1956 UK EP [London RE-U-1053].

LPs

THE LONDON CHUCK BERRY SESSIONS
Importa/Som 310.1008 • 1972
Same tracks and gatefold cover as the 1972 US LP [Chess CH-60020].

BIO
Toptape 53 • 1973
Same tracks as the 1973 US LP [Chess CH-50043]. However, I don't know whether this has a gatefold cover or not.

ROCK HITS
Fontana 6436 701 • 1973
Same tracks as all the European reissues containing Berry's Mercury re-recordings of his golden hits. (It was released in 1972 in the Netherlands as ROCK HITS [Fontana International 6430 022], in West Germany as ATTENTION! [Fontana 6430 022], in Norway and Spain as ROCK AND ROLL MUSIC [Fontana Special 6430 022 and Fontana 6430 022 respectively]. (However, the record label inside the Spanish issue actually says GOLDEN HITS.) In 1973 it was released in Italy as ROCK HITS [Fontana Special 6430 022], in France as ROCK AND ROLL MUSIC [Fontana 6430 022] and in the UK – with a different catalogue number from all the other variations – as BACK IN THE USA [Philips 6336 216].) Blue label with silver top.

SWEET LITTLE 16 ROCK'N'ROLL HITS
Mercury 9279 132 • 1980
Same tracks and cover as the 1976 UK LP [Philips Sonic Series SON-006]. The strange thing here is that these are actually the original Chess recordings released on the Mercury label!

REELIN' AND ROCKIN'
Topline 5067 • 1984
I don't have this, but the cover looks exactly like the 1984 UK LP [Topline TOP-117].

ROCKIT
Atco 6047225 • 1986
Same tracks and cover as the 1979 US LP [Atco SD-38.118].

THE BEST OF
Brasidisc Serie Rarity 50009 • 198?
Maybellene / Sweet Little Sixteen / *Medley:* Johnny B. Goode – Carol – Promised Land / Nadine / Memphis, Tennessee / Rock And Roll Music / Reelin' And Rockin' / My Ding-A-Ling / Hoochie Coochie Man**+**

The 1969 *Toronto Rock & Roll Revival* again.

HAIL! HAIL! ROCK'N'ROLL
MCA [BMG] 670.4012 • 1988
Original soundtrack. Same tracks and cover as the 1987 US LP [MCA MCA-6217].

THE LONDON CHUCK BERRY SESSIONS
Chess [MCA] 670.8150 ● 1990
   Same tracks as the 1989 US reissue [Chess CH-9295], but no gatefold cover.
Liner notes by Andy McKaie on back cover.

CD Albums

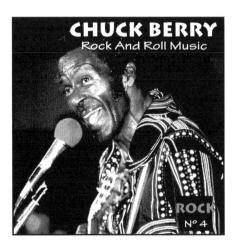

ROCK AND ROLL MUSIC
Altaya [Charly] Rock No. 4 ● 1996
Johnny B. Goode / Maybellene / Roll Over Beethoven / Carol / Almost Grown / Back In The USA /
Rock And Roll Music / School Day / Sweet Little Sixteen *(demo)* / Nadine *(stereo)* / Too Much
Monkey Business / Brown Eyed Handsome Man / Oh Baby Doll / Promised Land *(stereo)*

   This was pressed in Spain for the Brazilian market. Great picture of Berry on front
cover. Good sound quality too. 'Sweet Little Sixteen' is the demo version from 1957.

HIS GREATEST HITS
Rondo Hitline RONDO-22466 ● 1997
Rock And Roll Music / Back In The USA / Maybellene / Reelin' And Rockin' / Let it Rock / Sweet
Little Sixteen / School Day / Johnny B. Goode / You Never Can Tell / Roll Over Beethoven / Carol /
My Ding-A-Ling *(live, album version)* / Nadine / No Particular Place To Go

   CD pressed in Switzerland, cover (with a colour Berry photo I haven't seen before)
designed in the Netherlands. The last two tracks are in stereo; however 'You Never
Can Tell', which was recorded in stereo, is in mono. This CD came in a single
cardboard cover and was included with an A4 Chuck Berry magazine, *Coleção
Internacional Rock* (see *Chuck Berry In Print* for more information).

CANADA

Around 1980 I didn't have the slightest idea what had been released by Berry in Canada. Now I know about a whole host of singles, EPs and albums. Actually, almost everything that came out in the USA was released in Canada. From 1957 onwards, they followed the American EP and LP releases with the same covers, etc; however, all the original '50s and early '60s material was issued on Quality. Singles and EPs on the Quality label had red and beige labels with black print. LP label colours varied. 78 rpm singles did not have the 'K' prefix. I don't know why the catalogue number of the final single release is out of sequence.

From around 1964, Berry's records were released on Chess. The Canadian Chess label was black with silver lettering; promo labels were white. For singles, they used the US catalogue numbers with the prefix "CS-". After CS-1943, they adopted the 'light blue' US design with the Chess name in blue/white/red across the top.

To list everything released in Canada would be almost like repeating the US discography with new labels and record numbers. As stated above, I believe that almost everything released in the States came out in Canada, but I don't have a complete list, and if I had, there would still be problems about identifying any variations.

Therefore, what you get here is what Malte Koch and the author have in their respective collections, with comments where something is known to differ from the US releases.

Singles

Maybellene / Wee Wee Hours
Quality K-1413 • 1955

Thirty Days / Together (We Will Always Be)
Quality K-1430 • 1955

No Money Down / Down Bound Train
Quality K-1467 • 1956

Roll Over Beethoven / Drifting Heart
Quality K-1503 • 1956

Too Much Monkey Business / Brown Eyed Handsome Man
Quality K-1536 • 1956

You Can't Catch Me / Havana Moon
Quality K-1579 • 1956

School Day / Deep Feeling *(instr)*
Quality K-1611 • 1957

Oh Baby Doll / La Jaunda
Quality K-1631 • 1957

Quality 1413

Quality K-1611

Quality sleeve, late '50s

Quality 1631

Rock And Roll Music / Blue Feeling *(instr)*
Quality K-1663 ● 1957

Sweet Little Sixteen / Reelin' And Rockin'
Quality K-1703 ● 1957

Johnny B. Goode / Around And Around
Quality K-1727 ● 1958

Beautiful Delilah / Vacation Time
Quality K-1756 ● 1958

'I Got To Find My Baby' *b/w* 'Mad Lad' [US Chess 1763] and 'Come On' *b/w* 'Go, Go, Go' [US Chess 1799] were not released as singles in Canada.

Carol / Hey Pedro
Quality K-1775 • 1958

Sweet Little Rock And Roller / Jo Jo Gunne
Quality K-1808 • 1958

Run Rudolph Run+ / Merry Christmas Baby+
Quality K-1824 • 1958
>'Run Rudolph Run' is credited to *'(C. Berry) (Music: M. Brodie)'*.

Anthony Boy / That's My Desire+
Quality K-1838 • 1959

Almost Grown / Little Queenie
Quality K-1864 • 1959

Back In The USA / Memphis, Tennessee
Quality K-1920 • 1959

Childhood Sweetheart / Broken Arrow
Quality K-1956 • 1959

Too Pooped To Pop+ / Let It Rock
Quality 1989X • 1960

Bye Bye Johnny / Worried Life Blues+
Quality 1028X • 1960
>Quality restarted their label number system.

Jaguar And The Thunderbird / Our Little Rendezvous
Quality 1249X • 1960

I'm Talking About You / Little Star
Quality 1295X • 1961

I'm Talking About You / Diploma For Two
Chess [Quality] CS-1853X • 1963
>The white-label promo issue of this has a different prefix, C-1853X.

Nadine / O Rangutang *(instr)*
Chess [Quality] CS-1883X • 1964
>Vertical 'Chess' logo in silver. The promo issue of this was numbered C-1883X.

No Particular Place To Go / You Two
Chess [Quality] CS-1898 • 1964
>Vertical 'Chess' logo in silver. The promo issue of this was numbered C-1898X.

Chuck Berry & Bo Diddley* / Bo Diddley & Chuck Berry**
Chuck's Beat *(instr, single edit)** **/ Bo's Beat+** *(instr, single edit)***
Checker CH-1089 • 1964

You Never Can Tell / Brenda Lee
Chess [Phonodisc] CS-1906 • 1964
>Chess logo on top in silver.

271

Chess C-1853X (promo)

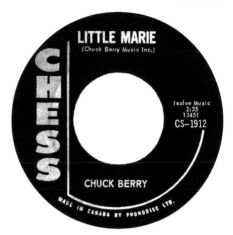

Chess CS-1912

Chess CS-1926

Chess CS-1963

Chess 1033-2131

Chess Golden Teasures CHGT-336X

272

Little Marie / Go, Bobby Soxer
Chess [Phonodisc] CS-1912 • 1964
    Vertical 'Chess' logo in silver.

Promised Land / The Things I Used To Do+
Chess [Phonodisc] CS-1916 • 1964
    Vertical 'Chess' logo in silver.

Dear Dad / Lonely Schooldays *(slow version)*
Chess [Phonodisc] CS-1926 • 1965
    Vertical 'Chess' logo in silver.

It Wasn't Me / Welcome Back Pretty Baby
Chess [Phonodisc] CS-1943 • 1965
    Vertical 'Chess' logo in silver.

Ramona Say Yes / Lonely School Days *(fast version)*
Chess [Phonodisc] CS-1963 • 1966
    Has the blue-fading-to-light blue US design with the Chess name in blue/white/red across the top. It would appear that 'Ramona Say Yes' was the 'A' side.

My Ding-A-Ling *(live, single edit)* **/ Johnny B. Goode** *(live)*
Chess [GRT] 1033-2131 • 1972
    Same label as CS-1963 above.

Reelin' And Rockin' *(live, single edit)* **/ Let's Boogie**
Chess [GRT] 1033-2136 • 1972
    Same label as the above two.

Johnny B. Goode / Rock And Roll Music
Mercury 'Celebrity' Series CS-6002 • 1973
    Blue label. It's strange, but in over 40 years collecting, I have never seen any other Mercury singles from Canada. They must surely have been out there...

Rock And Roll Music / Deep Feeling *(instr)*
Chess Golden Treasures [Quality] CHGT-317X • 1981

Sweet Little Sixteen / Reelin' And Rockin'
Chess Golden Treasures [Quality] CHGT-318X • 1981

Roll Over Beethoven / Nadine
Chess Golden Treasures [Quality] CHGT-326X • 1981

No Particular Place To Go / Thirty Days
Chess Golden Treasures [Quality] CHGT-336X • 1981
    Curry-coloured label.

Johnny B. Goode / Memphis, Tennessee
Quality Gold Collection GC-381X • 1982
    Label has brown top half, light brown bottom half.

Sweet Little Sixteen / Memphis (Tennessee)
Quality QGT-042 • 1980s

EPs

SWEET LITTLE 16
Quality XP-133 • 1958

    Same tracks and front cover as the 1958 US EP [Chess EP-5121].

AFTER SCHOOL SESSION
Quality XP-134 • 1958

    Same tracks and front cover as the 1957 US EP [Chess CH-5118].

ROCK AND ROLL MUSIC
Quality XP-135 • 1958

    Same tracks and front cover as the 1957 US EP [Chess EP-5119].

LPs

ROCK, ROCK, ROCK
Quality V-1561 • 1957

    Original soundtrack. Same tracks and cover as the 1956 US LP [Chess LP-1425]. Maroon label with silver lettering.

AFTER SCHOOL SESSION
Quality V-1598 • 1957

    Same tracks and cover as the 1957 US LP [Chess LP-1426]. Blue label with silver lettering.

ONE DOZEN BERRYS
Quality V-1616 • 1958

    Same tracks and cover as the 1958 US LP [Chess LP-1432]. Blue label with silver lettering.

CHUCK BERRY TWIST
Chess [Phonodisc] LP-1465 • 1962

    Same tracks and cover as the 1962 US LP, CHUCK BERRY TWIST [Chess LP-1465]. Black label, vertical Chess logo, silver lettering.

ON STAGE
Chess [Phonodisc] LP-1480(C) • 1963

Same tracks and cover as the 1963 US LP [Chess LP-1480] with 'Memphis' and 'Surfin' USA' at the top of the front cover. Black label, vertical Chess logo, silver lettering. No song titles printed on the label. 'How High The Moon' is faded out early.

MORE CHUCK BERRY
Chess [Phonodisc] LP-1465 • 1963

Same tracks and cover as the 1963 US reissue of MORE CHUCK BERRY [Chess LP-1465]. Black label, vertical Chess logo, silver lettering.

CHUCK BERRY'S GREATEST HITS
Chess [Phonodisc] LP-1485(C) • 1964

Same tracks and cover as the 1964 US LP [Chess LP-1485] with the three titles printed on the front cover: *'Featuring the hits Memphis – Maybellene – Johnny B. Goode'*.

Chuck Berry & Bo Diddley
TWO GREAT GUITARS
Checker [Phonodisc] LP-2991 *(mono)* **• 1964**

Same tracks and cover as the 1964 US LP [Chess LP-2991]. The label was black with vertical Checker logo. This album was probably also released in stereo, although I've never seen a copy.

ST. LOUIS TO LIVERPOOL
Chess [Phonodisc] CLP-1488 *(mono)* **CSLP-1488** *(stereo)* **• 1964**

Same tracks and cover as the 1964 US LP [Chess LP-1488]. Black label with vertical 'Chess' logo in silver.

CHUCK BERRY IN LONDON
Chess [Phonodisc] LP-1495 *(mono)* **LPS-1495** *(stereo)* **• 1965**

Same tracks and cover as the 1965 US LP [Chess LP-1495]. Black label.

FRESH BERRY'S
Chess [Phonodisc] LP-1498 *(mono)* **LPS-1498** *(stereo)* **• 1965**

Same tracks and cover as the 1965 US LP [Chess LP-/LPS-1498]. Blue label with silver lettering. Vertical Chess logo.

GOLDEN HITS
Mercury SR-61103 *(stereo)* **• 1967**

Same tracks and cover as the 1967 US LP [Mercury SR-61103]. Black label. Reissued in 1972 as Mercury 6336 500. This album was probably also released in mono, although I've never seen a copy.

CHUCK BERRY IN MEMPHIS
Mercury MG-21123 *(mono)* **SR-61123** *(stereo)* **• 1967**

Same tracks and cover as the 1967 US LP [Mercury MG-21123/SR-61123].

LIVE AT THE FILLMORE AUDITORIUM, SAN FRANCISCO
Mercury MG-21138 *(mono)* **SR-61138** *(stereo)* **• 1967**

Same tracks and cover as the 1967 US LP [Mercury MG-21138/SR-61138].

CHUCK BERRY'S GOLDEN DECADE
CHESS CLPS-1514D • 1968
> Second pressing, 'gold record' cover without the titles. Light blue label.

FROM ST. LOUIE TO FRISCO
Mercury SR-61176 *(stereo)* **• 1968**
> Same tracks and cover as the 1968 US LP [Mercury SR-61176].

CONCERTO IN B GOODE
Mercury SR-61223 *(stereo)* **• 1969**
> Same tracks and cover as the 1969 US LP [Mercury SR-61223].

BACK HOME
Chess [GRT] 9033-1550 • 1970
> Same cover as the US LP [Chess LPS-1550], but a nice purple label with black lettering.

SAN FRANCISCO DUES
Chess [GRT] 9033-50008 • 1971
> Same tracks and cover as the 1971 US LP [Chess CH-50008].

THE LONDON CHUCK BERRY SESSIONS
Chess [GRT] 9033-60020 • 1972
> Same tracks and gatefold cover as the 1972 US LP [Chess CH-60020]. Light blue-to-almost-white label, with the Chess logo on top in blue/white/red – the opposite of the US logo which was red/white/blue.

CHUCK BERRY'S GREATEST HITS
Chess [GRT] 9033-1485 • 1972
> Same tracks and cover as the 1964 LP [Chess LP-1485(C)]. Label colour as 9033-60020 above. It seems that this album was also issued with the later orange and blue label.

Chuck Berry & Bo Diddley
TWO GREAT GUITARS
Checker 9034-2991• 1972
> Reissue with black label.

GOLDEN HITS
Mercury 6336 500 • 1972
> Same tracks and cover as the 1967 US LP [Mercury SR-61103]. 'Skyscraper' label.

JOHNNY B. GOODE
Pickwick SPC-3327 • 1972
> Same tracks and cover as the 1972 US LP [Pickwick SPC-3327], but a little more colourful on the back. Black label with rainbow around the centre (however, see also the 1974 FLASHBACK double album below).

BIO
Chess [GRT] 9033-50043 • 1973
> Same tracks and gatefold cover as the 1973 US LP [Chess CH-50043]. However, you have to open the cover to take out the album. Orange and blue label.

SWEET LITTLE ROCK AND ROLLER
Pickwick SPC-3345 • 1973
Same tracks and cover (cigarette-smoking girl in a leather jacket) as the 1973 US LP [Pickwick SPC-3345]. Silver label (however, see also the 1974 FLASHBACK double album below).

CHUCK BERRY'S GOLDEN DECADE (VOLUME 3) [2-LP]
Chess [GRT] 9033-60028 • 1974
Same as the 1974 US LP [Chess 2CH-60028].

WILD BERRYS
Pickwick SPC-3392 • 1974
Same tracks and cover as the 1974 US LP [Pickwick SPC-3392].

FLASHBACK [2-LP]
Pickwick PTP-2061 • 1974
Same tracks as the 1974 US 2-LP [Pickwick PTP-2061], but without gatefold cover. Contains the original 1973 Canadian Pickwick albums SPC-3327 and SPC-3345, but with green labels and different lettering.

CHUCK BERRY
Chess [GRT] 9033-60032 • 1975
Same as the 1975 US LP [Chess CH-60032].

AMERICAN HOT WAX [2-LP]
A&M SP-6500 • 1978
See *Various Artists LPs*.

ROCKIT
Atlantic QSD-38-118 • 1979
Same tracks and cover as the 1979 US LP [Atco SD-38.118]. Label has green top, white borders, orange bottom.

ALIVE AND ROCKIN'
WAA A-9019 • 1981
Same tracks and cover as the 1981 US LP [Stack-O-Hits AG-9019].

CHUCK BERRY'S GOLDEN DECADE [2-LP]
Chess [Quality] CH-1514-2 • 1981
Same tracks as the 1972 US reissue [Chess 2CH-1514]. Same gatefold cover as the second pressing (pink radio). Yellow label.

CHUCK BERRY'S GOLDEN DECADE (VOLUME 2) [2-LP]
Chess [Quality] CH-60023-2 • 1981
Reissue. Same tracks and gatefold cover as the 1973 US 2-LP [Chess 2CH-60023]. Yellow label.

CHUCK BERRY'S GOLDEN DECADE (VOLUME 3) [2-LP]
Chess [Quality] CH-60028-2 • 1981
Reissue. Same tracks and gatefold cover as the 1974 US 2-LP [Chess 2CH-60028]. Yellow label.

BIO
Chess [GRT] CH-91510-2 • 1981
Reissue with green cover and yellow label.

THE GREATEST HITS OF CHUCK BERRY
Quality [Chess] SV-2090 • 1981
Same tracks as the 1964 US LP [Chess LP-1485] minus 'Brown Eyed Handsome Man' and 'Oh Baby Doll'. Different cover. A typically cheap one, dull cover and ten songs.

ST. LOUIS TO LIVERPOOL
Chess CH-9186 • 1984
Same tracks and cover as the 1984 US reissue [Chess CH-9186]. Distributed by Quality Records. Blue label.

HAIL! HAIL! ROCK'N'ROLL
MCA MCA-6217 • 1987
Original soundtrack. Same tracks and cover as the 1987 US LP [MCA MCA-6217].

CD Albums

BERRY IS ON TOP
Chess [MCA] CHMD-31260 • 1987
Same tracks and cover as the 1987 US CD [Chess CHD-31260].

GREATEST HITS
Soundsational CDMA-4003 • 199?
Rock And Roll Music / Sweet Little Sixteen / No Particular Place To Go / Johnny B. Goode / You Never Can Tell *(stereo)* / Maybellene / School Day / Carol / Back In The USA / Reelin' And Rockin' / My Ding-A-Ling *(live, single edit)* / Nadine / Almost Grown

This compilation of Chess recordings was released in the early 1990s.

LIVE AT THE FILLMORE AUDITORIUM
Polygram 314 558 135 • 1998
Sweet Little Sixteen / C.C. Rider+ / Driftin' Blues+ / Feelin' It *(instr)* / Flying Home+ / Hoochie Coochie Man+ / It Hurts Me Too+ *(duet with Steve Miller)* / Fillmore Blues *(instr)* / Reelin' And Rockin' / Johnny B. Goode

Don't be alarmed! The 'Sweet Little Sixteen' cut is the standard Mercury studio version and there is no overdubbed audience noise. Why do such a thing in 1998? What in the world were they thinking of? And this is not a cheap label issue.

Various Artists LPs

AMERICAN HOT WAX [2-LP]
A&M SP-6500 • 1978
Original soundtrack. Same tracks and gatefold cover as the 1978 US 2-LP [A&M SP-6500].

Chuck Berry – Fats Domino
ROCK'N'ROLL SHOW
K-Tel [Capitol] KF-205 • 1982
Sweet Little Sixteen / Maybellene / Rock And Roll Music / Carol / School Day / My Ding-A-Ling *(live, single edit)* / Roll Over Beethoven / Johnny B. Goode

The standard Chess recordings, plus eight songs by Fats Domino on Side 2. No pictures of the artists.

COSTA RICA

Various Artists LPs

ROCK AND ROLL: THE EARLY DAYS
RCA-Vik 1022027 • 1985
Maybellene

Same tracks and cover as the 1985 US LP [RCA AFM1-5463]. Blue label.

DENMARK

The Danish Sonet label was red and looked very similar to the Swedish and Norwegian ones. However, Danish Sonet releases had tri-centres – the other two had round ones – and the NCB (Nordic Copyright Bureau) logo was in a bolder rectangular box than the Swedish one. The Norwegian NCB logo was square.

Singles

Sonet T-7597

Sonet T-7610

Nadine / O'Rangutang *(instr)*
Sonet T-7591 • 1964
The picture sleeve (same both sides) looks very similar to the Swedish version, however, the colour on the top of the sleeve is turquoise and the paper is thinner. You can also find this Danish single in Swedish picture sleeves.

No Particular Place To Go / Liverpool Drive *(instr)*
Sonet T-7597 • 1964
The picture sleeve here is unique to Denmark and was also used for the following two releases. However, the two colours on the front are different on each. The one in my collection has a turquoise square top right and a red L-shaped block. The back of the sleeve contains a list of other Sonet singles.

You Never Can Tell / Brenda Lee
Sonet T-7605 • 1964
I have two variations of this picture sleeve. One with red square top right and a blue L-shaped block, the other a purple square top right and a brown L-shaped block. The back of one contains a list of Danish artists on the Sonet label and pictures of Suzie and Grethe Sønck. The other has pictures of the Sunbeams and Tommy Roe and a different list of artists.

Memphis, Tennessee / Johnny B. Goode
Sonet T-7610 • 1964

This coupling was exclusive to Denmark. The 'A' side is the version with overdubbed audience noise from the 1963 US LP, ON STAGE [Chess LP-1480]. I have three different variants of this picture sleeve: a blue square top right and a red L-shaped block with pictures of the Glencoves and Bobby Curtola on the back; an orange square top right and a purple L-shaped block with pictures of Suzie and Raquel Rastenni on the back; and a purple square top right and a brown L-shaped block with the same reverse as T-7605, listing Danish artists.

Later releases of Chuck Berry's Chess material were pressed in Sweden and sold throughout the whole of Scandinavia.

Club Nitty Gritty / Laugh And Cry
Mercury 127 260 • 1967

This was pressed in Norway for the Scandinavian market. The Norwegian release does not have a picture sleeve, but it is possible that the Danish one did. Unfortunately, no one I know has ever seen a copy. See Norwegian discography for more info.

―――――――――――

The following was a good series featuring various '50s and early '60s artists – Jerry Lee Lewis, Connie Francis, Sam Cooke, Buddy Holly, Fats Domino, Wilbert Harrison and many more. Most had very good colour photos of the artists, but unfortunately Berry's releases did not. All four records used the same picture with a different colour background. Only one thousand copies of each single were pressed. Bootlegs?

Maybellene / Roll Over Beethoven
Maybellene PD-3 • 1985

Picture disc.

Sweet Little Sixteen / Reelin' And Rockin'
Maybellene PD-50 • 1985

Picture disc.

Johnny B. Goode / Around And Around
Maybellene PD-51 • 1985

Picture disc.

Carol / Rock And Roll Music
Maybellene PD-63 • 1985

Picture disc.

Maybellene / Roll Over Beethoven
Maybellene 501 • 1986

I knew nothing about this release before I spotted it on eBay in April 2006. Black vinyl and yellow label. Art sleeve.

Maybellene PD-50 (front)   Maybellene PD-50 (back)

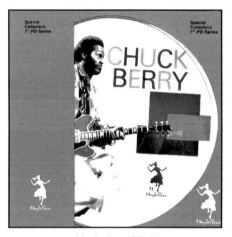

Maybellene PD-51   Maybellene 501

The following were one-sided picture flexi discs. The earliest pressings had black and white photos and came in plain sleeves. Later pressings had tinted photos and came in a similar-looking picture sleeve specially designed for the series.   Other releases were by Buddy Holly, Eddie Cochran, Little Richard, Elvis Presley, Jerry Lee Lewis and Gene Vincent. Both series carried the 'NCB' logo, though I'm not sure they were made in Denmark. Rumour has it they were actually made in West Germany and that we're probably talking about bootlegs.

Roll Over Beethoven / Maybellene
Masters of Rock & Roll PR-018 • 1987
   Picture flexi disc.

Johnny B. Goode / Sweet Little Sixteen
Masters of Rock & Roll PR-023 • 1987
   Picture flexi disc.

Masters of Rock & Roll PR-018

Masters of Rock & Roll PR-023

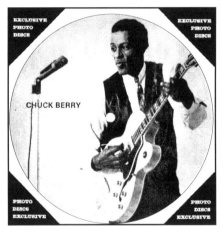

Masters of Rock & Roll PR-027

Masters of Rock & Roll PR-034

Carol / Rock And Roll Music
Masters of Rock & Roll PR-027 ● 1987
   Picture flexi disc.

Around And Around / School Day
Masters of Rock & Roll PR-034 ● 1987
   Picture flexi disc.

LPs

CHUCK BERRY'S GREATEST HITS
Gold Label GLP-957 ● 1981
   Same Mercury tracks as the 1976 US LP [Everest FS-321], but not in the same order. Different cover. Liner notes in Danish and English by Per Meistrup, who couldn't tell the difference between a freight train and a hummingbird. At the end he says: *'We have collected the greatest of Chuck's hits from the original recordings.'*

BACK IN THE USA
Picture disc, PD-50009 • 1983

Back In The USA / Good Lookin' Woman / Sweet Little Rock And Roller / I Do Really Love You / Oh Baby Doll / Thirty Days / Goodnight, Well It's Time To Go [It's Time To Go] / Back To Memphis / My Heart Will Always Belong To You+ / Reelin' And Rockin'

Mercury tracks. Picture disc pressed on red vinyl, with the same colour picture of Berry on both sides. It comes in a clear plastic cover with information about other picture discs on the back sleeve, but is also available in a plain pink LP cover. The album carries the same catalogue number as the two 1981 West German LPs on Time Wind and Vintage, and the picture of Berry is the same as the one used on those releases. See also the 1984 picture disc, BABY DOLL [AR-30026] below.

CHUCK BERRY
Picture disc, AR-30013 • 1983

Maybellene / Roll Over Beethoven / Too Much Monkey Business / You Can't Catch Me / School Day / Rock And Roll Music / Sweet Little Sixteen / Johnny B. Goode / Around And Around / Beautiful Delilah / Carol / Run Rudolph Run+

Chess tracks. Black and white picture disc with a different photo from the '50s on each side. 'Run Rudolph Run' is credited to *'C. Berry & M. Brodie'*. See also the 1984 picture disc, JOHNNY B. GOODE [All Round Trading DLP-2-773] and the 1985 LP, ROCK AND ROLL MUSIC [World Music WM-31013].

BABY DOLL
Picture disc, AR-30026 • 1984
Black and white picture disc with a different photo on each side. Same Mercury tracks as the 1983 picture disc, BACK IN THE USA [Unknown label, PD-50009].

JOHNNY B. GOODE
All Round Trading DLP-2-773 • 1984
Same Chess tracks as the 1983 picture disc, CHUCK BERRY [Unknown label, AR-30013]. See also next item.

ROCK AND ROLL MUSIC
World Music WM-31013 • 1985
Red label. Same Chess cuts as the 1983 picture disc, CHUCK BERRY [Unknown label, AR-30013] and the 1984 picture disc, JOHNNY B. GOODE [All Round Trading DLP-2-773]. Also issued on World Music PL-31013 with a different red label. This album also appeared with the same cover on All Round Trading DLP-2-773 with a dark blue label. Confused? I certainly am. And there is one more…

GREATEST HITS
Art AA-8616 • 1986
Same Chess cuts as the 1983 picture disc, CHUCK BERRY [Unknown label, AR-30013] The shot on the front cover is the same as one of the two used on the picture disc.

It appears that some of the above albums from PD-50009 to AA-8616 were issued in both West Germany and Denmark at the same time, in some instances using the same pictures for different LPs; in others, with Danish pressings inside German covers. Sometimes it's difficult to decide under which country to list such records!

CD Albums

THE BEST OF CHUCK BERRY
CéDé International 66037 • 1987
Maybellene / Thirty Days / Back To Memphis [Memphis, Tennessee] / Roll Over Beethoven / School Day / Rock And Roll Music / Sweet Little Sixteen / Johnny B. Goode / Carol / Too Much Monkey Business / You Can't Catch Me / Back In The USA / Oh Baby Doll / Beautiful Delilah / Around And Around / Reelin' And Rockin'

Chess tracks. 'Memphis' is mistitled 'Back To Memphis'. Sound is okay.

16 GOLDEN HITS
Music Stars 920190 • Early 1990s
Reelin' And Rockin' / Rock And Roll Music / How You've Changed / Sweet Little Sixteen / Rip It Up+ / Don't You Lie To Me+ / Guitar Boogie *(instr)* / I'm Talking About You / Diploma For Two / Thirteen Question Method / Away From You / Oh Baby Doll / Route 66+ / Run Around / Stop And Listen / Rock At The Philharmonic *(instr)*

Good selection of many obscure Berry tracks, but a strange album title in that respect. Unfortunately all tracks are destroyed by electronic stereo. Great cover of Berry on stage, probably taken in Copenhagen on 25 January 1973.

Various Artists LPs

Jive Bunny & The Mastermixers
ROCK'N'ROLL HALL OF FAME
Mega Records MRLP-3191 • 1991
Rock'n'Roll Hall Of Fame [includes 'Roll Over Beethoven' and 'Johnny B. Goode'] / *Jive Berry:* My Ding-A-Ling – Rock And Roll Music – Sweet Little Sixteen – Reelin' And Rockin' – Johnny B. Goode – Roll Over Beethoven – My Ding-A-Ling

'This album is a tribute to the Rock'n'Roll Greats that stormed the World in the '50s and '60s, the artists that changed the face of pop music forever.' Another of those 'megamix' albums. This is actually the most interesting one when it comes to Chuck Berry's music. Side A (the *Rock'n'Roll Hall Of Fame* mix) consists of 26 classic songs

A quiet moment backstage in Chicago, 16 August 1985.

from the era. Side B features *The Juke Box Story* (no Berry), *Jive Berry* (four minutes nine seconds), and finally a mix entitled *Rock'n'Roll Beethoven* which has nothing to do with Berry. The front cover has drawings of Berry, Presley, Richard, Holly and Haley.

See also 1994 UK Various Artists CD, PARTY MEGAMIX 2 [Prism Leisure PLATCD-3933] and the 1996 US Various Artists CD, CAN CAN YOU PARTY [Stardust 26666].

EAST GERMANY

LPs

CHUCK BERRY
Amiga 8.55.835 • 1981
Johnny B. Goode / Rock And Roll Music / Roll Over Beethoven / Reelin' And Rockin' / Sweet Little Sixteen / School Day / Feelin' It *(live, instr)* / Oh Baby Doll / Maybellene / Carol / Sweet Little Rock And Roller / Club Nitty Gritty / Back In The USA / Little Fox / It's Too Dark In There / Let It Rock

Mercury recordings, maroon label. Malte Koch has a promo release of this record (same label colour, but no cover). In my collection, I have what appears to be a test pressing with a blue label and *'Unverkäufliche Personalplatte' ('Staff copy – Not for sale')* stamped on Side A.

FINLAND

I have never seen, or heard of, any '50s, '60s or '70s Chuck Berry record releases from this country. All the following LPs listed below were pressed and issued in Finland in 1986 for the Scandinavian market. They have grey labels and the original US covers with session discographies printed on the back (but no discographies on the double albums).

LPs

ONE DOZEN BERRYS
Chess LP-104 • 1986
   Same tracks and cover as the 1958 US LP [Chess LP-1432].

NEW JUKE BOX HITS
Chess LP-105 • 1986
   Same tracks and cover as the 1961 US LP [Chess LP-1456].

AFTER SCHOOL SESSION
Chess LP-112 • 1986
   Same tracks and cover as the 1957 US LP [Chess LP-1426].

ROCKIN' AT THE HOPS
Chess LP-113 • 1986
   Same tracks and cover as the 1960 US LP [Chess LP-1448].

CHUCK BERRY'S GOLDEN DECADE (VOLUME 1) [2-LP]
Chess DLP-203 • 1986
   Same tracks and cover design (pink radio) as the second pressing of the 1972 US reissue [Chess 2CH-1514], but no gatefold cover.

CHUCK BERRY'S GOLDEN DECADE (VOLUME 2) [2-LP]
Chess DLP-210 • 1986
   Same tracks and cover design as the 1973 US 2-LP [Chess 2CH-60023], but no gatefold cover.

CHUCK BERRY'S GOLDEN DECADE (VOLUME 3) [2-LP]
Chess DLP-211 • 1986
   Same tracks and cover design as the 1974 US 2-LP [Chess 2CH-60028], but no gatefold cover.

CD Albums

ORIGINAL MASTERS OF CHUCK BERRY
Chess CD-3 • 1988

Sweet Little Sixteen / Rock At The Philarmonic *(instr)* / Guitar Boogie *(instr)* / Reelin' And Rockin' / It Don't Take But A Few Minutes / I'm Talking About You / Run Around / School Day / Deep Feeling *(instr)* / Too Much Monkey Business / No Money Down / Brown Eyed Handsome Man / Havana Moon / Bye Bye Johnny / Mad Lad+ *(instr)* / I Got To Find My Baby+ / Driftin' Blues+ / Let It Rock / Maybellene / Johnny B. Goode / Nadine / Roll Over Beethoven / Thirty Days / No Particular Place To Go / Back In The USA / You Never Can Tell / Beautiful Delilah / Confessin' The Blues+

This could have been a great compilation of Berry recordings. Unfortunately, the songs are destroyed by electronic stereo.

Various Artists CD Albums

MASTERS OF BLUES 1
Chess CD-1 • 1987

I Got To Find My Baby+ / Oh Yeah

Compilation featuring Berry and other Chess artists including Howlin' Wolf (3), Muddy Waters (3), Sonny Boy Williamson (2), Buddy Guy (2), B.B. King (2), John Lee Hooker (2), Albert King (2), Otis Rush (2), Little Walter (2) and Bo Diddley (2). Electronic stereo on the mono masters.

MASTERS OF BLUES 2
Chess CD-2 • 1987

Rock At The Philharmonic *(instr)* / Driftin' Blues+

Another compilation featuring Berry and other Chess artists including Muddy Waters (5), Howlin' Wolf (4), Sonny Boy Williamson (2), Hound Dog Taylor (1), Buddy Guy (2), John Lee Hooker (1), Albert King (2), Otis Rush (1), Little Walter (2) and Bo Diddley (2). Electronic stereo on the mono masters.

FRANCE

Only one record was released in France during the '50s and early '60s before Berry's comeback in 1963-64. This was a 1958 EP on the London label which has since become a sought-after item and now commands high prices. Today, a nice copy will set you back around £200. However, after Berry visited France in February 1965, the market was flooded with releases. Most EPs came with great picture sleeves, and many LPs did too. Although singles have also been listed below, it should be noted that, up until the early 1970s, they were generally issued for use in jukeboxes; the preferred commercial format during Berry's heyday was the four-track EP or 'Super 45'. It is particularly noteworthy that 'My Ding-A-Ling' was not issued as a single in France.

Singles

Barclay 60522

The five Barclay singles listed below may have been issued with picture sleeves, but no information is available.

Nadine / School Day
Barclay 60502 • 1964

You Never Can Tell / Too Pooped To Pop+
Barclay 60522 • 1964

Sweet Little Sixteen / Memphis, Tennessee
Barclay 60552 • 1965

Dear Dad / Promised Land
Barclay 60572 • 1965

Jamaica Farewell+ / I Want To Be Your Driver
Barclay 60618 • 1965
Now, this is an interesting coupling for a Berry single!

The ROCK REVIVAL series below all have great picture sleeves featuring photos taken at the Belgian TV show, *Face au Public*, broadcast 11 May 1965. (NB Chess 169528 and 169532 both have 'VOLUME 6' printed on the sleeve).

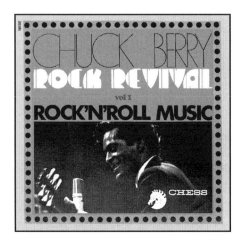

ROCK REVIVAL (VOLUME 1)
Rock And Roll Music / I Just Want To Make Love To You+
Chess [CED] 169512 ● 1968/69
The 'B' side has overdubbed audience noise and features the spoken French-language introduction by Berry taken from the 1965 *Chuck Berry à l'Olympia* album [Barclay 80 258], which makes the single pretty unique. Picture sleeve

ROCK REVIVAL (VOLUME 2)
Memphis, Tennessee / Brown Eyed Handsome Man
Chess [CED] 169513 ● 1968/69
Overdubbed audience noise. The 'B' side is the 1961 version. Picture sleeve.

ROCK REVIVAL (VOLUME 3)
Maybellene / Little Queenie
Chess [CED] 169514 • 1968/69
 Picture sleeve.

ROCK REVIVAL (VOLUME 4)
Roll Over Beethoven / School Day
Chess [CED] 169515 • 1968/69
 Picture sleeve.

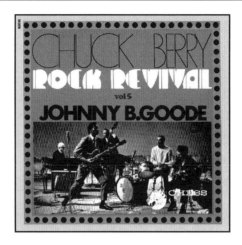

ROCK REVIVAL (VOLUME 5)
Johnny B. Goode / You Can't Catch Me
Chess [CED] 169516 • 1968/69
  Picture sleeve.

ROCK REVIVAL (VOLUME 6)
Nadine / Carol
Chess [CED] 169528 • 1969
  Picture sleeve.

ROCK REVIVAL (VOLUME 6)
Rip It Up+ / No Money Down
Chess [CED] 169532 ● 1969
    Picture sleeve. You will note that the French have a strange predilection for this particular version, but don't ask me why. It is a rare single track, though.

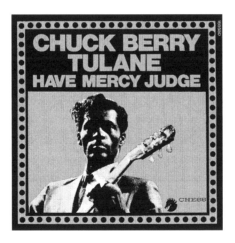

Tulane / Have Mercy Judge
Chess [CED] 169550 ● 1970
    Picture sleeve.

Reelin' And Rockin' *(live, single edit)* **/ Johnny B. Goode** *(live)*
Chess [CED] CH-25002 ● **1972**
   Picture sleeve.

Bio *(single edit)* **/ Hello Little Girl, Goodbye**
Chess [CED] CH-25006 ● **1974**
   Picture sleeve.

LES ROIS DU ROCK (VOLUME 3)
Johnny B. Goode / Roll Over Beethoven
Mercury 127.408.MCF ● **1974**
   Picture sleeve.

LES ROIS DU ROCK (VOLUME 6)
Sweet Little Sixteen / Memphis, Tennessee
Mercury 127.411.MCF • 1974
  Picture sleeve.

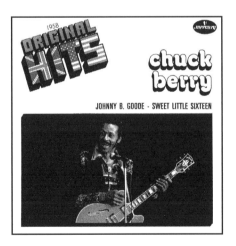

Johnny B. Goode / Sweet Little Sixteen
Mercury [Polygram] 6167 208 • 1977
  Both the cover and label proclaim '*1958 Original Hits*' – hardly credible that the originals would be on Mercury, but a nice picture sleeve nevertheless. Photo is from the Paris Olympia in 1975.

Nadine / You Never Can Tell
Vogue 101479 • 1981
Chess cuts. Picture sleeve.

EPs

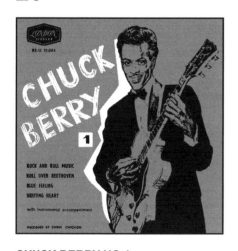 

CHUCK BERRY NO.1
London RE-U-10.004 • 1958
Rock And Roll Music / Roll Over Beethoven / Blue Feeling *(instr)* / Drifting Heart

Red label. There never was a 'NO. 2'. This is *very* rare!

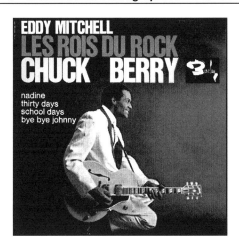

EDDY MITCHELL PRÉSENTE LES ROIS DU ROCK
Barclay 70668 • 1964
Nadine / Thirty Days / School Day / Bye Bye Johnny

Just recently I came across a white-label sample copy of this EP (see above).

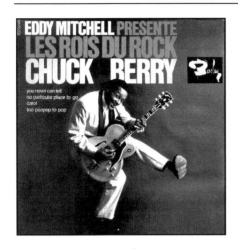

EDDY MITCHELL PRÉSENTE LES ROIS DU ROCK
Barclay 70739 • 1965
You Never Can Tell / No Particular Place To Go / Carol / Too Pooped To Pop+

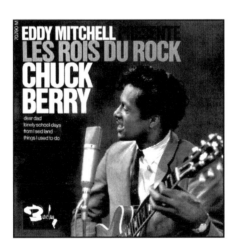

EDDY MITCHELL PRÉSENTE LES ROIS DU ROCK
Barclay 70790 • 1965
Dear Dad / Lonely Schooldays *(slow version)* / Promised Land / The Things I Used To Do+

This has one of the nicest Berry EP covers I have come across. The photo was taken at the Belgian TV show, *Face au Public*, broadcast 11 May 1965.

EDDY MITCHELL PRÉSENTE LES ROIS DU ROCK: CHUCK BERRY À LONDRES
Barclay 70858 • 1965
My Little Love-Light / You Came A Long Way From St. Louis+ / Jamaica Farewell+ / I Want To Be
Your Driver

'Jamaica Farewell' is the US version with the extra guitar.

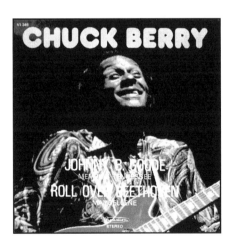

CHUCK BERRY
Visadisc VI-349 • 1973
Johnny B. Goode / Memphis, Tennessee / Roll Over Beethoven / Maybellene

Chess cuts.

LPs

EDDY MITCHELL PRÉSENTE LES ROIS DU ROCK –
VOLUME 1: CHUCK BERRY
Barclay 80 225 • June 1964
Nadine / I'm Talking About You / Bye Bye Johnny / Roll Over Beethoven / Thirty Days / Sweet Little Sixteen / Maybellene / Reelin' And Rockin' / Johnny B. Goode / Wee Wee Hours / Brown Eyed Handsome Man / School Day

Eddy Mitchell is the best and most famous rocker in France – he recorded a whole bunch of Berry songs – and this album was the first in a series of several introducing the pioneers of rock'n'roll. The second volume [Barclay 80 226] featured Bo Diddley. Berry performed live in France for the first time in February 1965, and VOLUME 1 introduced his music on LP to the French people. It was an extraordinary success and sold 25,000 copies. In fact, all the Barclay album sold quite well. The second pressing of this album featured a different small picture of Mitchell at the top right of the front cover (actually the same as that on VOLUMES 3 AND 11).

EDDY MITCHELL PRÉSENTE LES ROIS DU ROCK –
VOLUME 3: CHUCK BERRY
Barclay 80 245 • Late 1964
You Never Can Tell / Carol / Little Queenie / Confessin' The Blues+ / I Got To Find My Baby+ / Childhood Sweetheart / No Particular Place To Go / Almost Grown / Anthony Boy / Around And Around / Worried Life Blues+ / Too Pooped To Pop+

Unusual front cover. All these EDDY MITCHELL PRÉSENTE albums are a must for any Chuck Berry collection.

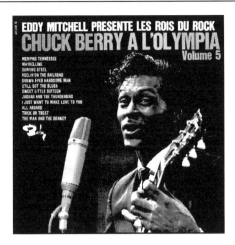

EDDY MITCHELL PRÉSENTE LES ROIS DU ROCK –
VOLUME 5: CHUCK BERRY À L'OLYMPIA
Barclay 80 258 ● May 1965

    This is very similar to the 1963 US LP, ON STAGE [Chess LP-1480]. However, this contains overdubs of Berry's voice recorded at his Olympia appearance in Paris 7 February 1965. The fake live show even has a French compere introducing Chuck, who shouts *'Viva la rock and roll'*, *'Viva la musica'*, *'Olé!'* and *'Ah, Paris'* between songs. It should be noted, however, that 'Go, Go, Go' and 'How High The Moon' are missing on this issue. Great picture on the cover, taken either at the Olympia itself or the Belgian TV show, *Face au Public*, broadcast 11 May 1965.

EDDY MITCHELL PRÉSENTE LES ROIS DU ROCK –
VOLUME 8: CHUCK BERRY À LONDRES
Barclay 80 279 ● 1965

    Same tracks as the 1965 US album, CHUCK BERRY IN LONDON [Chess LP-1495], but only released in mono. Same picture on the front cover.

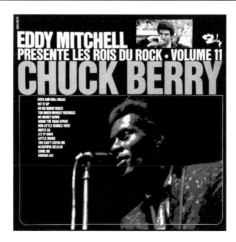

EDDY MITCHELL PRÉSENTE LES ROIS DU ROCK –
VOLUME 11: CHUCK BERRY
Barclay 080 318 • 1966
Rock And Roll Music / Rip It Up+ / Go Bobby Soxer / Too Much Monkey Business / No Money
Down / Down The Road A Piece+ / Our Little Rendezvous / Route 66+ / Let It Rock / Little Marie /
You Can't Catch Me / Beautiful Delilah / Come On / Brenda Lee

As is customary in France, a front cover with a goode concert photo.

LE DISQUE D'OR
Mercury 124.033-MDL *(mono)* **134.033-MCY** *(stereo)* • **1966**
Same tracks and almost the same front cover as the 1967 US LP, GOLDEN HITS
[Mercury MG-21103/ SR-61103]. The difference is that it has a small round picture of
Berry in the top left-hand corner. French liner notes. Reissued in stereo only as
LE DISQUE D'OR DE CHUCK BERRY [Mercury 134.033-MCY] with a different cover.

CHUCK BERRY IN MEMPHIS
Mercury 124.046-MDL *(mono)* **134.046-MCY** *(stereo)* **• 1967**
Same tracks and cover as the 1967 US LP [Mercury MG-21123/SR-61123]. French liner notes.

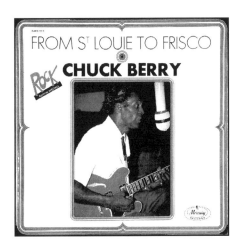

FROM ST. LOUIE TO FRISCO
Mercury 134.082-MCY *(stereo)* **• 1968**
Same tracks as the 1968 US LP [Mercury SR-61176], but a different cover. French liner notes. Reissued circa 1972 as Mercury 6463 015 with the same cover.

LIVE AT FILLMORE, SAN FRANCISCO
Mercury 134.057-MCY *(stereo)* **• 1968**
Same tracks as the 1967 US LP [Mercury SR-61138], but a different cover. The picture, by the way, is from the same shoot as the one used on the 1969 US CONCERTO IN B GOODE album. Reissued circa 1972 as Mercury 6463 016 with the same cover.

ROCK REVIVAL
Chess [CED] 69 502 • 1968
Carol / Rip It Up+ / Route 66+ / Let It Rock / Dear Dad / I Want To Be Your Driver / Thirty Days / Nadine / Around And Around / Reelin' And Rockin' / Bye Bye Johnny / No Particular Place To Go / Sweet Little Sixteen / Down The Road A Piece+

Once again, a very nice front cover. Picture of Berry and four musicians on stage, probably at the Paris Olympia in 1965.

CONCERTO IN B GOODE
Mercury 134.222-MCY *(stereo)* • 1969
Same tracks as the 1969 US LP [Mercury SR-61223], but a different cover.

THE LONDON CHUCK BERRY SESSIONS
Chess [Musidisc-Europe] CH-50001 • 1972
Same tracks and gatefold cover as the 1972 US LP [Chess CH-60020] and the 1972 UK LP [Chess 6310 122].

ST. LOUIE TO FRISCO TO MEMPHIS [2-LP]
Mercury 6619 008 • 1972
    Same tracks as the 1972 US 2-LP [Mercury SRM2-6501], but a different gatefold cover. For some strange, unknown reason this album came out with two completely different cover designs, but the same catalogue number!

ROCK AND ROLL MUSIC
Fontana 6430 022 • 1973
    Same tracks as the 1967 US LP, GOLDEN HITS [Mercury SR-61103], but a different cover. This reissue appeared in many European countries with substantially the same cover but different titles. It was released in 1972 in the Netherlands as ROCK HITS [Fontana International 6430 022], in West Germany as ATTENTION! [Fontana 6430 022], in Norway and Spain as ROCK AND ROLL MUSIC [Fontana Special 6430 022 and Fontana 6430 022 respectively]. (However, the record label inside the Spanish issue actually says GOLDEN HITS.) In 1973 it was released in Italy as ROCK HITS [Fontana Special 6430 022], in France as ROCK AND ROLL MUSIC [Fontana 6430 022] and in the UK – with a different catalogue number from all the other variations – as BACK IN THE USA [Philips 6336 216].

ROCK'N'ROLL WITH CHUCK BERRY [2-LP]
Chess [Musidisc-Europe] CH-50013 • 1973
❶ Sweet Little Sixteen / Let It Rock / My Mustang Ford / Little Queenie / No Particular Place To Go / Memphis, Tennessee / Roll Over Beethoven / Around And Around / Sweet Little Rock And Roller / Nadine / Promised Land / Reelin' And Rockin'
❷ School Day / Thirty Days / Oh Baby Doll / Almost Grown / Carol / You Never Can Tell / Johnny B. Goode / Rock And Roll Music / Brown Eyed Handsome Man / Little Marie / Too Much Monkey Business / Go, Bobby Soxer

    Most of the French album releases had great pictures of Berry on the cover. The shot on the front cover here is from the *Montreux Jazz Festival* in June 1972, and the one on the back is from the Olympia in Paris, July 1969. Because the '70s were the worst decade for the electronic stereo disaster, the photos are the primary reason why these albums are of interest to collectors.

SAN FRANCISCO DUES
Chess [Musidisc-Europe] CH-50014 • 1973
    Same tracks as the 1971 US LP [Chess CH-50008]. Same front cover, but a different picture on the back.

CHUCK BERRY'S GOLDEN DECADE [2-LP]*
Chess [Musidisc-Europe] CH-50024 • 1973
    Same tracks as the 1971 US Chess reissue [Chess 2CH-1514]. Same gatefold cover as first pressing (gold record).

CHUCK BERRY'S GOLDEN DECADE (VOLUME 2) [2-LP]*
Chess [Musidisc-Europe] CH-50028 • 1973
    Same tracks and gatefold cover as the 1973 US 2-LP [Chess 2CH-60023].

BIO
Chess [Musidisc-Europe] CH-50033 • 1973
    Same tracks and gatefold cover as the 1973 US LP [Chess CH-50043].

CHUCK BERRY'S GOLDEN DECADE (VOLUME 3) [2-LP]*
Chess [Musidisc-Europe] CH-50039 • 1974
    Same tracks and gatefold cover as the 1974 US 2-LP [Chess 2CH-60028].

CHUCK BERRY
Chess [Musidisc-Europe] CH-50047 • 1975
    Same tracks and cover as the 1975 US LP [Chess CH-60032].

LE ROI DU ROCK
Musidisc 30CV-1292 • 1975
Johnny B. Goode / Oh Baby Doll / Maybellene / Brown Eyed Handsome Man / You Can't Catch Me / Around And Around / Roll Over Beethoven / Too Much Monkey Business / Thirty Days / Deep Feeling *(instr)* / Nadine

    See also the 1976 2-LP Festival 219.

PROMISED LAND
Musidisc 30CV-1386 • 1975
Promised Land / Carol / Almost Grown / Let It Rock / You Never Can Tell / Reelin' And Rockin' / Little Queenie / Sweet Little Sixteen / It Don't Take But A Few Minutes / Rock And Roll Music / Bye Bye Johnny / School Day

    See also the 1976 2-LP Festival 219.

---

* In 1977, the three GOLDEN DECADE double albums were issued in France as a box set (see below). They were also reissued in the '80s as part of the CHICAGO GOLDEN YEARS series.

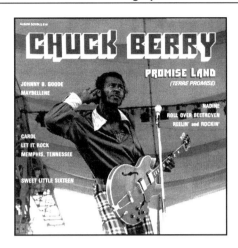

PROMISE LAND (TERRE PROMISE) [2-LP]
Festival 219 • 1976
This consists of the two Musidisc albums above. However, 30CV-1386 is Record 1 and 30CV-1292 is Record 2. Different cover, gatefold. 'Promised Land' was recorded by Johnny Hallyday as 'La Terre Promise' in 1975 and was very popular in France.

BACK HOME
Musidisc 30CV-1401 • 1977
Same tracks as the 1970 US LP [Chess LPS-1550]. Different cover (actually, the front cover picture was taken at the Olympia in Paris on 24 February 1975 – and I was even there!).

GOLDEN DECADE [6-LP]
Musidisc CCV-2601 • 1977
This contains the three French Chess GOLDEN DECADE double albums with the same catalogue numbers [CH-50024, CH-50028 and CH-50039] and was a budget-price package sold in supermarkets. Each record came in a clear plastic sleeve, and no liner notes were included. A small picture of Berry was used on the cover, which featured a gold record similar to that on the first pressings of the US VOLUME 1.

CHUCK BERRY
Impact [Phonogram] 6886 403 • 1980
Sweet Little Sixteen / Carol / Soul Rockin' / Ramblin' Rose+ / I Can't Believe / Bring Another Drink+ / Louie To Frisco / Sweet Little Rock And Roller / Little Fox / Oh Baby Doll / Wee Baby Blues+ *(live)* / Back To Memphis

Mercury recordings. Red label with silver stripes. This was reissued in 1981 with a lower catalogue number [Impact 6499 671] on a yellow label with pink stripes.

CHUCK BERRY (VOLUME 2)
Impact [Phonogram] 6886 407 • 1980
Johnny B. Goode / Misery / School Day / I Love Her, I Love Her / Check Me Out / Feelin' It *(live, instr)* / Ma Dear / Fillmore Blues *(live, instr)* / The Love I Lost / My Tambourine / Rock Cradle Rock / Rock And Roll Music

Mercury recordings.

In 1980/81, Berry's US Chess albums were all reissued in France with new catalogue numbers. These pressings initially appeared with the orange and blue Chess label. Strangely, later pressings carried a *red* label with the Chess 'horse head' logo top left. (I must admit that I have just recently come across this red Chess label and have only seen the 'Two Great Guitars' album with this kind of label.)

BERRY IS ON TOP
Chess [Phonogram] 9124 214 • 1980/81
    Same tracks and cover as the 1959 US LP [Chess LP-1435].

AFTER SCHOOL SESSION
Chess [Phonogram] 9124 215 • 1980/81
    Same tracks and cover as the 1957 US LP [Chess LP-1426].

ONE DOZEN BERRYS
Chess [Phonogram] 9124 216 • 1980/81
    Same tracks and cover as the 1958 US LP [Chess LP-1432].

ON STAGE
Chess [Phonogram] 9124 217 • 1980/81
    Same tracks and cover as the 1963 US LP [Chess LP-1480].

ROCKIN' AT THE HOPS
Chess [Phonogram] 9124 218 • 1980/81
    Same tracks and cover as the 1960 US LP [Chess LP-1448].

NEW JUKE BOX HITS
Chess [Phonogram] 9124 220 • 1980/81
    Same tracks and cover as the 1961 US LP [Chess LP-1456].

Chuck Berry & Bo Diddley
TWO GREAT GUITARS *(stereo)*
Chess [Phonogram] 9124 221 • 1980/81
    Same tracks and cover as the 1964 US LP [Checker LPS-2991].

FRESH BERRY'S *(stereo)*
Chess [Phonogram] 9124 223 • 1980/81
    Same tracks and cover as the 1965 US LP [Chess LPS-1498].

SAN FRANCISCO DUES
Chess [Phonogram] 9124 225 • 1980/81
    Same tracks and cover as the 1971 US LP [Chess CH-50008].

ST. LOUIS TO LIVERPOOL *(stereo)*
Chess [Phonogram] 9124 226 • 1980/81
    Same tracks and cover as the 1964 US LP [Chess LPS-1488].

BACK HOME *(stereo)*
Chess [Phonogram] 9124 227 • 1980/81
    Same tracks and cover as the 1970 US LP [Chess LPS-1550].

CHUCK BERRY
Impact [Phonogram] 6499 671 • 1981
    Reissue of the 1980 LP [Impact 6886 403].

MR. ROCK'N'ROLL
Mode [Vogue] 509075 • 1981
Same tracks as the 1964 US LP, CHUCK BERRY'S GREATEST HITS [Chess LP-1485], but a different cover.

ROLL OVER BEETHOVEN
Score [Hammer] SCO-8967 • 1981
Roll Over Beethoven / Goodnight, Well It's Time To Go [It's Time To Go] / Oh Baby Doll / Good Lookin' Woman / Thirty Days / Johnny B. Goode / Back To Memphis / Back In The USA / I Do Really Love You / My Heart Will Always Belong To You+

Mercury recordings.

SWEET LITTLE SIXTEEN [2-LP]
Impact [Phonogram] 6995 402 • 1981
❶ Hoochie Coochie Man+ *(live)* / Rock Cradle Rock / Oh Baby Doll / School Day / Soul Rockin' / Johnny B. Goode / Oh, Captain / Wee Baby Blues+ *(live)* / Ma Dear / Ramblin' Rose+ / Misery / Sweet Little Sixteen
❷ Thirty Days / The Love I Lost / I Can't Believe / Check Me Out / Louie To Frisco / Fillmore Blues *(live, instr)* / It Hurts Me Too+ *(live duet with Steve Miller)* / Sweet Little Rock And Roller / My Tambourine / Little Fox / I Love Her, I Love Her / Carol

This is a mess of Mercury recordings – and why include the execrable 'Oh, Captain'? Gatefold cover.

THE BEST OF CHUCK BERRY
Vogue [MFP] VMFP-521 • 1982
Maybellene / Deep Feeling *(instr)* / Johnny B. Goode / Wee Wee Hours / Nadine / Brown Eyed Handsome Man / Roll Over Beethoven / Thirty Days / Havana Moon / No Particular Place To Go / Memphis, Tennessee / Almost Grown

Chess cuts, all in mono. Great picture of Berry on the cover. See also the Belgian discography.

CHUCK BERRY
Carrere [Audiofidelity] 64.006 • 1983
Same tracks as the 1982 US album, Phoenix 10 PHX-351.

In the mid-'80s, Berry's US Chess albums were all reissued again on vinyl, the first ones as part of a CHICAGO GOLDEN YEARS series, all with a new catalogue numbers. These pressings initially appeared with the light blue Chess label with 'Chess' across the top in red and white. Later pressings carried a black label with the Chess 'horse head' logo at the top:

CHICAGO GOLDEN YEARS (VOLUME 8):
CHUCK BERRY'S GOLDEN DECADE [2-LP]
Chess [Vogue] 427008 • 1986
Same tracks and gatefold cover as the second pressing of the 1972 US reissue [Chess 2CH-1514] (pink radio).

CHICAGO GOLDEN YEARS (VOLUME 9):
CHUCK BERRY'S GOLDEN DECADE (VOLUME 2) [2-LP]
Chess [Vogue] 427009 • 1986
Same tracks and gatefold cover as the 1973 US 2-LP [Chess 2CH-60023].

CHICAGO GOLDEN YEARS (VOLUME 10):
  CHUCK BERRY'S GOLDEN DECADE (VOLUME 3) [2-LP]
Chess [Vogue] 427010 • 1986
  Same tracks and gatefold cover as the 1974 US 2-LP [Chess 2CH-60028].

ROCK'N'ROLL RARITIES [2-LP]
Chess [Vogue] 427018 • 1986
  Same tracks and gatefold cover as the 1986 US 2-LP [Chess CH2-92521]. Also
issued on CD [Vogue 600120].

Chuck Berry & Bo Diddley
CHICAGO GOLDEN YEARS (VOLUME 23): TWO GREAT GUITARS *(stereo)*
Chess [Vogue] 515023 • 1988
  Same tracks and cover as the 1964 US LP [Checker LPS-2991].

  All the following releases had session discographies printed on the back of the cover:
The labels were the late '60s light blue Chess ones with 'Chess' across the top in red
and white.

CHICAGO GOLDEN YEARS (VOLUME 30): AFTER SCHOOL SESSION
Chess [Vogue] 515030 • 1988
  Same tracks and cover as the 1957 US LP [Chess LP-1426].

CHICAGO GOLDEN YEARS (VOLUME 31): ONE DOZEN BERRYS
Chess [Vogue] 515031 • 1988
  Same tracks and cover as the 1958 US LP [Chess LP-1432].

NEW JUKE BOX HITS
Chess [Vogue] 515032 • 1988
  Same tracks and cover as the 1961 US LP [Chess LP-1456].

ROCKIN' AT THE HOPS
Chess [Vogue] 515033 • 1988
  Same tracks and cover as the 1960 US LP [Chess LP-1448].

ST. LOUIS TO LIVERPOOL *(stereo)*
Chess [Vogue] 515034 • 1988
  Same tracks and cover as the 1964 US LP [Chess LPS-1488].

THE LONDON CHUCK BERRY SESSIONS
Chess [Vogue] 515035 • 1988
  Same tracks and cover design as the 1972 US LP [Chess CH-60020], but no
gatefold cover.

CHUCK BERRY [2-LP]
Telstar STAR-2403 • 1989
❶ Johnny B. Goode / Almost Grown / Carol / You Never Can Tell / Let It Rock / School Day /
Sweet Little Rock And Roller / Thirty Days / Nadine / Back In The USA / Brown Eyed Handsome
Man / Maybellene / My Ding-A-Ling *(live, single edit)*
❷ Sweet Little Sixteen / Reelin' And Rockin' / Little Queenie / Roll Over Beethoven / No Particular
Place To Go / Promised Land / Rock And Roll Music / Too Much Monkey Business / Memphis,
Tennessee / Run Rudolph Run+ / No Money Down / Merry Christmas Baby+ *(single version)*

  Chess recordings.

LES TRIOMPHES DES STARS – CHUCK BERRY
WH [Carrere] 66.751 • 1989
Maybellene / Roll Over Beethoven / Brown Eyed Handsome Man / Rock And Roll Music / Sweet Little Sixteen / I'm Talking About You / Nadine / Johnny B. Goode / Memphis, Tennessee / Sweet Little Rock And Roller / Carol / Reelin' And Rockin'

Chess recordings. Also issued on CD [WH 96.751].

EDDY MITCHELL PRÉSENTE LES ROIS DU ROCK: CHUCK BERRY
Barclay [Universal] 980 817-9 • 2003
Same as the first French album from 1964 [Barclay 80 225]. Same cover and label. A collectors' item released in connection with Chess' *50th Anniversary of Rock'n'Roll* celebration. Limited edition and each LP is numbered (mine is 0676).

CD Albums

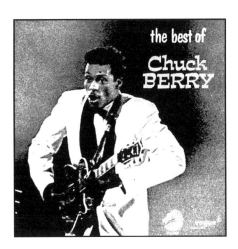

THE BEST OF CHUCK BERRY
Vogue [Chess] 600033 • 1984
Johnny B. Goode / Maybellene / Wee Wee Hours / Nadine / Havana Moon / No Particular Place To Go / Roll Over Beethoven / Bye Bye Johnny / Around And Around / Sweet Little Sixteen / Carol / Run Rudolph Run+ / Let It Rock / Sweet Little Rock And Roller / Little Queenie / Down The Road A Piece+ / Come On / Reelin' And Rockin' / School Day / Memphis, Tennessee / Almost Grown / Thirty Days

This was the very first CD I ever owned. I remember buying it from Bear Family Records in Germany. There is no year printed on it, however, I believe it was released in 1983. Anyway, this was at a very early stage when few people knew what a CD player was, and even fewer owned one. The sound quality is rather lousy – too much electronic stereo. I have never seen an LP release of this album. Even so, this CD is kinda rare as it must be one of the first, if not *the* first, CD released in Europe containing Berry material. The cover is a section of the US AFTER SCHOOL SESSION LP cover. Liner notes are in both French and English, as well as a session discography (not to be relied on these days).

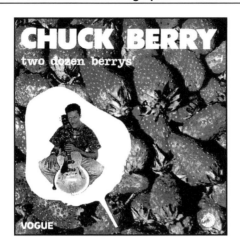

TWO DOZEN BERRYS
Vogue 600085 • 1986
Rock At The Philharmonic *(instr)* / No Money Down / Down Bound Train / Too Much Monkey Business / Roly Poly *(instr)* / Brown Eyed Handsome Man / Blue Feeling *(instr)* / School Day / Rock And Roll Music / Oh Baby Doll / Guitar Boogie *(instr)* / Go, Bobby Soxer / Betty Jean / Worried Life Blues+ / Berry Pickin' *(instr)* / Run Around / Confessin' The Blues+ / Thirteen Question Method / Route 66+ / I'm Talking About You / Rip It Up+ / Nadine / You Never Can Tell / Promised Land

I remember that, when I bought this back in 1986, I felt it contained a great combination of more obscure Berry tracks plus a few well-known classics, so to speak. I have never seen an LP release of this album. The CD has the same cover photo as the original US ONE DOZEN BERRYS LP. Unfortunately, the sound quality on some tracks is not good – electronic stereo again. Also note that the CD opens with an instrumental, which is very unusual on a Berry album (the only other instance was on TWO GREAT GUITARS).

ROCK'N'ROLL RARITIES
Vogue 600120 • 1986
Same tracks as the 1986 US 2-LP [Chess CH2-92521]. Also issued as a 2-LP set [Vogue 427018].

CHUCK BERRY
Festival FLD-763 • 1987
Roll Over Beethoven / Goodnight, Well It's Time To Go [It's Time To Go] / Oh Baby Doll / Good Lookin' Woman / Thirty Days / Johnny B. Goode / Back To Memphis / Back In The USA / I Do Really Love You / My Heart Will Always Belong To You+

Mercury recordings.

HAIL! HAIL! ROCK'N'ROLL
MCA 255 182-1 • 1987
Original soundtrack. Same tracks and cover as the 1987 US LP [MCA MCA-6217]. Also available on laserdisc [Philips 084 326-1].

16 GREATEST HITS
Rock 16 10003 • 1988
Roll Over Beethoven / Johnny B. Goode / Rock And Roll Music / Sweet Little Sixteen / School Day / Too Much Monkey Business / You Never Can Tell / Reelin' And Rockin' / Memphis, Tennessee / Carol / Maybellene / Almost Grown / Around And Around / Back In The USA / You Can't Catch Me / Nadine / No Particular Place To Go

Chess recordings. The last track – the 17th – is referred to as a *'special bonus track'*. It's worth noting that there was a similar Dutch CD released in 1991 with the same title and cover, but containing Mercury tracks [Rock 16 100<u>1</u>3].

LES TRIOMPHES DES STARS – CHUCK BERRY
WH [Carrere] 96.751 • 1989
Maybellene / Roll Over Beethoven / Brown Eyed Handsome Man / Rock And Roll Music / Sweet Little Sixteen / I'm Talking About You / Nadine / Johnny B. Goode / Memphis, Tennessee / Sweet Little Rock And Roller / Carol / Reelin' And Rockin'

Chess recordings. Also issued on LP [WH 66.751].

BEST OF CHUCK BERRY 1955-57 (VOLUME 1)
Vogue 670100 • 1989
Maybellene / Wee Wee Hours / Thirty Days / Down Bound Train / Rolly Polly *(instr)* / No Money Down / Berry Pickin' *(instr)* / Too Much Monkey Business / Roll Over Beethoven / Havana Moon / School Day / Blue Feeling *(instr)* / Oh Baby Doll / Thirteen Question Method *(1957)* / Rock And Roll Music

BEST OF CHUCK BERRY 1958-60 (VOLUME 2)
Vogue 670101 • 1989
Reelin' And Rockin' / Johnny B. Goode / Sweet Little Sixteen / Rock At The Philarmonic *(instr)* / Guitar Boogie *(instr)* / Carol / Around And Around / Sweet Little Rock And Roller / Run Rudolph Run+ / Memphis, Tennessee / Little Queenie / Almost Grown / Betty Jean / Let it Rock / Worried Life Blues+

BEST OF CHUCK BERRY 1960-65 (VOLUME 3)
Vogue 670102 • 1989
Bye Bye Johnny / Run Around / Down The Road A Piece+ / Confessin' The Blues+ / Route 66+ / I'm Talking About You / Rip It Up+ / Come On / Brown Eyed Handsome Man / Nadine / You Never Can Tell / Promised Land / No Particular Place To Go / Go, Bobby Soxer / St. Louis Blues+

I just can't understand why the French were so hung up on 'Rip It Up'.

Chuck Berry & Bo Diddley
TWO GREAT GUITARS
Vogue 670108 • 1989
Same tracks and cover as the 1964 US LP [Checker LPS-2991].

CHUCK BERRY STORY 1955-58 [2-CD]
Vogue 660501 • 1990
❶ Maybellene / Wee Wee Hours / Together (We Will Always Be) / Thirty Days / You Can't Catch Me / Down Bound Train / Roly Poly *(instr)* / Berry Pickin' *(instr)* / Too Much Monkey Business / Drifting Heart / Roll Over Beethoven / Brown Eyed Handsome Man / Havana Moon / Deep Feeling *(instr)* / School Day / La Jaunda / Blue Feeling *(instr)* / Oh Baby Doll
❷ Rock And Roll Music *(demo)* / Reelin' And Rockin' / Johnny B. Goode / Sweet Little Sixteen / Rock At The Philharmonic *(instr)* / Guitar Boogie *(instr)* / House Of Blue Lights+ / Ingo *(instr)* / It Don't Take But A Few Minutes / Carol / Blues For Hawaiians *(instr)* / Hey Pedro / Around And Around / Anthony Boy / Jo Jo Gunne / Sweet Little Rock And Roller / Run Rudolph Run+ / Merry Christmas Baby+ *(single version)*

See comments for next CD.

CHUCK BERRY STORY 1958-66 [2-CD]
Vogue 660514 • 1990
❶ Memphis, Tennessee / Little Queenie / Almost Grown / Back In The USA / Blue On Blue *(instr)* / Childhood Sweetheart / Broken Arrow / Let It Rock / Too Pooped To Pop+ / Driftin' Blues+ / Don't You Lie To Me+ / I Got To Find My Baby+ / Worried Life Blues+ / Our Little Rendezvous / Bye Bye Johnny / Run Around / Jaguar And The Thunderbird / Down The Road A Piece+
❷ Confessin' The Blues+ / Mad Lad+ / Route 66+ / I'm Talking About You / Rip It Up+ / Come On / Go, Go, Go / Man And The Donkey / Brown Eyed Handsome Man / Nadine / You Never Can Tell / Promised Land / No Particular Place To Go / Little Marie / Go, Bobby Soxer / My Little Love-Light / St. Louis Blues+ *(stereo)* / Viva, Viva Rock & Roll

36 Chess tracks on each volume = 72 altogether. 'Let It Rock' is without Berry's solo guitar. 'Brown Eyed Handsome Man' should have been the 1961 version, but it isn't. Somebody clearly made a mistake because the same 1956 version also appears on the first volume. Apart from 'St. Louis Blues', all tracks are mono or electronic stereo. Brief liner notes (same on both volumes) and recording details that are nothing to rely on these days. Stick with Fred Rothwell's *Long Distance Information*.

CHUCK BERRY – 3 ALBUMS ORIGINAUX
RFM [Polygram] 848 757-2 • 1990
This is a set of the three reissued US Mercury CD albums, CHUCK BERRY IN MEMPHIS, LIVE AT FILLMORE AUDITORIUM and FROM ST. LOUIE TO FRISCO, with the bonus tracks. The CDs and boxes were printed in France, but carry the same catalogue numbers as the US releases, 836 071, 836 072 and 836 073. No information is available about the other two reissued albums, GOLDEN HITS and CONCERTO IN B GOODE.

FRUIT OF THE VINE
Carrere 50033 • 1990
Same tracks and cover as the 1990 UK CD [Chess CDRED-19].

CHUCK BERRY – PLEIN SUCCÉS
Vogue 670646 • 1992
Maybellene / Too Much Monkey Business / Roll Over Beethoven / Rock And Roll Music *(demo)* / Johnny B. Goode / Carol / Around And Around / Sweet Little Rock And Roller / Come On / Sweet Little Sixteen / Memphis, Tennessee / Little Queenie / Bye Bye Johnny / Jaguar And The Thunderbird / Route 66+ / Rip It Up+ / Go, Go, Go / Nadine

Chess cuts.

BLUES BERRY (LES GÉNIES DU BLUES)
Éditions Atlas BLU-CD 3009 ● 1992
Memphis, Tennessee / Almost Grown / Maybellene / Johnny B. Goode / No Particular Place To Go / No Money Down / Thirty Days / Too Much Monkey Business / You Can't Catch Me / School Day / Sweet Little Sixteen / Around And Around / Carol / Little Queenie / Back In The USA / Nadine / You Never Can Tell / Promised Land

This album was a coverdisc given away with a magazine called *The Blues Collection*, and was not sold separately. Not much blues here except for one track. The series came out each Saturday, showcasing a different artist each week. Berry was number 9 in this series. It was also published in the UK in 1993 (see UK discography for details), albeit with a different cover.

THE VERY BEST [2-CD]
Vogue 74321116162 ● 1992
❶ Maybellene / Too Much Monkey Business / Roll Over Beethoven / Brown Eyed Handsome Man / Havana Moon / School Day / Oh Baby Doll / Rock And Roll Music / Johnny B. Goode / Sweet Little Sixteen / Carol / Around And Around / Jo Jo Gunne / Run Rudolph Run+ /Sweet Little Rock And Roller
❷ Memphis, Tennessee / Little Queenie / Back In The USA / Let It Rock / Bye Bye Johnny / Run Around / Route 66+ / Rip It Up+ / Come On / Nadine / You Never Can Tell / Promised Land / No Particular Place To Go / St. Louis Blues+ / Viva, Viva Rock & Roll

Chess cuts. This is an abbreviated version (30 tracks) of the 1990 2-CD sets, CHUCK BERRY STORY 1958-66 [Vogue 660514] and CHUCK BERRY STORY 1955-58 [Vogue 660501]. Great picture of Berry (taken in Paris in 1965) on the front cover.

BERRY IS ON TOP
MCA MCD-30487 ● 1993
Same tracks and cover as the original 1959 US LP [Chess LP-1435], plus eight bonus tracks: 'Down The Road A Piece', 'No Money Down', 'Down Bound Train', 'Jaguar And The Thunderbird', 'Things I Used To Do' *(stereo)*, 'No Particular Place To Go', 'Fraulein' *(stereo)* and 'Nadine'. Also released in Germany in 1993 and in the UK in 1994.

LES GÉNIES DU ROCK – JOHNNY B. GOODE
Atlas RK-CD401 ● 1993
Roll Over Beethoven / Johnny B. Goode / Maybellene / Rock And Roll Music / Carol / My Mustang Ford / Sweet Little Sixteen *(alt. version)* / Thirteen Question Method *(alt. version)* / Oh Baby Doll / Let's Boogie *(stereo)* / Beautiful Delilah / I Want To Be Your Driver *(stereo)* / Let It Rock / Sweet Little Rock And Roller / Route 66+ / Run Rudolph Run+ / You Never Can Tell *(stereo)* / Jo Jo Gunne

Interesting compilation of Chess recordings. Liner notes in French only. This was in a series of over one hundred CDs issued by a French record club. Other artists featured included the Nice, Iggy Pop, John Lee Hooker, the Shirelles.

CHUCK BERRY – GOLD
Columbia COL-476858-2 ● 1994
Maybellene / Thirty Days / No Money Down / Roll Over Beethoven / Brown Eyed Handsome Man / Too Much Monkey Business / You Can't Catch Me / School Day / Rock And Roll Music / Sweet Little Sixteen / Reelin And Rockin' / Johnny B. Goode / Around And Around / Beautiful Delilah / Carol / Sweet Little Rock And Roller / Almost Grown / Little Queenie / Back In The USA / Memphis, Tennessee / Let It Rock / Bye Bye Johnny / I'm Talking About You / Come On / Nadine / No Particular Place To Go / You Never Can Tell / Promised Land

Good compilation with the best of the best from Berry. All these 28 songs have actually become classics in music history. Good to see that that darned 'Ding-A-Ling' was left out. This CD was probably also sold in both Germany and the Netherlands. The track selections are actually very similar to the 1982 US 2-LP, THE GREAT 28 [Chess CH-8201].

LES ORIGINAUX
Vogue 7452119 2642 • 1994
Memphis, Tennessee / School Day / Roll Over Beethoven / St. Louis Blues+ *(stereo)* / Nadine / Sweet Little Sixteen / Back In The USA / Johnny B. Goode / Sweet Little Rock And Roller / Oh Baby Doll / Maybellene / Rock And Roll Music *(demo)* / Too Much Monkey Business / Come On / No Particular Place To Go / Route 66+ / Let It Rock / Viva, Viva Rock And Roll

Chess cuts. 'Let It Rock' is the version without Berry's solo guitar. The CD comes in a jewel case with a cardboard sleeve that is identical to the CD insert.

Shabba Ranks
A MI SHABBA
Epic 477482-2 • 1995
Go Shabba Go

Song by Jamaican deejay/toaster Shabba Ranks (real name Rexton Rawlston Fernando Gordon) featuring Chuck Berry on vocals and guitar. If we can speak of a 'final' Berry studio recording, this is it. What can one say about the song? It's not rock'n'roll, and Berry's guitar is low down in the mix, which makes it sound very thin. The song was included as a bonus track on the European pressing of the album above, but not on the respective US pressing. Although it was released by EMI France, the disc itself was manufactured in Austria, and was also distributed in the UK, Germany, etc.

CHUCK BERRY
Locomotive International LMM-81 • 1996
Rock And Roll Music / Nadine / Hail Hail Rock'n'Roll [School Day] / In The Wee Wee Hours [Wee Wee Hours] / *Medley:* Carol / Blues Time / Sweet Little Sixteen [Johnny B. Goode / Maybellene]

This is a CD release we all should stay away from – it's probably the worst ever. See the 1983 Swiss LP, ROCK [Blue Vox BV/129-LP] and you will understand what I'm talking about. Several songs are mistitled (the correct titles are shown in square brackets). Also, the last three titles printed on the cover and CD ('Carol', 'Blues' and 'Sweet Little Sixteen') are not there at all, and the total playing time for this six-track CD is just 29:22! What a waste!! It says in bold letters '*Tous les titres composés par Chuck Berry*' ('*All titles composed by Chuck Berry*'), which at least is correct. You have been warned!

CHUCK BERRY
Universal 112 172-2 • 2000

Johnny B. Goode / Roll Over Beethoven / Maybellene / School Day / Rock And Roll Music / Oh Baby Doll / Too Much Monkey Business / Let It Rock / Carol / Sweet Little Rock And Roller / My Ding-A-Ling *(live, single edit)* / Reelin' And Rockin' / No Particular Place To Go / Sweet Little Sixteen / Little Queenie / Brown Eyed Handsome Man / Nadine / Too Pooped To Pop+ / Back In The USA / Bye Bye Johnny

I thought this album really looked great with the red cover and a good black and white picture of Berry. Well... apart from this there is nothing fancy about it, as we simply have 20 greatest hits, a digipak with credits and recording year for each track, but no liner notes, just a list of the other releases in the series. No stereo either – even 'My Ding-A-Ling' is in mono – and some of the older songs are still in electronic stereo, would you believe!

 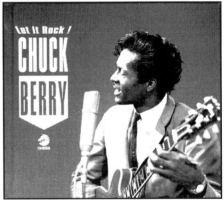

LET IT ROCK!
Chess [Universal] 112 871-2 • 2002

Maybellene / Roll Over Beethoven / Wee Wee Hours / Thirty Days / You Can't Catch Me / No Money Down / Rock And Roll Music / Sweet Little Sixteen / Johnny B. Goode / Around And Around / Carol / Memphis, Tennessee / Little Queenie / Almost Grown / Back In The USA / Childhood Sweetheart / Let It Rock / Don't You Lie To Me+ / Bye Bye Johnny / Nadine / You Never Can Tell / Promised Land / No Particular Place To Go / Dear Dad

A MUST HAVE! I'm glad to see songs like 'Childhood Sweetheart' and 'Dear Dad' included. However, this particular CD has a cover and 30-page booklet you have never seen the likes of! This is probably the best Berry booklet published anywhere as far as pictures go. You've just got to see it to believe it! It contains several photos from 1965 (Paris and Belgium), and the shot on the front cover is from the 1965 Belgian TV show, *Face au Public*. The text is in French, but it is the pictures that count. (Well, the sound is goode too!)

319

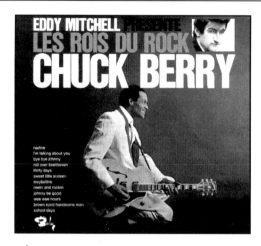

EDDY MITCHELL PRÉSENTE LES ROIS DU ROCK: CHUCK BERRY
Barclay [Universal] 980 817-8 • 2003
 Same as the 1964 LP [Barclay 80 225]. Digipak, but same cover.

ROLL OVER BEETHOVEN: THE SINGLES 1955-1956
Saga All Stars Series 984 967-4 • 2007
Maybellene / Wee Wee Hours / Thirty Days / Together (We Will Always Be) / No Money Down / Down Bound Train / Roll Over Beethoven / Drifting Heart / Too Much Monkey Business / Brown Eyed Handsome Man / You Can't Catch Me / Havana Moon / Maybellene *(live, 1956 Alan Freed radio show)* / Roll Over Beethoven *(live, 1956 Alan Freed radio show)*

 A new digipak series from France: *'Saga proudly presents the All Stars series. A family-friendly collection of all-time classic tunes, sung by your favourite artists. For cool cats and hip chicks!'*
 Great cover which you fold out and get a '50s black and white picture of Berry's face. On the other side there is a list of the songs in big lettering, which looks almost like an old concert poster. The first twelve titles are the Chess singles from the first two years, and the last two are from a 1956 Alan Freed radio show (see the 1978 Various Artists bootleg LP, ROCK'N'ROLL RADIO [Radiola MR-1087] for more information).

Various Artists LPs

 There are dozens of compilation albums issued in France which feature Chuck Berry tracks, but only a few of these are of interest to the Berry collectors. Despite the fact that they feature Berry's Mercury recordings, the LA FANTASTIQUE EPOPÉE DU ROCK albums below actually good compilations, in that they have nice pictures of the artists and liner notes (in French). They came out in the late '60s. VOLUME 3 is Johnny Hallyday's JOHNNY À NASHVILLE.

LA FANTASTIQUE EPOPÉE DU ROCK (VOLUME 1)
Mercury 6338 005 • 1968
Carol / Memphis, Tennessee / Maybellene

 Picture of Berry on the cover. Other artists include Screamin' Jay Hawkins (2), Jerry Lee Lewis (3), the Platters, Fats Domino, Blue Cheer (!?) and Billy Lee Riley.

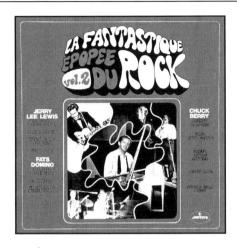

LA FANTASTIQUE EPOPÉE DU ROCK (VOLUME 2)
Mercury 134 093-MCY • 1968
Johnny B. Goode / Club Nitty Gritty / Sweet Little Sixteen / Thirty Days / Rock And Roll Music

Picture of Berry on the cover. Other artists include Jerry Lee Lewis (4) and Fats Domino (3).

LA FANTASTIQUE EPOPÉE DU ROCK (VOLUME 4)
Mercury 138 000-MCY • 1968
Sweet Little Rock And Roller

Picture of Berry on the cover. Other artists include Jerry Lee Lewis (2 tracks including 'Roll Over Beethoven'), Clyde McPhatter (2), Charlie Rich (2), Billy Lee Riley, Marty Wilde (2), Fats Domino and Little Richard. (NB: Both sides of the cover state that the old Arthur Crudup tune, 'So Glad You're Mine', is by Berry; however, the label says Marty Wilde performs the song, which is correct.)

LA FANTASTIQUE EPOPÉE DU ROCK (VOLUME 5)
Mercury 138 001-MCY • 1968
Oh Baby Doll

Picture of Berry on the cover. Other artists include Jerry Lee Lewis (2), Marty Wilde, Billy Lee Riley, Charlie Rich (2), Buddy Knox, Gary 'US' Bonds, Clyde McPhatter, Bo Diddley and Frankie Lymon.

32 ROCKERS & ROLLERS [2-LP]
Festival 203 • 1976
Roll Over Beethoven / Let It Rock

Chess cuts. Picture of Berry on the cover. Good compilation featuring various Chess artists including Bo Diddley (3), Bobby Tuggle, the Rays, Clarence 'Frogman' Henry (2), Paul Gayten, Bobby Cisco (2), Bobby Charles (2), Jimmy McCracklin (2), Ray Stanley, Johnnie & Joe, Lee Andrews & The Hearts, Lowell Fulson, Dale Hawkins, Eddie Boyd, O. Wills, Bobby Dean, Eddie Fontaine, Rusty York, Piano Red, the Monotones, the Re-Vels, the Students, the Ideals and the Miracles. Gatefold cover.

Chuck Berry – Jerry Lee Lewis – Little Richard
LET'S DANCE ROCK'N'ROLL [3-LP]
Score SCO-8605 • 1981
Sweet Little Sixteen / School Day / Maybellene / Rock And Roll Music / Ramblin' Rose+ / Carol / C.C. Rider+ *(live)* / Memphis, Tennessee / Sweet Little Rock And Roller / Reelin' And Rockin'

Berry, Lewis and Richard get one record each. Picture of Berry on the cover. Mercury recordings. The cover says these are live recordings, but apart from one they're not.

GOSPEL, BLUES, JAZZ & CO [3-LP]
Mode [Vogue] 000358 • 1982
Chuck's Beat *(with Bo Diddley) (instr, album version)*

Picture of Berry on the cover. You don't often find Chuck on an album with jazz and gospel legends like Mahalia Jackson, Count Basie, Erroll Garner and Louis Armstrong, but that's exactly what you get on this set. But why on earth include this Berry number? I could have made a better suggestion: 'Rock At The Philharmonic' and Diddley's 'Crackin' Up' would have worked just fine. Other artists include the Stars of Faith, the Swanee Quintet, the Clara Ward Singers, the Original Gospel Harmonettes, Memphis Slim, Champion Jack Dupree, Big Bill Broonzy, Jimmy Witherspoon, the Aces, Buddy Guy (3), John Lee Hooker, Muddy Waters (2), Sonny Boy Williamson (2), Sidney Bechet, Stephane Grappelli, Django Reinhardt, Dizzy Gillespie, Max Roach and Art Blakey.

SUPER RHYTHM'N'BLUES (VOLUME 3)
MFP 2M026-64.829 • 1982
Maybellene / Sweet Little Sixteen

Chess recordings. Picture of Berry on the cover. Other artists include Billie Holiday, Ray Charles, Wilson Pickett, Jimi Hendrix, Little Richard and the Platters.

ORIGINAL RHYTHM'N'BLUES HITS [3-LP]
Mode [Vogue] 000365 • 1983
Sweet Little Sixteen / Maybellene

Okay compilation of Chess artists and 38 tracks. However, the publication dates printed next to each song should not be relied upon. Berry's two songs were *not* first published in 1968 and 1967 respectively. No pictures of any of the performers.

LES OSCARS DU ROCK AND ROLL
AB Productions 831 351-1 • 1986
Johnny B. Goode *(live)* / Nadine *(live)*

The 1969 *Toronto Rock & Roll Revival* again, but it says '1958' and '1964' respectively. This is utter humbug! The cover says 'original versions', but many are not. Two songs from each artist: Bill Haley (live), Sonny Burgess (1970s), Billy Lee Riley (Sun), Warren Smith (Sun), Johnny Cash (Sun), Roy Orbison (Sun), Carl Perkins (Sun), Jerry Lee Lewis (Sun), Gene Vincent (1960s), Little Richard (live, 1960s) and Fats Domino (live). The record features Sonny Burgess and his version of 'Memphis, Tennessee' from 1976! Original? Jerry Lee Lewis and his version of 'Be-Bop-A-Lula'. Original? Live versions of 'The Fat Man' and 'Blueberry Hill' by Fats Domino, are claimed to date from 1949 and 1956 respectively. Unbelievable. To be perfectly honest, there are a few originals, but the sound quality is not that good either. So, I just can't understand why such crap was released in the first place (money, of course). I've included this album as a warning for you to stay clear if you should be unlucky enough come across it. Which hopefully you won't.

Various Artists CD Singles

Chuck Berry – Jimi Hendrix – Texas
LA GRANDE AVENTURE DU ROCK
Polygram, no number • 199?
Johnny B. Goode

Three-track 3" CD single issued in the early 1990s. Berry's track is the original Chess recording. The others are 'Hey Joe' by Jimi Hendrix (1967) and 'I Don't Want A Lover' by Texas (1989). This was probably issued as a sample for an upcoming album of some sort, but it doesn't say.

Chuck Berry – Nina Simone – Joe Tex – James Brown
ESPACE RHYTHM & BLUES
PMGBH JMS-2693 • 1993
No Particular Place To Go

Five-track CD single. Berry's song is the original Chess studio recording. Others are 'My Baby Just Cares For Me' *(live)* by Nina Simone, 'Show Me' by Joe Tex, 'Rock Me Baby' by Ike And Tina Turner and 'It's A Man's Man's Man's World' *(live)* by James Brown.

Chuck Berry – Dick Dale
YOU NEVER CAN TELL
MCA MCD-33130 • 1994
You Never Can Tell

Two track CD single taken from the soundtrack of the movie, *Pulp Fiction*. This is almost a Chuck Berry CD single, as his name and song title both appear on the front side of the sleeve (although the cover illustration is taken from the *Pulp Fiction* movie CD, which the single was of course released to promote). Berry's song is the original Chess recording. The other track on the CD is 'Misirlou' by Dick Dale & His Del-Tones.

ROCK'N'ROLL 39-59 [promo]
Body & Soul 11001 • 2007
Roll Over Beethoven

This complimentary 4-track CD was given to visitors to the rock'n'roll exhibition at the Fondation Cartier museum in Paris from 22 June to 28 October 2007.

See also Various Artists CD, ROCK'N'ROLL 39-59 [Body & Soul BS-2971] below, and *Section 15 (Chuck Berry in Print)* for details of a huge and comprehensive book + more info about the exhibition.

Various Artists CD Albums

JOHNNY HALLYDAY PRÉSENTE
 TOUTE LA MUSIQUE QUE J'AIME: LE ROCK'N'ROLL
Atoll 191 416.2-PY • 1995
Maybellene / Roll Over Beethoven

A collection of classics compiled by Johnny Hallyday to celebrate 40 years of rock'n'roll. At least that must have been the intention. However, the tracks here are mostly re-recordings by the original artists (though there are a few original songs). True to form, Berry's cuts are his Mercury recordings. Liner notes (in French) are by Hallyday, whose picture also appears on the cover, but there are no pictures of the artists. The album also includes a bonus track by Johnny entitled 'Le Bon Temps du Rock'n'Roll', which is his version of the Bob Seger classic, 'Old Time Rock And Roll'. Other artists include Gene Vincent (2 re-recordings), Johnny Burnette's Rock & Roll Trio, Bill Haley (2 live cuts), Bo Diddley, Carl Perkins, Jerry Lee Lewis (2), Little Richard (2 re-recordings), Johnny Kidd & The Pirates, Fats Domino (live), Ray Charles (live), Buddy Holly and Eddie Cochran.

ROCK'N'ROLL 39-59 [promo]
Body & Soul 11001 • 2007
Roll Over Beethoven

ROCK'N'ROLL 39-59
Body & Soul BS-2971 • 2007
Maybellene

Issued in connection with the rock'n'roll exhibition at the Fondation Cartier museum in Paris from 22 June to 28 October 2007, the CD [BS-2971] contains 12 rock'n'roll classics and 12 records that inspired them – like Bill Haley's version of 'Shake, Rattle And Roll' and Joe Turner's original, Elvis' 'Blue Moon Of Kentucky' and Bill Monroe's original, etc. Berry's 'Maybellene' is followed by Roy Acuff's 1939 version of 'Ida Red' (strange choice). This interesting compilation also includes a 20-page booklet.

See also Various Artists CD EP, ROCK'N'ROLL 39-59 [Body & Soul 11001] above, and *Section 15 (Chuck Berry in Print)* in *Volume 2* for details of a huge and comprehensive book + more info about the exhibition.

(WEST) GERMANY

In the 1950s, a few of the Chess recordings were released as singles on the London label (black with gold print, in green company sleeves)... but where's 'Johnny B. Goode'? As far as I know there were no Berry EPs produced in Germany at any time. However, in the early and mid-'60s (1963-66) the Funckler singles and EPs from the Netherlands were sold in West Germany.

Most Berry LPs sold in West Germany during the '60s were Funckler pressings imported from the Netherlands. From 1970 onwards, a great many were released on Bellaphon, a West German independent label formed in 1964. In 1968 they became really huge due to a contract with Fantasy Records which gave them the German rights to all Creedence Clearwater Revival records. Following the rock'n'roll revival, they secured the rights to the Sun and Chess catalogue and other labels.

At first sight Bellaphon's numbering scheme appears confusing, but Dietmar Rudolph has provided an interesting and logical explanation: catalogue numbers beginning with '19' were assigned to new releases; those beginning with '15' to reissues on single LPs; those beginning with '55' and '65' to reissues on 2-LPs. It makes sense. However, the sequence of the Bellaphon numbers is apparently unrelated to year of release, and no dates appear on any of the early issues.

Singles

You Can't Catch Me / Havana Moon
London DL-20.085 • 1957

Roll Over Beethoven / Rock And Roll Music
London DL-20.151 • 1958

Sweet Little Sixteen / Reelin' And Rockin'
London DL-20.170 • 1958

Carol / Hey Pedro
London DL-20.195 • 1958

Almost Grown / Little Queenie
London DL-20.253 • 1959

Lonely School Days *(fast version)* **/ Ramona Say Yes**
Vogue DV-14547 • 1966
    Picture sleeve.

Misery / Little Fox
Mercury 6052 257 • 1972
    This is a rare Berry single because these two songs have not been available in this format in any other countries. It was released to promote the 2-LP, ST. LOUIE TO FRISCO TO MEMPHIS [Mercury 6619 008]. Great picture sleeve.

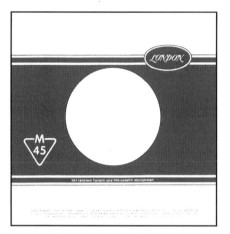

London sleeve, 1950s

London DL-20.151

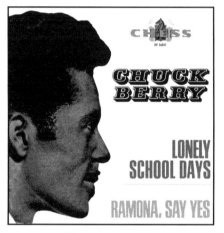

Vogue DV-14547

Vogue DV-14547

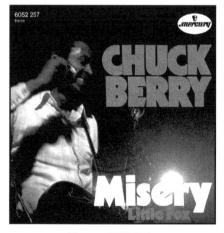

Mercury 6052 257

Mercury 6052 257

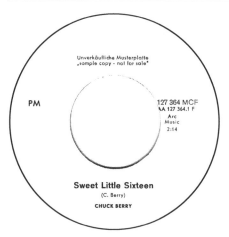

Mercury 127 364-MCF (promo)

Bellaphon BF-18108

Bellaphon BF-18108

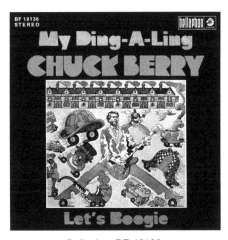

Bellaphon BF-18138

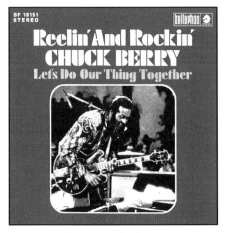

Bellaphon BF-18151

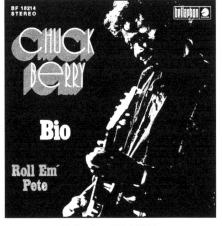

Bellaphon BF-18214

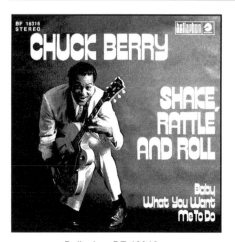

Bellaphon BF-18316

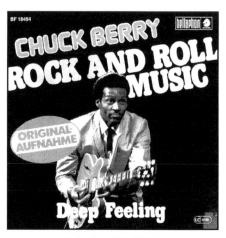

Bellaphon BF-18454

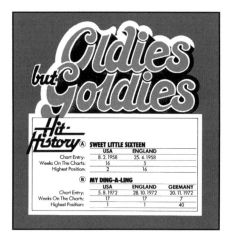

Chess 'Oldies But Goldies' 6.13013

Chess 'Big Hits' 6.14941 (test pressing)

Chess 'Big Hits' 6.14941

Chess 'Big Hits' 6.14941

Johnny B. Goode / Back In The USA
Mercury 'Kings Of Rock'n'Roll' Series 127 356-MCF • 1972
> Picture sleeve.

Sweet Little Sixteen / Roll Over Beethoven
Mercury 'Kings Of Rock'n'Roll' Series 127 364-MCF • 1972
> Picture sleeve. As was customary with West German Mercury, promo copies of this single and the one above were issued with plain white labels with no label name printed on them.

Johnny B. Goode / School Day
Mercury 'Legendary Oldies' Series 811 058-7 • 1972

Roll Over Beethoven / Back In The USA
Mercury 'Yesterday' Series 6052 480 • 1972
> Art sleeve.

Johnny B. Goode / Memphis, Tennessee
Mercury 'Yesterday' Series 6167 409 • 1972
> Art sleeve.

Johnny B. Goode / Sweet Little Sixteen
Bellaphon BF-18108 • 1972
> Chess cuts. Picture sleeve.

My Ding-A-Ling *(live, single edit)* **/ Let's Boogie**
Bellaphon BF-18138 • 1972
> Picture sleeve.

Reelin' And Rockin' *(live, single edit)* **/ Let's Do Our Thing Together**
Bellaphon BF-18151 • 1973
> Picture sleeve. This was also issued with a promo sheet dated 10 January 1973.

Roll Over Beethoven / Rock And Roll Music
Bellaphon BO-101 • 1973
> Chess cuts. Art cover. Issued as part of an *'Echoes Of A Rock Era'* series.

Bio *(single edit)* **/ Roll 'Em Pete+** *(live)*
Bellaphon BF-18214 • 1973
> Picture sleeve.

Shake, Rattle And Roll+ / Baby What You Want Me To Do+
Bellaphon BF-18316 • 1975
> Picture sleeve with great picture of Berry.

Rock And Roll Music / Deep Feeling *(instr)*
Bellaphon BF-18454 • 1976
> Chess cuts. Picture sleeve.

Johnny B. Goode / Maybellene
Chess 'Oldies But Goldies' 6.13011 • 1981
> Art cover.

Rock And Roll Music / Roll Over Beethoven
Chess 'Oldies But Goldies' 6.13012 • 1981
  Art cover.

Sweet Little Sixteen *(demo)* **/ My Ding-A-Ling** *(live, single edit)*
Chess 'Oldies But Goldies' 6.13013 • 1981
  Rare issue on 45 rpm of the demo version. Art cover.

Johnny B. Goode / Carol
Chess 'Big Hits' 6.14941 • 1987
  Art cover.

Sweet Little Sixteen / Roll Over Beethoven
Chess 'Big Hits' 6.14942 • 1987
  Art cover. Even as late as 1987 you could find test pressings of these with a plain white label without the label-name (Chess) printed on it. The label says *'Ungeprüftes Muster – Unverkäuflich'* *('Unchecked sample – Not for sale')* on it.

Maybellene / Sweet Little Sixteen
ZYX *'Golden Oldies Revival'* 1956-7 • 1988
  Chess cuts. Art cover. Most of the releases in this series were '60s artists/music, with catalogue numbers starting at 1901-7 and ending at 1960-7. See also *Various Artists Singles.*

A MYSTERY BOX SET

CHUCK BERRY – A RETROSPECTIVE
BX-45367 • Germany(?), late 1990s
  This box set containing nine Berry singles – eight on the Collectables label (COL.3401, 3404, 3405, 3422, 3437, 3438, 3471, 3474) and one on Eric (224) – appeared sometime in the late '90s! Some of the records came in company sleeves, others just in plain white sleeves. Some of the Collectables releases had the old label, others the newer one with *'Chess – MCA Special Products'* printed on it. The box itself was black and yellow with no picture or liner notes. Despite containing only US singles, it looks as though this package might have originated in Germany.

LPs

CHUCK BERRY'S GREATEST HITS
Chess [Deutsche Grammophon] 275 003 • 1965
Same tracks as the 1964 US LP [Chess LP-1485]. Same front cover, but different back cover with pictures.

FRESH BERRY'S
Chess [Deutsche Grammophon] 275 004 *(stereo)* • **1965**
Same tracks as the 1965 US LP [Chess LPS-1498]. Different front cover (great picture of Berry). This was also pressed as a white promo with no company name on the label.

CHUCK BERRY
Pye MAL-611 *(mono)* • **1967**
Same tracks and cover as the 1966 UK LP [Marble Arch MAL-611]. However, it's on a cherry-coloured Pye label stating *'Made in Germany'*. Rumour has it that the 10-track stereo version of YOU NEVER CAN TELL [Marble Arch MALS-702] was released on the Vogue label in Germany in 1967, but this remains unconfirmed.

CHUCK BERRY IN MEMPHIS
Mercury SM-858027-FPY *(stereo)* • **1967**
Same tracks and cover as the 1967 US LP [Mercury SR-61123].

LIVE AT THE FILLMORE AUDITORIUM, SAN FRANCISCO
Mercury SM-858047-FPY *(stereo)* • **1967**
Same tracks and cover as the 1967 US LP [Mercury SR-61138].

FROM ST. LOUIE TO FRISCO
Mercury SM-134082-MCY • 1968
Same tracks and cover as the 1968 US LP [Mercury SR-61176].

CONCERTO IN B GOODE
Mercury SM-134222-MCY • 1969
Same tracks and cover as the 1969 US LP [Mercury SR-61223].

THE BEST OF CHUCK BERRY [2-LP]
Bellaphon BLST-6506 • 1970
❶ Sweet Little Sixteen / Let It Rock / My Mustang Ford / Little Queenie / No Particular Place To Go / Memphis, Tennessee / Roll Over Beethoven / Around And Around / Sweet Little Rock And Roller / Nadine / Promised Land / Reelin' And Rockin'
❷ School Day / Thirty Days / Oh Baby Doll / Almost Grown / Carol / You Never Can Tell / Johnny B. Goode / Rock And Roll Music / Brown Eyed Handsome Man / Little Marie / Too Much Monkey Business / Go, Bobby Soxer

Gatefold cover. Same front cover picture as the 1965 US LP, CHUCK BERRY IN LONDON [Chess LPS-1495]. Liner notes edited from the 1964 US LP, ST. LOUIS TO LIVERPOOL [Chess LP-/LPS-1488], still signed by 'Marshall Paul' (Marshall Chess).

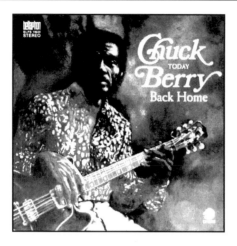

CHUCK BERRY TODAY – BACK HOME
Bellaphon BLPS-19034 • 1970
      Same tracks as the 1970 US LP, BACK HOME [Chess LPS-1550]. Almost the same front cover, but in psychedelic pink and purple. Different back cover.

SAN FRANCISCO DUES
Bellaphon BLPS-19055 • 1971
      Same tracks and cover as the 1971 US LP [Chess CH-50008].

THE LONDON CHUCK BERRY SESSIONS
Bellaphon BLPS-19098 • 1972
      Same tracks and gatefold cover as the 1972 US LP [Chess CH-60020].

ST. LOUIE TO FRISCO TO MEMPHIS [2-LP]
Mercury 6619 008 • 1972
      Same tracks and gatefold cover as the 1972 US 2-LP [Mercury SRM2-6501].

ATTENTION!
Fontana 6430 022 • 1972
      Same tracks as the 1967 US LP, GOLDEN HITS [Mercury SR-61103], but a different cover. This reissue appeared in many European countries with substantially the same cover but different titles. It was released in 1972 in the Netherlands as ROCK HITS [Fontana International 6430 022], in West Germany as ATTENTION! [Fontana 6430 022], in Norway and Spain as ROCK AND ROLL MUSIC [Fontana Special 6430 022 and Fontana 6430 022 respectively]. (However, the record label inside the Spanish issue actually says GOLDEN HITS.) In 1973 it was released in Italy as ROCK HITS [Fontana Special 6430 022], in France as ROCK AND ROLL MUSIC [Fontana 6430 022] and in the UK – with a different catalogue number from all the other variations – as BACK IN THE USA [Philips 6336 216].

CHUCK BERRY'S GOLDEN DECADE 1955-65 [2-LP]
Bellaphon BLST-6545 • 1972
　　Same tracks as the 1972 US reissue [Chess 2CH-1514]. Different gatefold cover, however the inside is the same as the cover of the second pressing (pink radio)

CHUCK BERRY'S GOLDEN DECADE (VOLUME 2) [2-LP]
Bellaphon BLST-6548 • 1972
　　Same tracks as the 1973 US 2-LP [Chess 2CH-60023]. Gatefold cover, different front and back, but the inside is almost identical, except that the original US record numbers have been erased from the sessionography.

BIO
Bellaphon BLPS-19169 • 1973
　　Same tracks and gatefold cover as the 1973 US LP [Chess CH-50043].

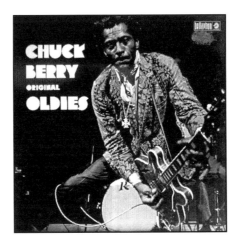

ORIGINAL OLDIES
Bellaphon BI-1547 • 1973
Roll Over Beethoven / Reelin' And Rockin' / Brown Eyed Handsome Man / Too Pooped To Pop+ / Around And Around / Bye Bye Johnny / Rock And Roll Music / Maybellene / Deep Feeling *(instr)* / Anthony Boy / You Can't Catch Me / Back In The USA

　　'Too Pooped To Pop' is credited to Berry.

333

ORIGINAL OLDIES (VOLUME 2)
Bellaphon BI-1551 • 1973
Sweet Little Sixteen / Let's Do Our Thing Together / Almost Grown / Your Lick *(instr)* / St. Louis Blues+ / Johnny B. Goode / She Once Was Mine / My Little Love-Light / Dear Dad / Ain't That Just Like A Woman+ / It's My Own Business

Features one of the best cover shots ever on a Berry album!

THE STORY OF ROCK AND ROLL
Ariola 28.911-XAT • 1973
Mercury recordings. Same tracks as the 1976 US LP, GREATEST HITS [Everest FS-321], but a different cover.

BOXEN HITS
Bellaphon BI-15112 • 1974
Same tracks as the 1961 US LP, NEW JUKE BOX HITS [Chess LP-1456], but different cover.

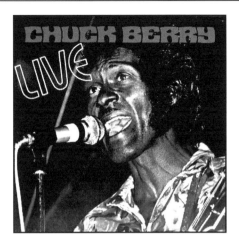

CHUCK BERRY LIVE
Bellaphon BI-15102 ● 1974
  Same tracks as the 1963 US LP, ON STAGE [Chess LP-1480], except 'How High The Moon' is faded earlier and is not mentioned on the cover or label. Different cover.

CHUCK BERRY'S GOLDEN DECADE (VOLUME 3) [2-LP]
Bellaphon BLST-6561 ● 1974
  Same tracks and gatefold cover as the 1974 US 2-LP [Chess 2CH-60028].

ORIGINAL OLDIES (VOLUME 3)
Bellaphon BI-15107 ● 1974
Let It Rock / Nadine / No Money Down / Sweet Little Rock And Roller / Thirty Days / You Never Can Tell / Little Queenie / Memphis, Tennessee / Jo Jo Gunne / Brenda Lee / Guitar Boogie *(instr)* / Route 66**+**

24 OLDIES ORIGINAL [2-LP]
Bellaphon BLS-5522 • 1975
  Record 1 is the same as the 1973 LP, ORIGINAL OLDIES [Bellaphon BI-1547]. Record 2 is the same as the 1973 LP, ORIGINAL OLDIES (VOLUME 2) [Bellaphon BI-1551]. Different gatefold cover.

CHUCK BERRY
Bellaphon BLPS-19204 • 1975
  Same tracks and cover as the 1975 US LP [Chess CH-60032].

CHUCK BERRY – PORTRAIT [2-LP]
Bellaphon BLS-5540 • 1976
❶ Rock And Roll Music / Carol / Sweet Little Sixteen / No Particular Place To Go / Memphis, Tennessee / Johnny B. Goode / Roll Over Beethoven / Too Much Monkey Business / Reelin' And Rockin' / Around And Around / I'm Talking About You / Go, Go, Go
❷ Maybellene / Oh Baby Doll / Back In The USA / Deep Feeling *(instr)* / Sweet Little Rock And Roller / Wee Wee Hours / My Ding-A-Ling *(live, single edit)* / Guitar Boogie *(instr)* / Brown Eyed Handsome Man / Promised Land *(stereo)* / You Can't Catch Me / Route 66+

  Another repackaging of Berry's best with a gatefold cover. Germany must surely be the country that has released the most 'greatest hits' album compilations. I would love to know how many albums Berry has sold in this country.

CHUCK BERRY
Pickup [Bellaphon] BPU-14001 • 1976
Around And Around / Roll Over Beethoven / Rock And Roll Music / Johnny B. Goode / Sweet Little Sixteen / Maybellene / She Once Was Mine / Brown Eyed Handsome Man / Too Pooped To Pop+ / Back In The USA / Dear Dad / It's My Own Business

  'Too Pooped To Pop' is credited to Berry.

CHUCK BERRY LIVE IN CONCERT [2-LP]
Bellaphon BLS-5573 • 1979
  Same tracks as the 1978 US 2-LP [Magnum MR-703]. Different gatefold cover. Germany is the only country outside the USA to issue this (in)famous LP in its original form.

ROCKIT
Atco ATL-50.648 ● 1979
Same cover and tracks as the 1979 US LP [Atco SD-38.118].

20 SUPER HITS
Chess 6.24372-AP ● 1980
Johnny B. Goode / Roll Over Beethoven / School Day / Maybellene / Rock And Roll Music / Oh Baby Doll / Too Much Monkey Business / Carol / Let It Rock / Sweet Little Rock And Roller / My Ding-A-Ling *(live, single edit)* / Reelin' And Rockin' / No Particular Place To Go / Sweet Little Sixteen / Little Queenie / Brown Eyed Handsome Man / Nadine / Too Pooped To Pop+ / Back In The USA / Bye Bye Johnny

Also issued on CD [Chess 8.24372-ZR] circa 1988.

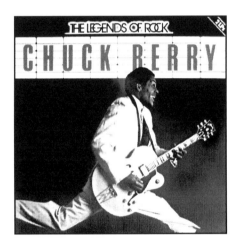

THE LEGENDS OF ROCK [2-LP]
Chess 6.28500-DP ● 1980
❶ Maybellene / No Money Down / Too Much Monkey Business / You Can't Catch Me / Wee Wee Hours / Deep Feeling *(instr)* / Roll Over Beethoven / Rock And Roll Music / Sweet Little Sixteen *(alt. take)* / Around And Around / Little Queenie / Johnny B. Goode
❷ Almost Grown / Carol / Blues For Hawaiians *(instr)* / Worried Life Blues+ / Down The Road A Piece+ / Driftin' Blues+ / Let It Rock / Come On / I Got To Find My Baby+ / I Love You / Mean Old World+ / Chuck's Beat *(with Bo Diddley) (instr, album version)*

This is a good compilation of Berry tracks, but as was often the case on German issues, most of the earlier songs are destroyed by electronic stereo. 'Sweet Little Sixteen' is the unreleased take that first appeared on the 1979 bootleg LP, AMERICA'S HOTTEST WAX [Reelin' 001], and later on the 1983 UK legal release [Chess CXMP-2011]. However, the Germans were actually the very first to issue this version legally. Good liner notes by Norbert Hess (in German only), who also provided the picture of Berry on the inside of the gatefold cover. Great pictures of Berry on the back cover. (Berry is also featured on the Bo Diddley LEGENDS OF ROCK compilation [Chess 6.28524] on the cut, 'Bo's Beat'.)

ROCK! ROCK! ROCK'N'ROLL!
Mercury 6463 044 • 1980
Maybellene / Back In The USA / Johnny B. Goode / Rock And Roll Music / Carol / Sweet Little Sixteen / Roll Over Beethoven / Reelin' And Rockin' / Let It Rock / Sweet Little Rock And Roller / Oh Baby Doll *(Chess)* / Goodnight, Well It's Time To Go [It's Time To Go]

Mostly Mercury recordings. The Mercury version of 'Let It Rock' was issued here for the very first time. For some unknown reason, they also included the Chess version of 'Oh Baby Doll' in dreadful electronic stereo! Plus the main picture of Berry is the wrong way round.

BACK IN THE USA
Time Wind F-50009 • 1981
Back In The USA / Good Lookin' Woman / Sweet Little Rock And Roller / I Do Really Love You / Oh Baby Doll / Thirty Days / Goodnight, Well It's Time To Go [It's Time To Go] / Back To Memphis / My Heart Will Always Belong To You+ / Reelin' And Rockin'

Mercury recordings. 'Good Lookin' Woman' is mistitled 'Good Lovin' Woman'. They've probably got that from the 1974 US LP, WILD BERRYS [Pickwick SPC-3392], where the error appeared the first time. This LP was also issued on Vintage F-50009 with almost the same cover. This is the same compilation of tracks that was issued in Denmark in 1983 as a picture disc with the same catalogue number. See also 1984 2-LP, BACK IN THE USA [Historia DLP2-773] and Danish discography.

PROFILE – CHUCK BERRY
Chess 6.24472-AL • 1981
Memphis, Tennessee / Bye Bye Johnny / I'm Talking About You / Reelin' And Rockin' / Down The Road A Piece+ / Let It Rock / Go, Go, Go / School Day / Sweet Little Sixteen / Havana Moon / Thirty Days / Confessin' The Blues+

Terrible electronic stereo! 'Go, Go, Go' is with the overdubbed live audience.

Chuck Berry & Bo Diddley
TWO GREAT GUITARS
Chess 515 023-AO • 1981
Same tracks and cover as the 1964 US LP [Checker LPS-2991].

AFTER SCHOOL SESSION
Chess 515 030-AO ● 1981
    Same tracks and cover as the 1957 US LP [Chess LP-1426].

ONE DOZEN BERRYS
Chess 515 031-AO ● 1981
    Same tracks and cover as the 1958 US LP [Chess LP-1432].

NEW JUKE BOX HITS
Chess 515 032-AO ● 1981
    Same tracks and cover as the 1961 US LP [Chess LP-1456].

ST. LOUIS TO LIVERPOOL
Chess 515 034-AO ● 1981
    Same tracks and cover as the 1964 US LP [Chess LPS-1488].

ST. LOUIE TO FRISCO TO MEMPHIS
Karussell 2872 103 ● 1981
Louie To Frisco / Flying Home+ *(instr)* / Fillmore Blues *(live, instr)* / Check Me Out / Little Fox / Johnny B. Goode / C.C. Rider+ / Misery / Ma Dear / Soul Rockin' / My Tambourine / Back To Memphis

    Mercury recordings. Single album (the original US compilation was a double).

AUSGEWÄHLTE GOLDSTÜCKE
Karussell 2876 035 ● 1982
Sweet Little Sixteen / Carol / Soul Rockin' / Ramblin' Rose+ / I Can't Believe / C.C. Rider *(live)* / Louie To Frisco / Little Fox / Wee Baby Blues+ *(live)* / Ma Dear / My Tambourine / Back To Memphis

    Mercury recordings.

THE LONDON CHUCK BERRY SESSIONS
Chess 6.24722-AS ● 1982
    Same tracks and gatefold cover as the 1972 US LP [Chess CH-60020].

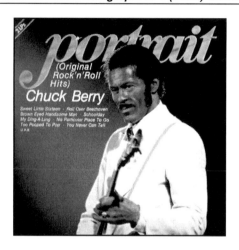

PORTRAIT – ORIGINAL ROCK'N'ROLL HITS [2-LP]
Chess 6.28584-DO • 1982
❶ Sweet Little Sixteen / School Day / Oh Baby Doll / Brown Eyed Handsome Man / Rock And Roll Music / Jo Jo Gunne / Sweet Little Rock And Roller / Roll Over Beethoven / Carol / Reelin' And Rockin' / Merry Christmas Baby+ / Anthony Boy / Almost Grown
❷ Johnny B. Goode / Little Queenie / Back In The USA / Let It Rock / Too Pooped To Pop+ / Nadine / No Particular Place To Go / My Ding-A-Ling *(live, single edit)* / You Never Can Tell / Little Marie / Promised Land / Dear Dad / Bye Bye Johnny

Side 4 (starting with 'My Ding-A-Ling') features the stereo versions, except for 'Bye Bye Johnny'. The rest are mono, or rather electronic stereo. 'Merry Christmas Baby' is the single version.

AFTER SCHOOL SESSION / ONE DOZEN BERRYS [2-LP]
Chess 6.28595-DT • 1982
Gatefold cover comprising the two original US covers. Same tracks as the original US LPs from 1957 and 1958 [Chess LP-1426 and LP-1432 respectively]. The sound is in electronic stereo. The back cover tells us that both albums were first published in 1956, which is not correct for either album.

ON STAGE / ROCKIN' AT THE HOPS [2-LP]
Chess 6.28596-DT • 1982
Gatefold cover comprising the two original US covers. Same tracks as the original US LPs from 1963 and 1960 [Chess LP-1480 and LP-1448 respectively], except that 'How High The Moon' is not included on the ON STAGE LP. Again the sound is in electronic stereo. On the back cover it says that this was first published in 1956, which of course is wrong. (Note: There is a strange issue involving this album and the one above. Dietmar Rudolph has come across a 2-LP set with the cover of ON STAGE/ROCKIN' AT THE HOPS but containing the discs for AFTER SCHOOL SESSION/ONE DOZEN BERRYS. Even more strangely, the album cover has the correct catalogue number for AFTER SCHOOL SESSION/ONE DOZEN BERRYS!)

GREATEST HITS [2-LP]
Time Wind DB-50126 • 1982
Record 1 is the 1982 UK LP, CHUCK BERRY LIVE [Everest CBR-1007] featuring live recordings from the 1969 *Toronto Rock & Roll Revival* show. Record 2 is the 1981 (West German) LP, BACK IN THE USA [Time Wind F-50009] featuring Mercury recordings. Great and unusual picture of Berry on the front cover.

MOTIVE
Mercury 6463 129 • 1982
Roll Over Beethoven / Sweet Little Rock And Roller / Louie To Frisco / Back To Memphis / Wee Baby Blues+ *(live)* / Johnny B. Goode / Club Nitty Gritty / Sweet Little Sixteen / School Day / Feelin' It *(live, instr)* / Let It Rock / Carol

Part of a series featuring everybody from Gentle Giant and Lee Hazlewood to Paul Mauriat and Zarah Leander. Apart from a goode cover, the album itself is not important – not even in a serious Berry collection (?)

SWEET LITTLE ROCK'N'ROLLER [2-LP]
Mercury 6619 039 • 1982
❶ Maybellene / Back In The USA / Johnny B. Goode / Rock And Roll Music / Roll Over Beethoven / Reelin' And Rockin' / Club Nitty Gritty / Sweet Little Sixteen / School Day / Feelin' It *(live, instr)* / Let It Rock / Carol
❷ Concerto In B Goode *(instr)* / Sweet Little Rock And Roller / Little Fox / It's Too Dark In There / It Hurts Me Too+ *(live, duet with Steve Miller)* / Oh Baby Doll *(Chess)* / Goodnight, Well It's Time To Go [It's Time To Go]

Another repackaging of Mercury tracks – plus one from Chess. 'Concerto In B Goode' takes up the whole of Side 3. Gatefold cover with some interesting pictures, including several previously unseen.

TAKEOFF – LIVE IN TORONTO
RCA International NL-45338 • 1982
Reelin' And Rockin' / Maybellene / Rock And Roll Music / My Ding-A-Ling / Too Much Monkey Business / Nadine / School Day / *Medley:* Johnny B. Goode – Carol – Promised Land / Sweet Little Sixteen

The 1969 *Toronto Rock & Roll Revival* again.

ROCK'N'ROLL SUPERSTAR – CHUCK BERRY
Chess Club Edition 46.675.5 • 1983
Rock And Roll Music / Roll Over Beethoven / Johnny B. Goode / School Day / No Particular Place To Go / Oh Baby Doll / Carol / Reelin' And Rockin' / My Ding-A-Ling *(live, single edit)* / Sweet Little Rock And Roller / Let It Rock / Sweet Little Sixteen / Maybellene / Nadine / Too Pooped To Pop+ / Back In The USA

This has almost the same front cover as the 1980 2-LP, THE LEGENDS OF ROCK [Chess 6.28500-DP]. The back cover includes a short list of various artists and groups who have recorded Berry's songs. However, Stanley Clarke has most definitely *not* recorded 'School Day'!

BACK IN THE USA [2-LP]
Historia DLP2-773 • 1984
Contains the same Mercury tracks as the 1981 LP, BACK IN THE USA [Time Wind F-50009], and the following Chess tracks on Record 2: 'Maybellene', 'Roll Over Beethoven', 'Too Much Monkey Business', 'You Can't Catch Me', 'School Day', 'Rock And Roll Music', 'Sweet Little Sixteen', 'Johnny B. Goode, 'Around And Around', 'Beautiful Delilah', 'Carol' and 'Run Rudolph Run'. The two vinyl albums in this set are identical to Berry LPs released in Denmark in the mid-'80s, but with slight cover and title variations. Both records have 'NCB' (Nordic Copyright Broadcasting) printed on the labels, which indicates Scandinavia. However, the cover here looks German and probably is, so we can assume they produced their own gatefold cover and repackaged the two LPs from Denmark. I'm sure this must have been a collaboration between Denmark and Germany. 'Run Rudolph Run' is credited to *'C. Berry– M. Brodie'*. See also Time Wind F-50009 and Danish discography.

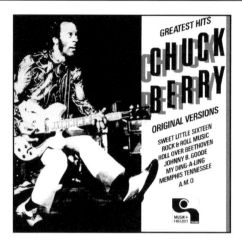

GREATEST HITS – ORIGINAL VERSIONS
Chess [Teldec] 6.26004-AF • 1984
Sweet Little Sixteen / Rock And Roll Music / Carol / You Never Can Tell / Reelin' And Rockin' / No Particular Place To Go / Roll Over Beethoven / Memphis, Tennessee / School Day / Johnny B. Goode / Nadine / My Ding-A-Ling *(live, single edit)*

These are the original versions okay, but we all hate electronic stereo!

CHUCK BERRY SPECIAL [2-LP]
World Star Collection DLP1-773/ DLP2-773 • 1985
This is the 1981 LP, BACK IN THE USA [Time Wind F-50009] again, plus the 1984 picture disc LP, JOHNNY B. GOODE [All Round Trading DLP-2-773]. Different cover, gatefold. I actually thought this was from Denmark, but the cover says '*Seite A/B/C/D'*. It seems that some of the albums on Time Wind and All Round Trading were issued in both Germany and Denmark at the same time, sometimes using the same pictures for different LP titles, and also packaging the Danish albums inside German covers. Sometimes it is difficult to decide which country to list them under.

ROCK'N'ROLL RARITIES [2-LP]
Chess 254 200-1 • 1986
Same tracks and cover as the 1986 US 2-LP, ROCK'N'ROLL RARITIES [Chess CH2-92521].

HAIL! HAIL! ROCK'N'ROLL
MCA 255 182-1 • 1987
Original soundtrack. Same tracks and cover as all the other issues of this album. In Germany, this LP also came with a sticker on the front cover saying '*Recorded live in October 1986. Produced by Keith Richards.*' Also issued on CD [MCA 222 182-2].

THAT GOOD OLD TIMES – CHUCK BERRY LIVE
Bellaphon 230-07-126 • 1988
Rock And Roll Music / Sweet Little Sixteen / Nadine / School Day / My Ding-A-Ling / Memphis, Tennessee / *Medley:* Johnny B. Goode – Carol – Promised Land / Reelin' And Rockin' / Maybellene

The 1969 *Toronto Rock & Roll Revival* again. Also issued on CD [Bellaphon 288-07-126].

HAIL! HAIL! ROCK'N'ROLL [2-LP]
ZYX 20116 • 1989

Not the movie soundtrack. Same as the 1988 UK 2-LP [Chess DETD-207]. Also issued on CD [ZYX 9067].

THE VERY BEST OF CHUCK BERRY
Bellaphon 230-07-171 • 1991

Rock And Roll Music / Back In The USA / Maybellene / Reelin' And Rockin' / Let It Rock / Sweet Little Sixteen / School Day / Johnny B. Goode / You Never Can Tell / Roll Over Beethoven / Carol / My Ding-A-Ling *(live, album version)*

Chess tracks. Also issued on CD [Bellaphon 288-07-171].

ANOTHER MYSTERY BOX SET

BIO
Number unknown • Germany(?), date unknown

This box set was brought to my attention by Dietmar Rudolph when it came up for sale on eBay in 2004. I have no idea what this particular set was all about or when it came out. The seller described it as an 11-LP box consisting of the GOLDEN DECADE albums 'VOLUMES 1-6' (ie the three double albums), ROCK'N'ROLL RARITIES (VOLUMES 1&2), NEW JUKE BOX HITS, BIO and the 1984 Danish BABY DOLL picture disc. The latter especially made me suspicious as it contains Mercury recordings; all the others are Chess. As I haven't seen this I don't know if the albums came in a box or some other kind of packaging. The front cover of the 'Bio' album was portrayed on eBay. There's no mention of any record number or label, which is understandable since this had to be something put together by someone who thought they could make some easy money.

CD Albums

HAIL! HAIL! ROCK'N'ROLL
MCA 255 182-2 • 1987

Original soundtrack. Same tracks and cover as all the other issues of this album. In Germany this LP also came with a sticker on the front cover saying *'Recorded live in October 1986. Produced by Keith Richards.'* Also issued on LP [MCA 222 182-1].

THAT GOOD OLD TIMES – CHUCK BERRY LIVE
Bellaphon 288-07-126 • 1988

Rock And Roll Music / Sweet Little Sixteen / Nadine / School Day / My Ding-A-Ling / Memphis, Tennessee / *Medley:* Johnny B. Goode – Carol – Promised Land / Reelin' And Rockin' / Maybellene

The 1969 *Toronto Rock & Roll Revival* again. Also issued on LP [Bellaphon 230-07-126].

20 SUPER HITS
Chess 8.24372-ZR • 1988?

Same tracks and cover as the 1980 LP [Chess 6.24372-AP].

JOHNNY B. GOODE
Karussell 839 218-2 • 1989

A combination of Chess tracks and live material from the 1969 *Toronto Rock & Roll Revival*. Poor sound quality, and the songs are not even worth mentioning.

HAIL! HAIL! ROCK'N'ROLL
ZYX 9067 • 1989

Not the movie soundtrack. Same as the 1988 UK 2-LP [Chess DETD-207]. Also issued on 2-LP [ZYX 20116].

GOLDEN HITS
Mercury 826-256-2 • 1990

Same tracks and cover as the 1989 US CD reissue with four bonus cuts [Mercury 826-256-2]. Pressed in the Netherlands.

CHUCK BERRY IN MEMPHIS
Mercury 836 071-2 • 1990

Same tracks and cover as the 1989 US CD reissue with one bonus cut [Mercury 836-071-2]. Pressed in the Netherlands.

LIVE AT FILLMORE AUDITORIUM
Mercury 836 072-2 • 1990

Same tracks and cover as the 1989 US CD reissue with five bonus cuts [Mercury 836 072-2]. Pressed in the Netherlands.

FROM ST. LOUIE TO FRISCO
Mercury 836 073-2 • 1990

Same tracks and cover as the 1989 US CD reissue with four bonus cuts [Mercury 836 073-2]. Pressed in the Netherlands.

CONCERTO IN B GOODE
Mercury 836 074-2 • 1990

Same tracks and cover as the 1989 US CD reissue [Mercury 836 074-2]. Pressed in the Netherlands.

THE VERY BEST OF CHUCK BERRY
Bellaphon 288-07-171 • 1991

Rock And Roll Music / Back In The USA / Maybellene / Reelin' And Rockin' / Let It Rock / Sweet Little Sixteen / School Day / Johnny B. Goode / You Never Can Tell / Roll Over Beethoven / Carol / My Ding-A-Ling *(live, album version)*

Chess tracks. Also issued on LP [Bellaphon 230-07-171].

KING OF ROCK'N'ROLL GUITAR
Galaxis GLX-9052 • 1991

17 Mercury tracks with really terrible sound quality! To be quite honest, this is one of those releases you *don't* need. The cover isn't any good either.

THE COLLECTION
MCA MCD-17751 ● 1991
Maybellene / Roll Over Beethoven / School Day / Sweet Little Rock And Roller / Back In The USA / Little Queenie / Promised Land *(stereo)* / My Ding-A-Ling *(live, single edit)* / No Particular Place To Go / You Never Can Tell *(stereo)* / Rock And Roll Music / Sweet Little Sixteen / Nadine / Johnny B. Goode / Carol / Memphis, Tennessee

Chess recordings. A good compilation of Berry's greatest. Unfortunately some of the tracks are in dreadful electronic stereo (and this as recently as 1991!).

Chuck Berry & Bo Diddley
TWO GREAT GUITARS
MCA MCD-09170 ● 1992
Chess recordings. Reissue with four additional instrumental tracks, three by Diddley and one by Berry ('Chuckwalk'). Same tracks and cover as the 1992 US CD [Chess CHD-9170].

BERRY IS ON TOP
MCA MCD-30487 ● 1993
Chess Recordings. 20 tracks. Contains the 12 songs from the original 1950 US LP, BERRY IS ON TOP [Chess LP-1435], plus the following additional tracks: 'Down The Road A Piece', 'No Money Down', 'Down Bound Train', 'Jaguar And The Thunderbird', 'Things I Used To Do' *(stereo)*, 'No Particular Place To Go', 'Fraulein' *(stereo)*' and 'Nadine'. Same front cover as the original US LP. New liner notes by Colin Escott. 'Down The Road A Piece' is the short, faded version. This CD was also released in France in 1993, and in the UK in 1994.

MR. ROCK'N'ROLL
Laserlight 12.190 ● 1993
Again, a combination of eight original Chess tracks and seven live cuts from the 1969 *Toronto Rock & Roll Revival*. The sound quality is not that good either. The songs are not worth mentioning; however, the picture of Berry on the front cover is quite good.

GREATEST HITS
Legend WZ-90070 ● 1993
18 original Chess tracks. Nothing fancy, and you don't need this if you have any of his other 'greatest hits' or 'best of' compilations. It keeps the music of the Legend alive, though.

THE BEST OF CHUCK BERRY
MCA MCD-19510 ● 1994
Same tracks and cover as the 1994 UK CD [MCA MCBD-19510] featuring 20 Chess classics. See also UK discography.

ROLL OVER BEETHOVEN
Back Biter BB-61003 • 1995
Maybellene / Roll Over Beethoven / Oh Baby Doll / Let It Rock / School Day / Sweet Little Sixteen / Johnny B. Goode / Rock And Roll Music / Carol / Sweet Little Rock And Roller / Little Queenie / Around And Around / I'm Talking About You / Route 66+ / Run Rudolph Run+ / Memphis, Tennessee / Thirty Days / Bye Bye Johnny

Nice compilation of Chess tracks with good sound quality. Great cover and pictures! 'Run Rudolph Run' is credited to *'Berry–Brodie'*, just like the original US Chess single.

Shabba Ranks
A MI SHABBA
Epic 477482-2 • 1995
See French discography.

JAZZ ON A SUMMER'S DAY –
   HIGHLIGHTS FROM THE ORIGINAL FILM SOUNDTRACK
Charly CDGR-196 • 1998
See *Various Artists CD Albums.*

ANTHOLOGY [2-CD]
MCA [Universal] 112 304-2 • 2000
Same tracks and cover as the 2000 US 2-CD set on MCA 088 112 304-2. This was made in the EU, which means you could buy it in several countries in Europe, even in Norway.

GREATEST HITS
Hit Box – ZYX Music HIB-10114-2 • 2004
Maybellene / Oh Baby Doll / Beautiful Delilah / No Particular Place To Go / Rip It Up+ / Brown Eyed Handsome Man / Roll Over Beethoven / School Day / Sweet Little Sixteen / Reelin' And Rockin' / Johnny B. Goode / Sweet Little Rock And Roller / Back In The USA / Nadine / Bye Bye Johnny *(stereo)* / You Never Can Tell / Promised Land / Little Queenie

'Rip It Up' is a long way from being a 'greatest hit' by Berry and should be ignored by every compiler. Interesting to note that they actually managed to include the stereo version of 'Bye Bye Johnny', which is very rare indeed. No recording info on the cover, and the standard black and white picture of Berry looking straight at you, knees bent, on the front.

346

GOLD
Geffen [Universal] 0602498805589 ● 2005
Same tracks and cover as the 2005 2-CD on Geffen B0004364-02. Made in the EU, which means you could buy it in several countries in Europe, even in Norway.

CHUCK BERRY ROCKS
Vintage RocknRoll GTR-39508 ● 2007
Maybellene / Roll Over Beethoven / Down Bound Train / Too Much Monkey Business / Brown Eyed Handsome Man / Wee Wee Hours / Thirty Days / No Money Down / Drifting Heart / Havana Moon / Together (We Will Always Be) / You Can't Catch Me / Oh Maria+ / I Hope These Words Will Find You Well+

With five ballads and blues tracks this is not much of a rockin' album, and if you add the two last tracks with Joe Alexander & The Cubans from 1954 featuring 'Charles Berryn' on rhythm guitar, it becomes fifty/fifty. Therefore it's not really a representative album to show off Berry as a composer and songwriter. However, it *is* interesting to have the two tracks from '54 on one album, although you can hear that they are dubbed from disc.

I haven't kept up with the CD releases in Germany, and there were certainly more issues between 1995 and 2007. However, I believe very few are of special interest to collectors.

Various Artists Singles

Memphis, Tennessee
ZYX 'Golden Oldies Revival' 1943-7 ● 1987
Chess cut. Art cover. Flip is 'Barefootin' ' by Robert Parker. Most of the releases in this series were '60s artists/music, with catalogue numbers starting at 1901-7 and ending at 1960-7. See also *Singles.*

Various Artists LPs

There must surely be hundreds of compilation albums in Germany featuring a song or two by Berry. I have only included the ones I feel that are of particular interest to the Berry collector.

ROCK AROUND THE CLUB
Philips 6300 081 • 1973
Misery

Mercury recording. No picture of Berry or any of the other artists, but the album is listed here because of the unusual inclusion of this obscure Berry track, and also the variety of non-rock'n'roll performers. Other artists include Jerry Lee Lewis, Mama Lion, Graham Bell, Atomic Rooster, the Rattles, Rod Stewart, Status Quo, the Spencer Davis Group, the Sensational Alex Harvey Band, Nazareth and Atlantis.

Chuck Berry – Bo Diddley – Jerry Lee Lewis – Carl Perkins
4 ROCK GIANTS – TALKS & HITS
Bellaphon BI-15119 • 1973
Berry interview / Maybellene / Sweet Little Sixteen / School Day

Chess recordings. Picture of Berry on the cover. Interview with Berry probably taped on 20 January 1973 at the Hilton Hotel in Amsterdam, Netherlands. The interview is only available on this album and on the original 1973 Dutch bootleg release, ROCK SMUK [Sun/Chess NQCS-1], which has a different cover. Also contains interviews and tracks by Jerry Lee Lewis, Bo Diddley and Carl Perkins. See *Section 4 (Bootlegs)* for more information.

Chuck Berry – Jerry Lee Lewis – Fats Domino
ROCK'N'ROLL
Fontana 701 629-WPY • 1974
Mercury recordings with overdubbed live audience. Same tracks and cover as the 1969 UK LP [Fontana SFL-13120]. Picture of Berry on the cover.

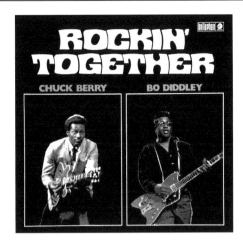

Chuck Berry – Bo Diddley
ROCKIN' TOGETHER
Bellaphon Bl-1557 • 1974
Chuck Berry: Reelin' And Rockin' / Tulane / Childhood Sweetheart / I'm A Rocker / Don't You Lie To Me+ / Let's Do Our Thing Together /
Bo Diddley: Hey Bo Diddley / I'm A Man / She's Alright / Road Runner / I'm Looking For A Woman / Bo Diddley

Berry is on Side 1, and Diddley on Side 2. A misleading title, as the two men do not 'rock together' on any of the tracks. 'Don't You Lie To Me' is credited to Berry.

Chuck Berry – Bill Haley – Little Richard
THE KINGS OF ROCK'N'ROLL [2-LP]
Bellaphon BLS-5516 • 1975
Johnny B. Goode / School Day / Around And Around / No Particular Place To Go / Wee Wee Hours / Sweet Little Sixteen / Roll Over Beethoven / Reelin' And Rockin' / Dear Dad / Brown Eyed Handsome Man / Havana Moon / Rock And Roll Music

Chess recordings. Picture of Berry on the cover. One side contains Bill Haley live recordings licensed from Sonet Records in Sweden, another consists of Little Richard live recordings licensed from Modern in the USA. Berry has the remaining two sides.

WORLDSTAR-SESSION (VOLUME 1: LIVE USA)
Imtrat 880.08 • 1981
My Ding-A-Ling *(live, edited – 3:21)*

The 1969 *Toronto Rock & Roll Revival* again. This is also quite an intriguing compilation featuring mostly non-rock'n'roll artists alongside Berry. There are also a couple of Berry songs. No pictures of artists. Other artists (all live recordings) include Dire Straits, Bruce Springsteen, Rod Stewart ('Sweet Little Rock And Roller', 1974), Fleetwood Mac, Peter Gabriel, Atomic Rooster, Billy Idol, Stevie Wonder, Frank Zappa, the Animals ('I Got To Find My Baby', 1963) and the Rolling Stones.

OLDIES BUT GOLDIES
Chess 6.24403-AQ • 1981
Bye Bye Johnny / Reelin' And Rockin' / Maybellene

OLDIES BUT GOLDIES
Chess 6.24497-AQ • 1981
Sweet Little Sixteen / Roll Over Beethoven / Johnny B. Goode / Rock And Roll Music

BLACK & WHITE BLUES – THE LITTLE RED ROOSTER [2-LP]
Chess 6.28537-DP • 1981
Mean Old World**+**

Great album with the best of the black and white blues artists. Sides 1 and 2 have a black label and feature black performers, while sides 3 and 4 have white labels and feature white artists. I like it that they have included the above Berry recording because it's one of my all-time favourites. If you want to convince anyone that Berry really could sing and play the blues, this is it! Liner notes in German. Several pictures, but unfortunately no Berry. Other artists on the 'black' sides include Howlin' Wolf (2), Otis Spann, Elmore James, Bo Diddley, Willie Mabon, Eddie Boyd, Muddy Waters, John Lee Hooker, Tommy Tucker, Sonny Boy Williamson, Otis Rush, Little Walter, Big Bill Broonzy and Washboard Sam. White artists include Alexis Korner's Blues Incorporated, John Mayall's Bluesbreakers, Eric Burdon & The Animals, Rod Stewart, Canned Heat, Peter Green, Ten Years After, Captain Beefheart & His Magic Band, Eric Clapton, Savoy Brown, Johnny Winter, Das Dritte Ohr, Them and the Rolling Stones.

Chuck Berry – Bill Haley – Fats Domino – Little Richard
THE GIANTS OF ROCK'N'ROLL – DIE SUPER-HITS DER GROSSEN 4
K-Tel TG-1367 • 1982
Sweet Little Sixteen *(demo)* / Rock And Roll Music / Johnny B. Goode / Roll Over Beethoven

Chess recordings. Also includes cuts by Bill Haley And His Comets (5), Fats Domino (4) and Little Richard (5). Drawing of Berry on the cover.

THE GREATEST HITS OF ROCK'N'ROLL [2-LP]
RCA International NL-45337 • 1982
Too Much Monkey Business / Nadine / Maybellene / School Day

The 1969 *Toronto Rock & Roll Revival* again, plus a very dull gatefold cover with a picture of Berry on the inside. Other artists include Little Richard (7), Jerry Lee Lewis (7, including 'Sweet Little Sixteen'), Bill Haley And His Comets (5) and Roy Orbison (3).

K-TEL ROCK'N'ROLL SHOW
K-Tel TG-155 • 1982
Sweet Little Sixteen / Memphis, Tennessee / Johnny B. Goode

25 Chess studio recordings, mostly big ones and a few that ain't. Either way, you've heard them all before. Interesting cover picture, but not worth the price of the album, so...

REAL STONES [2-LP]
Provogue PRL-7012-1 • 1989
Come On / Bye Bye Johnny / Route 66**+** / Carol / Confessin' The Blues**+** / Around And Around / Don't You Lie To Me**+** / Memphis, Tennessee / Roll Over Beethoven / Down The Road A Piece**+** / You Can't Catch Me / I'm Talking About You / Little Queenie / Let it Rock / Run Rudolph Run**+**

Now this is interesting. A compilation of 30 tracks that inspired the Rolling Stones. 15 are by Berry – including four that he didn't write – although I don't think that they got 'Confessin' The Blues' from him. Good booklet with pictures of Chuck, Marshall Chess and Muddy Waters, Howlin' Wolf, Willie Dixon, Dale Hawkins, Bo Diddley, Barrett Strong and Arthur Alexander. Also issued on CD [Provogue PRD-7012-2].

Various Artists CD Albums

REAL STONES
Provogue PRD-7012-2 • 1989
Come On / Bye Bye Johnny / Route 66+ / Carol / Confessin' The Blues+ / Around And Around / Don't You Lie To Me+ / Memphis, Tennessee / Roll Over Beethoven / Down The Road A Piece+ / You Can't Catch Me / I'm Talking About You / Little Queenie / Let it Rock / Run Rudolph Run+

Now this is interesting. A compilation of 30 tracks that inspired the Rolling Stones. 15 are by Berry – including four that he didn't write – although I don't think that they got 'Confessin' The Blues' from him. Good booklet with pictures of Chuck, Marshall Chess and Muddy Waters, Howlin' Wolf, Willie Dixon, Dale Hawkins, Bo Diddley, Barrett Strong and Arthur Alexander. Also issued on 2-LP [Provogue PRL-7012-1].

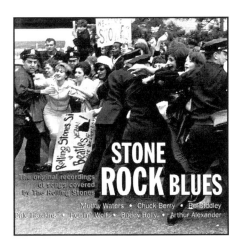

STONE ROCK BLUES
Chess [MCA] MCD-09347 • 1994
Carol / Little Queenie / Around And Around / You Can't Catch Me / Come On / I'm Talking About You / Bye Bye Johnny

'The original recordings of songs covered by the Rolling Stones', so reads the front cover. 17 tracks by artists like Muddy Waters (5), Bo Diddley (2), Howlin' Wolf, Arthur Alexander, Dale Hawkins and Buddy Holly. As always, when it comes to the Stones, Berry songs are in the majority. Reissue produced and compiled by Andy McKaie, which means quality work. Original mono tracks. Berry picture on the back cover and also in the booklet. Informative session and record discography for each track. The number CHD-9347 which is printed on the cover indicates that this first came out in the US, but I have never seen a copy.

JAZZ ON A SUMMER'S DAY –
HIGHLIGHTS FROM THE ORIGINAL FILM SOUNDTRACK
Charly CDGR-196 • 1998
Sweet Little Sixteen (*live*)

Recorded live at the *Newport Jazz Festival* on 5 July 1958. As far as I know, this particular CD was only released in Germany. Informative liner notes by David Shrimpton. This Berry track plus three others were previously included on a Swedish CD as far back as 1992 [Phontastic PHONT NCD-8815]. See also Swedish discography.

GESCHICHTE DER POPULÄREN MUSIK [52-CD]
Bear Family BCD-16300 • 1998
Introduction / Chuck Berry Interview 1 / Beach Boys – Beatles – Stones – Hendrix medley / Bio / Chuck Berry Interview 2 / Johnny B. Goode / One O'Clock Jump+ / Down The Road A Piece+ / Chuck Berry Interview 3 / Drifting Heart / Beans And Cornbread (*Louis Jordan*) / Jaguar And The Thunderbird / Ain't That Just Like A Woman (*Louis Jordan*) / Blue Light Boogie (*Louis Jordan*) / Chuck Berry Interview 4 / Ida Red (*Pete Seeger*) / Maybellene / Roll Over Beethoven / School Day / The Yellow Rose Of Texas (*Mitch Miller*) / On Top Of Old Smokey (*Mitch Miller*)

Yes, this is a (*very* expensive) 52-CD set of a German radio series titled *'The History of Popular Music'*. It consists of all 52 shows as broadcast by Radio Bremen between 1984 and 1986, along with a 300+ page book containing a complete transcript of each show. Chuck Berry is featured on CD 15 (tracks listed above), which also includes some lengthy spoken passages. The Berry interview segments are from a 1972 interview conducted by Radio Bremen. Several pictures of Berry are also included in the book, two of which I haven't seen before.

STAR-CLUB HAMBURG 1960-69 [3-CD]
Star-Club 585 878 • 2001
Maybellene / Sweet Little Rock And Roller

The legendary Star-Club in Hamburg opened on 13 April 1962 and launched its own record label in 1964. This is a good set featuring many of the American, English and German artists and groups who have played at this famous club. Berry played the Star-Club on 5 June 1964, and there are some great pictures of him from that gig. Unfortunately, the tracks by him here are the original Chess recordings, so offer nothing new. I haven't heard this set, so I can't vouch for the other tracks.

ELVIS' FAVORITES
Traditional Line TL-1368 • 2003
Promised Land

23 originals later recorded by Elvis, although some are a little dubious. A few of the songs on this compilation are *not* the originals, but rather the hit versions that Elvis listened to and subsequently recorded. Anyhow, this CD has a good selection of country and rhythm & blues songs and features titles by Arthur 'Big Boy' Crudup, Bill Monroe, the Drifters, Jack Greene, Chuck Willis, Arthur Gunter, Ketty Lester, Carl Perkins and others.

RUDOLPH THE RED NOSED REINDEER
Bear Family BCD-16718AR • 2005
Run Rudolph Run+

A compilation of 27 versions of the title song! I won't list all the featured artists here, but will just tell you that you get the original by Gene Autry (of course), and versions as diverse as Perry Como, the Chipmunks and Fats Domino. There are also three Rudolph-related songs: Johnny Horton's 'They Shined Up Rudolph's Nose', Homer & Jethro's 'Randolph, The Flat-Nosed Reindeer' and Berry's 'Run Rudolph Run'. The full story of the song is, of course, contained in the accompanying booklet. However, we still get no clue as to exactly what happened with the copyright of 'Run Rudolph Run'.

Bear Family have done it again with the amazing *'Blowing The Fuse'* series, covering 1945 to 1960. Beautiful digipak covers and thick booklets with pictures and stories of each song. A must for any serious collector.

29 R&B CLASSICS THAT ROCKED THE JUKEBOX IN 1955
Bear Family BCD-16710AS • 2005
Maybellene

30 R&B CLASSICS THAT ROCKED THE JUKEBOX IN 1956
Bear Family BCD-16711AS • 2006
Roll Over Beethoven

31 R&B CLASSICS THAT ROCKED THE JUKEBOX IN 1957
Bear Family BCD-16712AS • 2006
School Day

31 R&B CLASSICS THAT ROCKED THE JUKEBOX IN 1958
Bear Family BCD-16713AS • 2006
Johnny B. Goode

29 R&B CLASSICS THAT ROCKED THE JUKEBOX IN 1959
Bear Family BCD-16714AS • 2006
Almost Grown

GREECE

LPs

ROCKIT
Atlantic 50648 • 1980
Same tracks and cover as the 1979 US LP [Atco SD-38.118].

CD Albums

20 SUPER HITS
Unknown label and catalogue number • 1996
Same tracks and same front cover as the 1980 German LP [Chess 6.24372] and 1988 CD [Chess 8.24372-ZR]. I picked this information up from the Internet, where it said that this CD was a promo-only release given away with a Greek magazine in 1996. It has Greek writing on the front and back cover, and on the disc itself, but other than that is not particularly noteworthy.

HUNGARY

LPs

20 SUPER HITS
Gong SLPXL-37480 • 1980
Identical front cover and tracks to the 1980 West German LP, 20 SUPER HITS [Chess 6.24372-AP]. White label with black printing.

INDIA

I don't have anything like a complete list of what's been released in India, however... The London singles below had black labels with silver lettering. The 45 rpm copies I know of have round push-out centres, and are very similar to the original UK issues. The only real difference is that '*Made in India*' is printed at the bottom of the label in small letters.

Singles

Beautiful Delilah / Vacation Time
London HLM-8677 • 1958

Carol / Hey Pedro
London HL-8712 • 1958

Too Pooped To Pop / Let it Rock
London HLM-9069 • 1960

CD Albums

CHUCK BERRY
Unknown label and catalogue number • 1990s
Maybellene / Sweet Little Sixteen / School Day / Rock And Roll Music / Johnny B. Goode / Carol / Memphis, Tennessee / Roll Over Beethoven / Back In The USA / Sweet Little Rock And Roller / Reelin' And Rockin' / C.C. Rider+

Mercury recordings. Unfortunately I haven't seen or heard this album, so can't comment further.

INDONESIA

Cassette Tapes

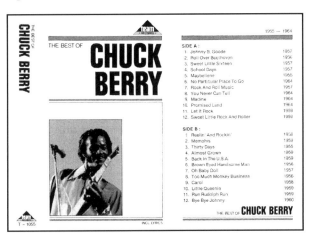

THE BEST OF CHUCK BERRY
Team T-1055 • 1983

Johnny B. Goode / Roll Over Beethoven / Sweet Little Sixteen / School Day / Maybellene / No Particular Place To Go / Rock And Roll Music / You Never Can Tell / Nadine / Promised Land / Let It Rock / Sweet Little Rock And Roller / Reelin' And Rockin' / Memphis, Tennessee / Thirty Days / Almost Grown / Back In The USA / Brown Eyed Handsome Man / Oh Baby Doll / Too Much Monkey Business / Carol / Little Queenie / Run Rudolph Run+ / Bye Bye Johnny

Yeah, this is surely 'the best of', by all means – Chess stuff and all. However, in order to squeeze 12 tracks onto each side of this tape, the songs run too fast. That's a new angle! The booklet has lyrics to all songs (which are in electronic stereo, by the way). 'Let It Rock' is the version without Berry's solo guitar. Either way, it's nice to have something from this country.

357

ISRAEL

Singles

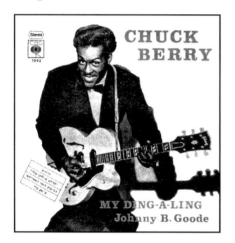

My Ding-A-Ling (*live, single edit*) / **Johnny B. Goode** (*live*)
CBS 1093 • 1972

   Not often you see Chuck Berry on CBS! Picture sleeve.

LPs

GOLDEN HITS
Mercury AN 69-42 • 1967

   Same tracks and cover as the US LP [Mercury MG-21103 / SR-61103]. Black Mercury label with silver lettering, monaural cover but has a gold 'stereo' sticker. The liner notes on the back are the same as on the US release. Made by Hed-Arzi Ltd, Israel.

MOTORVATIN'
Epic EPC-82060 • 1977

   Same tracks and cover as the 1977 UK LP [Chess 9286 690]. Interesting to see a Berry LP on the Epic label! A rare treat.

ITALY

Back in the mid-'80s I didn't know of any singles released in Italy and all I had was a list of six albums! Now the list has grown to a bunch of singles, one EP, and a respectable number of LPs and CDs.

Singles

Derby sleeve, mid-'60s   Derby DB-5115

Too Pooped To Pop / Let It Rock
Argo 1747 • 1961

Rock And Roll Music / Maybellene
Derby DB-5108 • 1965

No Particular Place To Go / School Day
Derby DB-5115 • 1965
This came as a surprise when it surfaced on eBay in January 2007! I'd never seen or heard of this label before. And then DB-5108 above turned up!

Tulane / Have Mercy Judge
Cadet [Durium] DE-2742 • 1970
Also pressed as a jukebox single with white labels ('*Vietata la vendita. Utilizzazione esclusiva per JUKE-BOX*'). Picture sleeve.

My Ding-A-Ling *(live, single edit)* **/ Johnny B. Goode** *(live)*
Cadet [Durium] DE-2790 • 1972
Picture sleeve. Also pressed as a jukebox single with white labels ('*Vietata la vendita. Utilizzazione esclusiva per JUKE-BOX*').

359

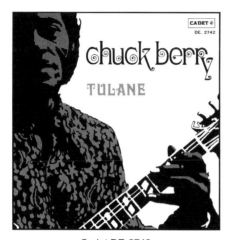

Cadet DE-2742

Cadet DE-2742

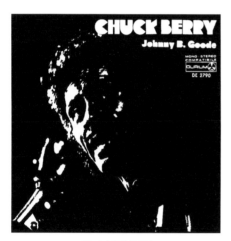

Cadet DE-2790

Cadet DE-2790 (jukebox pressing)

Chess CH-2169

Chess CH-2169

Reelin' And Rockin' *(live, single edit)* / **I Will Not Let You Go**
Cadet [Durium] DE-2796 • 1973
   Picture sleeve.

Reelin' And Rockin' *(live, single edit)*
Durium LdA-7811 • 1973
   This was only a jukebox single. Flip is 'Don't Ha Ha' by Casey Jones.

Shake, Rattle And Roll+ / Baby, What You Want Me To Do+
Chess CH-2169 • 1975
   Picture sleeve (but no Berry). The 'B' side features vocals by Ingrid Gibson Berry and Chuck Berry.

Johnny B. Goode / Roll Over Beethoven
Chess 6078 705 • 1977
   Dark blue label. Art sleeve.

LPs

GOLDEN HITS
Fontana **FPY-858002 • Early 1970s**
   Probably the same tracks as the 1967 US LP, GOLDEN HITS [Mercury SR-61103].

Chuck Berry & Bo Diddley
TWO GREAT GUITARS
Cadet [Durium] 2991 • September 1971
   Same tracks as the 1964 US LP [Checker LPS-2991], but no more information available.

ST. LOUIS TO LIVERPOOL
Cadet [Durium] CQ-20.062 • 1972
   Same tracks as the 1964 US LP [Chess LPS-1488], but with a different front cover. The record number, however, is the same as that used for the 1973 Dutch release.

THE LONDON CHUCK BERRY SESSIONS
Cadet [Durium] CH-60020 • 1972
   Same as the 1989 US reissue [Chess CH-9295], but without the gatefold cover.

ROCK HITS
Fontana Special 6430 022 • 1973
   Same tracks as the 1967 US LP, GOLDEN HITS [Mercury SR-61103], but a different cover. This reissue appeared in many European countries with substantially the same cover but different titles. It was released in 1972 in the Netherlands as ROCK HITS [Fontana International 6430 022], in West Germany as ATTENTION! [Fontana 6430 022], in Norway and Spain as ROCK AND ROLL MUSIC [Fontana Special 6430 022 and Fontana 6430 022 respectively]. (However, the record label inside the Spanish issue actually says GOLDEN HITS.) In 1973 it was released in France as ROCK AND ROLL MUSIC [Fontana 6430 022] and in the UK – with a different catalogue number from all the other variations – as BACK IN THE USA [Philips 6336 216].

ROCK'N'ROLL HITS
Philips 9279 138 ● 1974
Reissue of the above album, but with a slightly more stylish cover – although it's the same picture as on the others mentioned above. The only interest, collector-wise, must be the Italian liner notes!

CHUCK BERRY'S GOLDEN DECADE
Frog ABRP-22011 ● 1981
Same tracks as the 1972 US reissue [Chess 2CH-1514]. Almost identical gatefold cover to the second pressing (pink radio).

THE GREAT 28 [2-LP]
Green Line GLPA-02402 ● 1982
Same as the 1982 US 2-LP [Chess CH-8201], but a slightly different gatefold cover, especially the colours. Reissued on CD in 1988 as ROCK'N'ROLL MUSIC [Contact CDCON-119] with a different cover. (NB This is not in the same numerical series as the other Green Line Chess releases.)

CHUCK BERRY (VOLUME 1: ROLL OVER BEETHOVEN)
Joker SM-3983 ● 1982
Roll Over Beethoven / School Day / It Hurts Me Too+ *(live duet with Steve Miller)* / Carol / C.C. Rider+ *(live)* / Bring Another Drink+ / Oh Baby Doll / So Long+ / Reelin' And Rockin' / My Heart Will Always Belong To You+ / Back In The USA / Sweet Little Rock And Roller

Mercury recordings. Great picture of Berry on front cover.

CHUCK BERRY (VOLUME 2: MAYBELLENE)
Joker SM-3984 ● 1982
Maybellene / Good Lookin' Woman / I Do really Love You / Memphis, Tennessee / My Woman / Rock And Roll Music / Thirty Days / Ramblin' Rose+ / Back To Memphis / Goodnight, Well It's Time To Go [It's Time To Go] / Sweet Little Sixteen / Put Her Down

Mercury recordings. Nice to see 'My Woman' and 'Put Her Down' included, as they haven't appeared very often on Mercury compilations.

CHUCK BERRY [2-LP]
Joker SM-3989/2 ● 1982
Reissue of the two Joker albums above. Almost same front cover as VOLUME 1 above. Gatefold – but there's nothing on the inside!

20 GREATEST HITS
Lotus LOP-14107 ● 1985
This is the same as the Joker albums above, except 'My Woman', 'Put Her Down', 'Back To Memphis' and 'Good Lookin' Woman' are not included.

THE CHUCK BERRY COLLECTION – 20 ROCK'N'ROLL GREATS
Déjà Vu DVLP-2068 ● 1986
Maybellene / Carol *(live)* / Johnny B. Goode *(live)* / Roll Over Beethoven / Hoochie Coochie Man+ *(live)* / Brown Eyed Handsome Man / Oh Baby Doll / Around And Around / School Day *(live)* / Thirty Days / Sweet Little Sixteen *(live)* / Memphis, Tennessee *(live)* / Reelin' And Rockin' / Too Much Monkey Business / You Can't Catch Me / Wee Wee Hours *(live)* / Rock And Roll Music / Havana Moon / No Particular Place To Go / Little Queenie

Assortment of live tracks from the 1969 *Toronto Rock & Roll Revival* and Chess studio cuts. 'Maybellene' is the Chess original with overdubbed live audience. This is also one of those albums you don't need, and should actually never have been released in the first place. Released on CD in 1987 [Déjà Vu DVCD-2068]. This had liner notes which were not present on the LP cover.

ST. LOUIS TO LIVERPOOL
Chess [Green Line] CH-18007 ● 1986
Same tracks and cover as the 1964 US LP [Chess LPS-1488]. Also distributed in the UK by Charly as Chess GCH-8007.

NEW JUKE BOX HITS
Chess [Green Line] CH-18008 ● 1986
Same tracks and cover as the 1961 US LP [Chess LP-1456]. Also distributed in the UK by Charly as Chess GCH-8007.

ROCKIN' AT THE HOPS
Chess [Green Line] CH-18041 ● 1986
Same tracks and cover as the 1960 UK LP [Chess LP-1448]. Also distributed in the UK by Charly as Chess GCH-8041.

BERRY IS ON TOP
Chess [Green Line] CH-18043 ● 1986
Same tracks and cover as the 1959 US LP [Chess LP-1435]. Also distributed in the UK by Charly as Chess GCH-8043.

BIO
Chess [Green Line] CH-18046 ● 1986
Same tracks and cover as the 1984 US LP with green cover [Chess CH-91510]. Also distributed in the UK by Charly as Chess GCH-8046.

DUCK WALK
The Entertainers ENT-LP-13.046 ● 1988
Roll Over Beethoven / You Never Can Tell / No Particular Place To Go / Sweet Little Sixteen / Wee Wee Hours / Brown Eyed Handsome Man / Rock And Roll Music / Memphis, Tennessee / Maybellene / Nadine / Johnny B. Goode / Promised Land / School Day / Back In The USA / Oh Baby Doll / Reelin' And Rockin'

16 Chess tracks. Fancy picture of Berry on the cover. A similarly-titled CD, but with a different cover and 30 Chess tracks in bad sound quality [The Entertainers CD-0263], was released either in Germany, Austria or France in 1987. Nuff said.

THE CHAMPIONS RECORDS 7 - CHUCK BERRY
Targa VTAL-1430 ● 1988
Down Bound Train / Drifting Heart / Beautiful Delilah / Hey Pedro / Roly Poly *(instr)* / Johnny B. Goode* / House Of Blue Lights+ / Roll Over Beethoven* / My Little Love Light / Time Was+ *(faster version)* / Oh Baby Doll* / Ingo *(instr)* / Sweet Little Sixteen* / Oh Yeah / Childhood Sweetheart / Maybellene*

Interesting selection of songs, obscurities mixed with classics – or so it seems! Unfortunately, the classics are the dreadful Mercury versions (*), and not Chess like the rest. No picture of Berry here, just a black cover with silver, red and white print. Liner notes both in English and Italian: *'Between 1955 and 1959 Charles Edward Berry wrote the most important and lasting group of songs in the history of rock…'* Well said, folks! However, you forgot to point out that the classics included here are the Mercury re-recordings.

CHUCK BERRY
Targa IGDA-1053/54 • 1989
Supplement to the magazine *Il Rock* No. 26, published by DeAgostini. Same songs as on Targa 1430 above. Different cover with the same picture of Berry front and back.

ROLL OVER BEETHOVEN
Success 2103-LP • 1989
16 Mercury tracks. The cover is not good, the sound is not good, and I hate this kind of album with the same dreadful tracks over and over again. Sometimes I feel it would have been better if Berry had stayed with Chess. Also issued on CD [Success 2103-CD].

CD Albums

THE CHUCK BERRY COLLECTION – 20 ROCK'N'ROLL GREATS
Déjà Vu DVCD-2068 • 1987
Maybellene / Carol *(live)* / Johnny B. Goode *(live)* / Roll Over Beethoven / Hoochie Coochie Man+ *(live)* / Brown Eyed Handsome Man / Oh Baby Doll / Around And Around / School Day *(live)* / Thirty Days / Sweet Little Sixteen *(live)* / Memphis, Tennessee *(live)* / Reelin' And Rockin' / Too Much Monkey Business / You Can't Catch Me / Wee Wee Hours *(live)* / Rock And Roll Music / Havana Moon / No Particular Place To Go / Little Queenie

Assortment of live tracks from the 1969 *Toronto Rock & Roll Revival* and Chess studio cuts. 'Maybellene' is the Chess original with overdubbed live audience. This is also one of those albums you don't need, and should actually never have been released in the first place. Originally released on LP in 1986 [Déjà Vu DVLP-2068]. The CD had liner notes which were not present on the LP cover.

ROCK'N'ROLL MUSIC
Contact CDCON-119 • 1988
CD reissue of the 1982 2-LP, THE GREAT 28 [Green Line GLPA-02402]. Same tracks, different cover.

ROLL OVER BEETHOVEN
Success 2103-CD • 1989
16 Mercury tracks. The cover is not good, the sound is not good, and I hate this kind of album with the same dreadful tracks over and over again. Sometimes I feel it would have been better if Berry had stayed with Chess. Also issued on LP [Success 2103-LP].

CHUCK BERRY – IL GRANDE ROCK DEAGOSTINI
Mercury CDDEA-2259 • 1991
Same tracks as the 1989 US CD reissue of GOLDEN HITS [Mercury 826-256-2], but a different cover.

THE CHUCK BERRY STORY
Déjà Vu DVRECD-66 • 1992
Roll Over Beethoven *(live, 1956 Alan Freed radio show)* / Hoochie Coochie Man+ *(live)* / Sweet Little Sixteen *(live)* / Memphis, Tennessee *(live)* / School Day *(live)* / Rock And Roll Music *(live)* / Nadine *(live)* / School Day *(live)* / Reelin' And Rockin' *(live)* / Too Much Monkey Business *(live)* / My Ding-A-Ling *(live)* / Maybellene / Thirty Days / Sweet Little Rock And Roller / Little Queenie / Brown Eyed Handsome Man / Carol / Route 66+ / Wee Wee Hours / Johnny B. Goode

'Roll Over Beethoven' is a live recording from a 1956 Alan Freed radio show (see the 1978 Various Artists bootleg LP, ROCK'N'ROLL RADIO [Radiola MR-1087] for more information). The live tracks from 'Hoochie Coochie Man' to 'My Ding-A-Ling' are from the 1969 *Toronto Rock & Roll Revival*. The rest are Chess recordings. Too much monkey business!

REELIN' AND ROCKIN' [3-CD]
Green Line CD3GLP-466 • 1993
❶ Maybellene / Thirty Days / You Can't Catch Me / Too Much Monkey Business / Brown Eyed Handsome Man / Roll Over Beethoven / Havana Moon / School Day / Rock And Roll Music / Oh Baby Doll / Reelin' And Rockin' / Sweet Little Sixteen / No Money Down / You Never Can Tell / Carol
❷ Let's Boogie / Mean Old World+ / I Will Not Let You Go / London Berry Blues *(instr)* / I Love You / Reelin' And Rockin' *(live, album version)* / My Ding-A-Ling *(live, album version)* / Johnny B. Goode *(live)*
❸ Johnny B. Goode / Around And Around / Beautiful Delilah / Memphis, Tennessee / Sweet Little Rock And Roller / Little Queenie / Almost Grown / Back In The USA / Let It Rock / Bye Bye Johnny / I'm Talking About You / Come On / Nadine / No Particular Place To Go / I Want To Be Your Driver

Discs 1 and 3 contain 30 Chess tracks altogether, with good sound quality (no stereo, though). All the classics are here. Disc 2 is the complete LONDON CHUCK BERRY SESSIONS album from 1972. This is actually quite a goode Berry compilation, so it's sad that it looks so anonymous.

THE VERY BEST
Millennium Edition MILCD-25 • 1995
Maybellene *(live, 1956 Alan Freed radio show)* / Roll Over Beethoven *(live, 1956 Alan Freed radio show)* / Wee Wee Hours / Johnny B. Goode – Carol / Hoochie Coochie Man+ / Sweet Little Sixteen / Memphis, Tennessee / School Day / Rock And Roll Music / Nadine / Reelin' And Rockin' / Too Much Monkey Business / My Ding-A-Ling

The first two songs are live recordings from a 1956 Alan Freed radio show (see the 1978 Various Artists bootleg LP, ROCK'N'ROLL RADIO [Radiola MR-1087] for more information). The rest are from the 1969 *Toronto Rock & Roll Revival*. Why bother?

LIVE GOODE!
Univers UV-155 • 2005
Maybellene / Rock And Roll Music / Nadine / School Day / Hoochie Coochie Man+ / *Medley: Carol – Promised Land* / Johnny B. Goode / Reelin' And Rockin' / Memphis, Tennessee / Sweet Little Sixteen / Wee Wee Hours / My Ding-A-Ling

Nice digipak featuring the Toronto 1969 show again. This time 'Too Much Monkey Business' and 'Johnny B. Goode' are missing. Also 'My Ding-A-Ling' is edited down to 2:47 from 9:33. And, as you can see from the track listing, 'Johnny B. Goode' has been edited out of the medley! Strangely, the booklet contains not one but two biographies – one by Cub Koda, the other by Bruce Pegg – as well as some great pictures of Berry and others on stage with Billy Peek in 1973. The sound is not any better than most other Toronto issues: kinda woolly.

Various Artists LPs

Chuck Berry – B.B. King – Ray Charles – Ike & Tina Turner
SOUL MUSIC [3-LP]
Joker C-83/3 • 1983
Oh Baby Doll / So Long+ / Reelin' And Rockin' / My Heart Will Always Belong To You+ / Back In The USA / Sweet Little Rock And Roller

This appears to be three single LPs repackaged as a set. The Berry songs are all Mercury recordings. On the other side of the record [Joker SM-4044] are six songs by B.B. King. The second record [SM-3926] contains 10 songs by Ray Charles, and the third [SM-3913] 12 songs by Ike & Tina Turner.

THE BEST OF CHESS ROCK'N'ROLL [2-LP]
Chess [Green Line] CH2-16024 • 1987
    Same tracks and gatefold sleeve as the US 2-LP [Chess CH2-6024]. Also distributed in the UK by Charly as Chess GCH2-6024.

Various Artists CD Albums

ROCK, ROCK, ROCK
Chess [Green Line] CDCHESS-1016 • 1989
    Same tracks as the 1956 US LP [Chess LP-1425], but the cover is the one used for the 1986 US LP reissue with the 1965 picture of Berry [Chess CH-9254].

ROCK'N'ROLL RADIO COLLECTION: LIVE ROCK'N'ROLL BROADCAST FROM 1956
Déjà Vu CD-51302 • 1990s
Maybellene *(live, 1956 Alan Freed radio show)* / Roll Over Beethoven *(live, 1956 Alan Freed radio show)*

    These are the two live recordings from a 1956 Alan Freed radio show (see the 1978 Various Artists bootleg LP, ROCK'N'ROLL RADIO [Radiola MR-1087] for more information).

JAMAICA

Singles

Sweet Little Sixteen / Reelin' And Rockin'
Down Beat 234 • 1958

    78 rpm release with red label. I suspect this was also issued as a 45 rpm vinyl single. I am certain that other Berry singles from the '50s must also have been released in Jamaica, but unfortunately have no more information.

JAPAN

Now, this is a difficult task. I wonder if anyone knows exactly what's been released in this country over the years, and when it comes to Berry records it's almost impossible. It is not known if anything by Berry was issued in Japan in the '50s. However, I have seen a single by Little Richard on the London label from that decade. The Berry singles I have come across and bought are from 1964 onwards.

The first LP came out in 1964. Berry's Japanese releases almost always have very good covers and are therefore collector's items. Two LPs are of particularly great interest to Berry fans and music lovers as they contain recordings not available anywhere else (the 1981 LP, TOKYO SESSION [East World WTP-90072] and the 1982 Various Artists LP, THE DAY OF R&B [East World WTP-72403]). As far as I know all the LPs from the 1970s onwards had the usual Japanese 'obi' strip down the left side. The text on the inside covers (gatefold if available) is in Japanese and sometimes also in English. Most albums have a lyric sheet inlay, if they are not printed on the cover itself.

There have also been many CDs issued in Japan. In fact, they have released sooo many CDs throughout the years that they are impossible to keep track of. There are many Berry compilations, as well as reissues of original US albums. I only have the title, label and catalogue number for many of them, but most are 'Best Of' and 'Greatest Hits' compilations, and, as far as I know, contain nothing new under the (rising) sun.

Singles

No Particular Place To Go / You Two
Globe JET-1442 ● 1964
Chess cuts. Red label, name in silver and black lettering. Picture sleeve.

St. Louie To Frisco / Soul Rockin'
Mercury SM-1061 ● 1968
This has a great picture sleeve, very similar to the 1968 US LP cover of FROM ST. LOUIE TO FRISCO [Mercury SR-61176]. Blue label with silver lettering.

Rock And Roll Music / Johnny B. Goode
Globe 'Golden Couple Series' SJET-1087 ● 1970?
Chess cuts. Red label, name in silver and black lettering (same as JET-1442 above). Picture sleeve.

Sweet Little Sixteen / Roll Over Beethoven
Chess 'Golden Couple Series' SJET-1179 ● 1970?
Blue label with the Chess name across the top in red/white/blue. Picture sleeve.

My Ding-A-Ling *(live, single edit)* / Johnny B. Goode *(live)*
Chess JET-2146 ● 1972
Art sleeve.

Globe JET-1442

Globe JET-1442

Mercury SM-1061

Globe SJET-1087

Chess SJET-1179

Chess JET-2146

Chess JET-2163

Chess JET-2163 (promo)

Chess JET-2163

Chess FD-2044

East World PRT-1076

East World PRT-1076 (promo)

Reelin' And Rockin' *(live, single edit)* / **Let's Boogie**
Chess JET-2163 • 1972
    Blue label with the Chess name across the top in red/white/blue. Promos were issued with plain white labels with no label name printed on them. Picture sleeve.

Johnny B. Goode / Sweet Little Sixteen
Chess FD-2044 • 1977
    Orange label with a blue border. Promos were issued with plain white labels with no label name printed on them. Picture sleeve.

Johnny B. Goode *(live)* / **Roll Over Beethoven** *(live)*
East World PRT-1076 *(promo)* • **1981**
    Picture sleeve. This was probably only issued as a white label promo, to promote the fabulous live TOKYO SESSION LP from 1981 [East World WTP-90072].

EPs

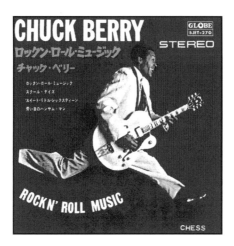

ROCK'N'ROLL MUSIC [33⅓ rpm]
Globe SJET-270 • 1965
Rock And Roll Music / School Day / Sweet Little Sixteen / Brown Eyed Handsome Man

    Chess cuts.

BEST FOUR [33⅓ rpm]
Globe SJET-296 *(stereo)* ● **1965**
No Particular Place To Go / Little Marie / You Never Can Tell / Promised Land

Chess cuts. This is just fabulous! A stereo EP with an exceptional cover featuring a black and white picture of Berry from England, taken 14 May 1964.

SONGS FROM MOTION PICTURE 'T.A.M.I.' [33⅓ rpm]
Globe SJET-388 ● **1965**
Sweet Little Sixteen / Maybellene / Johnny B. Goode / Nadine

Great cover! Despite the title, the songs are the original Chess studio recordings.

LPs

CHUCK BERRY'S GREATEST HIT (THE BEST OF CHUCK BERRY)
Globe DJET-7198 • 1964

No Particular Place To Go / You Never Can Tell / Maybellene / Nadine / Brenda Lee / You Two / Memphis, Tennessee / Sweet Little Sixteen / Roll Over Beethoven / Rock And Roll Music / Johnny B. Goode / Brown Eyed Handsome Man

Probably Berry's very first album release in Japan. This has the same tracks and front cover as the 1964 US LP [Chess LP-1485] with the 'sticker' listing the original hits 'Memphis', 'Maybellene' and 'Johnny B. Goode'. The back cover has *The Best Of Chuck Berry'* printed across the top and lyrics beneath. See also Taiwan discography.

ON STAGE
Globe DJET-7204 • 1964

Same tracks as the 1963 US LP [Chess LP-1480], although 'How High The Moon' is the version with the longer fade. Different and fabulous cover!

ST. LOUIS TO LIVERPOOL
Globe SJET-7690 • 1964

No Particular Place To Go / Little Marie / You Never Can Tell / Go, Bobby Soxer / Brenda Lee / Promised Land / Memphis, Tennessee / Sweet Little Sixteen / Roll Over Beethoven / Rock And Roll Music / Johnny B. Goode / Brown Eyed Handsome Man

Same front cover as US Chess LP-1488 with the same title, but, as you can see, a different selection of tracks. Different back cover with five smaller pictures of Berry, covering ⅓ of the cover. See also Taiwan discography.

GOLDEN HITS
Mercury SFX-7238 *or* SM-7272 • 1967

Same tracks and cover as the 1967 US LP, *Golden Hits* [Mercury SR-61103]. The correct number here is uncertain as I don't have the albums myself and I have seen both numbers referred to this particular LP. (Could SM-7272 be a 1968 reissue?)

ST. LOUIE TO FRISCO
Mercury SM-7283 • 1968
Same tracks and cover as the 1968 US LP [Mercury SR-61176].

GOLDEN HITS
Mercury SFL-9100 • 197?
Reissue. Same tracks and cover as the 1967 US LP [Mercury SR-61103].

LIVE AT THE FILLMORE AUDITORIUM, SAN FRANCISCO
Mercury SFL-9101 • 197?
Same tracks and cover as the 1967 US LP [Mercury SR-61138].

BACK HOME
Chess [Globe] SJET-8280 • 1970
Same tracks and probably same cover as the 1970 US LP [Chess LPS-1550].

SAN FRANCISCO DUES
Chess [Globe] SJET-8345 • 1971
Same tracks and cover as the 1971 US LP [Chess CH-50008].

THE LONDON CHUCK BERRY SESSIONS
Chess SWG-7583 • 1972
Same tracks and gatefold cover as the 1972 US LP [Chess CH-60020]. Also lyric sheet. Reissued in 1976 both as Chess BT-5301 and Chess BT-8057, but without the gatefold cover.

Most of the information about above albums was extracted from the booklet of the 3-LP box set below. However, there are a few errors which makes it difficult to be absolutely certain about the album titles. SJET-7690, I first thought, was the 1964 ST. LOUIS TO LIVERPOOL LP with the same tracks, especially since 'Brenda Lee' and 'Go, Bobby Soxer' were included, but this is incorrect. It also seems that GOLDEN HITS was issued with different numbers on at least three occasions in the late '60s and early '70s (see above). The LP later also appeared under different titles: ATTENTION! [Fontana PAT-19] in 1973, CHUCK BERRY [Mercury FD-200] in 1975, JOHNNY B. GOODE – CHUCK BERRY'S GOLDEN HITS [Mercury EVER-22] in 1982, and JOHNNY B. GOODE – CHUCK BERRY'S GOLDEN HITS [Mercury 25PP-19] in the mid-1980s.

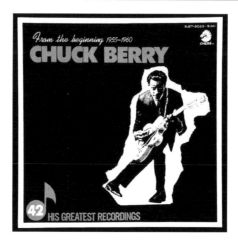

FROM THE BEGINNING 1955-60 [3-LP]
Chess SJET-9523-5(M) • 1973?

❶ *1955-57:* Maybellene / Wee Wee Hours / Thirty Days / Together (We Will Always Be) / No Money Down / Down Bound Train / Roll Over Beethoven / Brown Eyed Handsome Man / Too Much Monkey Business / You Can't Catch Me / Deep Feeling / School Day / Oh Baby Doll / Rock And Roll Music

❷ *1958-59:* Sweet Little Sixteen / Reelin' And Rockin' / It Don't Take But A Few Minutes / Johnny B. Goode / Around And Around / Beautiful Delilah / Carol / Sweet Little Rock And Roller / Jo Jo Gunne / Run Rudolph Run+ / Anthony Boy / Little Queenie / Almost Grown / Memphis, Tennessee

❸ *1959-60:* Back In The USA / Childhood Sweetheart / Broken Arrow / Down The Road A Piece+ / Confessin' The Blues+ / Let It Rock / Too Pooped To Pop+ / Worried Life Blues+ / Bye Bye Johnny / I Got To Find My Baby+ / Jaguar And The Thunderbird / Don't You Lie To Me+ / I'm Talking About You / Come On

On Record 1, the black inner sleeve with white print has a copy of the first pressing (silver top label) of 'Maybellene' on one side and 'Wee Wee Hours' on the other. On Record 2, 'Run Rudolph Run' is credited to *'C. Berry Music Inc.–M. Brodie'.* The inner sleeve has a copy of the Chess single, 'Sweet Little Sixteen', on one side and 'Reelin' And Rockin'' on the other. On Record 3, all songs are credited to Berry (or *'E. Anderson'*) except 'Too Pooped To Pop', which is correctly credited to *'B. Davis'.* The inner sleeve has a copy of the single 'Back In The USA' and 'Memphis, Tennessee', one on either side. There is also a 28-page booklet full of information (in Japanese and English) with pictures, labels, album covers, etc. Lyrics to all songs. There must surely have been a second box set issued, but I have no more information.

ATTENTION!
Fontana PAT-19 • 1973
 Same tracks as the 1967 US LP, GOLDEN HITS [Mercury SR-61103], but a different cover.

AMERICAN GRAFFITI [2-LP]
MCA MCA-9254/55 • 1973
 See *Various Artists LPs.*

BIO
Chess SWX-6051 • 1973
 Same tracks and gatefold cover as the 1973 US LP [Chess CH-50043], but with the addition of a lyric sheet. However, this cover actually has the best print of any from across the world. The pictures and print are so clear they are a joy to see. A must have!

Speaking of lyrics, did you know that there actually were lyrics to the instrumental 'Woodpecker'? Well, they're here. The Japanese never fail to surprise me.

CHUCK BERRY'S GOLDEN DECADE – TWIN DELUXE [2-LP]
Chess SJET-9227-28 • 1973
Same tracks and probably same cover as the second pressing of the 1972 US reissue [Chess 2CH-1514] (pink radio).

CHUCK BERRY'S GOLDEN DECADE (VOLUME 2) [2-LP]
Chess SJET-9229-30 • 1974
No information.

CHUCK BERRY – EXCELLENT 20
Chess SWX-30013 • 1974
Maybellene / Roll Over Beethoven / Brown Eyed Handsome Man / Too Much Monkey Business / School Day / Rock And Roll Music / Sweet Little Sixteen / Reelin' And Rockin' / Johnny B. Goode / Carol / Sweet Little Rock And Roller / Little Queenie / Almost Grown / Memphis, Tennessee / Back In The USA / Too Pooped To Pop+ / Nadine / No Particular Place To Go / Promised Land / My Ding-A-Ling *(live, single edit)*

The best of the best of Chess, except they missed off 'You Never Can Tell'. Four-page inlay card with Japanese liner notes, pictures and lyrics.

GREATEST HITS 24 [2-LP]
Chess SWX-9019-20 • 1975
Almost the same songs as the LP above, except 'Little Queenie' is omitted and 'No Money Down', 'Beautiful Delilah', 'Let It Rock', 'I'm Talking About You' and 'Come On' are added. Great gatefold cover, front and back. Most often the album covers from Japan are really good. It's amazing how they came up with all these good photos of Berry. As always with Japanese issues, you get the lyrics to all the songs.

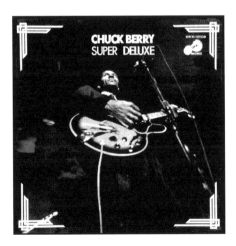

CHUCK BERRY SUPER DELUXE
Chess SWX-10109 • 1975?
14 tracks, which are all on the above two albums. However, the front cover is just marvellous! Berry in a dark suit pictured on stage against a black background. The photo is taken from a low angle in front of the stage which provides a very distinctive view. Gatefold cover with more pictures inside, plus lyrics to all the songs.

ATTENTION!
Mercury BT-5032 • 1975
Johnny B. Goode / Sweet Little Sixteen / C.C. Rider+ *(live)* / School Day / Carol / Back In The USA / Rock And Roll Music / Maybellene / Memphis, Tennessee / I Can't Believe / Hoochie Coochie Man+ *(live)* / Roll Over Beethoven

This has one of the greatest front cover pictures I have ever seen of Berry: another stage shot, this time with Chuck dressed in a white jacket and grey pants in front of a dark background. Pity that these are the Mercury remakes, not the Chess originals.

CHUCK BERRY
Chess SWX-6180 • 1975
Same tracks and cover as the 1975 US LP [Chess CH-60032]. The copy I bought unusually did not have an inlay card.

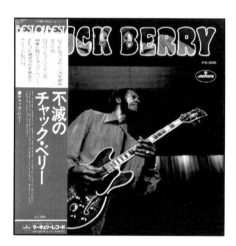

CHUCK BERRY
Mercury FD-200 • 1975
Same tracks as the 1967 US LP, GOLDEN HITS [Mercury SR-61103], but a different cover. Also lyric sheet inlay.

THE HISTORY OF CHUCK BERRY (VOLUME 1)
Chess BT-5269 • 1976
Maybellene / Thirty Days / No Money Down / Roll Over Beethoven / Brown Eyed Handsome Man / Too Much Monkey Business / You Can't Catch Me / School Day / Oh Baby Doll / Rock And Roll Music / Sweet Little Sixteen / Reelin' And Rockin'

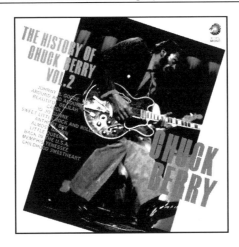

THE HISTORY OF CHUCK BERRY (VOLUME 2)
Chess BT-5270 • 1976
Johnny B. Goode / Around And Around / Beautiful Delilah / Carol / Jo Jo Gunne / Sweet Little Rock And Roller / Anthony Boy / Almost Grown / Little Queenie / Back In The USA / Memphis, Tennessee / Childhood Sweetheart

THE HISTORY OF CHUCK BERRY (VOLUME 3)
Chess BT-5271 • 1976
Too Pooped To Pop+ / Bye Bye Johnny / I Got To Find My Baby+ / Our Little Rendezvous / Little Star / Come On / Nadine / No Particular Place To Go / Little Marie / Promised Land / My Ding-A-Ling *(live, edited to 6:54 (the usual edited length is 4:16))*

'Little Marie' is credited to one Colin Wilkie! Where do they get these names from? Nevertheless, the above three volumes are pretty nice releases with goode covers.

THE LONDON CHUCK BERRY SESSIONS
Chess BT-5301 • 1976
Reissue without the gatefold cover but with lyric sheet inlay. Orange and blue label. See also below.

THE LONDON CHUCK BERRY SESSIONS
Chess BT-8057 • 1976
Reissue without the gatefold cover. Part of a *'Chess Black Sounds Collection'* series. Tan and black label, titles in silver print. It says 1976 on the back cover, on both this LP and the one above. Very strange indeed. Why release the same album in the same year? They look exactly the same except that *'Chess Black Sound Collection'* is printed on the back cover in the upper left-hand corner of this release. The labels are also identical in layout apart from the colours. The original Japanese Chess album with gatefold cover, SWG-7583, came out in 1972.

SPOTLIGHT ON CHUCK BERRY [2-LP]
Chess FDX-9241-42 • 1976

❶ Maybellene / Thirty Days / Brown Eyed Handsome Man / Too Much Monkey Business / You Can't Catch Me / School Day / Oh Baby Doll / Roll Over Beethoven / Rock And Roll Music / Sweet Little Sixteen / Reelin' And Rockin' / Beautiful Delilah / Almost Grown / Carol / Sweet Little Rock And Roller / Memphis, Tennessee

❷ Johnny B. Goode / Jo Jo Gunne / Little Queenie / Back In The USA / Childhood Sweetheart / Confessin' The Blues+/ Let It Rock / Too Pooped To Pop+/ Bye Bye Johnny / Worried Life Blues+/ Jaguar And The Thunderbird / I Got To Find My Baby+ / Come On / Nadine / No Particular Place To Go / Promised Land

Strange they didn't include any instrumentals. Nice gatefold cover, back and front. Lyric sheet inlay, but inside the cover there is nothing but a list of all the other albums in the Spotlight series.

REFLECTION
Chess FDX-7064 • 1977

Maybellene / Roll Over Beethoven / School Day / Rock And Roll Music / Sweet Little Sixteen / Reelin' And Rockin' / Johnny B. Goode / Around And Around / Carol / Almost Grown / Little Queenie / Back In The USA / Memphis, Tennessee / Bye Bye Johnny / Come On / Nadine / My Ding-A-Ling *(live, single edit)*

Another great cover!

ROCKIT
Atco P-10985T • 1979

Same cover and label design as the 1979 US LP [Atco SD-38.118]. However, you also get the lyrics to all the songs.

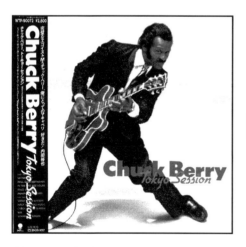 

TOKYO SESSION
East World WTP-90072 • 1981

School Day / Roll Over Beethoven / Wee Wee Hours / My Ding-A-Ling* / Memphis, Tennessee* / Sweet Little Sixteen / Rock And Roll Music / *Medley:* Carol – Little Queenie / Bio / Johnny B. Goode

If there ever was a latter-day Berry rarity, then this is it! Compiled from two Tokyo concert dates (27 April 1981 at Shinjuku Koseinenkin Hall and 29 April 1981 at Shibuya Kokaido). It must surely be Berry's best live album ever. I have never heard him sounding so good. He plays terrific guitar and the band (Jim Marsala on bass, Shigeru Narumo on piano and Tsutomu Maki on drums) provide top-notch backing. Ingrid Berry also appears on a couple of songs (marked *). Even for those who, like myself, have heard all the songs time and again, these versions come across as new and fresh thanks to Berry's enthusiasm. The sound quality is superb too. The cover is also a sight to see, and even on the reverse there's a close-up of his trademark 'Berrywalk'. You know exactly who it is by just looking at the picture. As always the album comes with a biography in Japanese text biography, an English lyrics insert and an obi strip.

Sadly, this great LP was only released in Japan and South Korea. According to the cover, it was recorded under license from the Chuck Berry Communications System Inc. However, when a friend of mine, Rune Halland, went backstage in Oslo in 1987 and asked Berry to autograph his copy, he appeared not to know anything about it and became rather suspicious. But he did sign it!

THE DAY OF R&B
East World WTP-72403 •1982
See *Various Artists LPs.*

JOHNNY B. GOODE – CHUCK BERRY'S GOLDEN HITS
Mercury EVER-22 • 1982
Same tracks as the 1967 US LP, GOLDEN HITS [Mercury SR-61103]. Great different cover, also lyric sheet inlay. Probably the only way that you can get the lyrics to 'Club Nitty Gritty' is to buy one of the albums issued in Japan! Carries the legend *'Ever Bright Collection'.* Digitally remastered.

TORONTO ROCK'N'ROLL REVIVAL 1969
Overseas UPS-331-V • 1982
Same tracks as the 1981 US LP, CHUCK BERRY LIVE (VOLUME 1) [SSS International SSS-36] and the 1982 US LP, TORONTO ROCK'N'ROLL REVIVAL 1969 – VOLUME III [Accord SN-7172]. This has – surprisingly for a Japanese album – a very dull cover: three small pictures of Berry on the back of an otherwise black cover. Four-page inlay with Japanese liner notes, and lyrics to each song are transcribed as sung on the recording.

AFTER SCHOOL SESSION
Chess [P-Vine] PLP-803 • 1983
A faithful reproduction of the 1958 US LP [Chess LP-1426]. Cover is thick cardboard just like original US album and looks exactly like its American counterpart apart from the Japanese 'ID' strip and lyric inlay sheet. The record inside sports the original black US Chess label with vertical silver 'Chess logo.

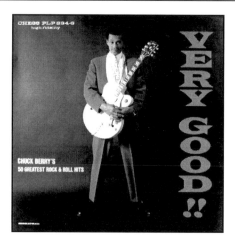

VERY GOOD!! CHUCK BERRY'S 50 GREATEST ROCK & ROLL HITS [3-LP]
Chess [P-Vine] PLP-834-6 ● 1983

❶ Maybellene / Wee Wee Hours / Thirty Days / You Can't Catch Me / No Money Down / Brown Eyed Handsome Man / Roll Over Beethoven / Too Much Monkey Business / Havana Moon / School Day / Rock And Roll Music / Oh Baby Doll / Sweet Little Sixteen / Rock At The Philharmonic *(instr)* / Reelin' And Rockin' / Johnny B. Goode / It Don't Take But A Few Minutes
❷ Around And Around / Beautiful Delilah / Carol / Anthony Boy / Jo Jo Gunne / Memphis, Tennessee / Sweet Little Rock And Roller / Run Rudolph Run+ / Little Queenie / Almost Grown / Back In The USA / Let It Rock / Too Pooped To Pop+ / I Got To Find My Baby+ / Don't You Lie To Me+ / Worried Life Blues+ / Bye Bye Johnny
❸ Jaguar And The Thunderbird / Diploma For Two / Down The Road A Piece+ / Confessin' The Blues+ / I'm Talking About You / Route 66+ / Rip It Up+ / Come On / Rocking On The Railroad [Let It Rock] / Nadine / No Particular Place To Go / Promised Land / You Never Can Tell / Liverpool Drive *(instr)* / Run Joe+ / Jamaica Farewell+

This is a terrific album! Great picture of Berry from the mid-'60s on the front cover, more pictures in the enclosed booklet, and the lyrics to 50 Berry songs. The labels are facsimiles of the original black US Chess labels from the late '50s and early '60s. 'Rocking On The Railroad' [*aka* 'Let It Rock'] is the version from the 1963 US LP, ON STAGE [Chess LP-1480] with overdubbed audience noise – a strange inclusion since the unadulterated version of 'Let It Rock' appears on Side D of the second LP. 'Jamaica Farewell' is the full-length version (see 1965 US LP, CHUCK BERRY IN LONDON [Chess LP-/LPS-1495] for details), albeit in mono.

ONE DOZEN BERRYS
Chess [P-Vine] PLP-848 ● 1984

A faithful reproduction of the 1958 US LP [Chess LP-1432]. Cover is thick cardboard just like original US album and appears exactly like its American counterpart apart from the obi and lyric inlay sheet. The record inside sports the original black US Chess label with vertical silver 'Chess logo.

JOHNNY B. GOODE – CHUCK BERRY'S GOLDEN HITS
Mercury 25PP-19 ● 1985

Same tracks as the 1967 US LP [Mercury SR-61103]. Same front cover, but it has a different small picture on the back cover.

THE GREATEST HITS 21
Overseas UXP-763-V • 1986
Maybellene / Sweet Little Sixteen / School Day / Rock And Roll Music / Johnny B. Goode / Carol / Reelin' And Rockin' / Memphis, Tennessee / Bring Another Drink+ / Good Lookin' Woman / Roll Over Beethoven / Back In The USA / Sweet Little Rock And Roller / Oh Baby Doll / C.C. Rider+ *(live)* / Thirty Days / Goodnight, Well It's Time To Go [It's Time To Go] / Back To Memphis / Check Me Out / My Heart Will Always Belong To You+ / I Do Really Love You

Mercury recordings. All songs credited to Berry except 'C.C. Rider'. The LP contains a four-page inlay and the cover bears the legend: *'Golden Juke Box Hit Series - 21 Timeless Treasures'*. If the Mercury versions qualify as timeless treasures, I'll rest my case! Also issued on CD [Overseas 30CP-83].

CD Singles

No Particular Place To Go *(stereo)* / **Johnny B. Goode**
MCA 10P3-6051 • 1988
Chess cuts. This is a 3" CD single in a specially-made 'box' which you can fold in half to make a frame.

Merry Christmas Baby+ / Run Rudolph Run+
Overseas [Xmas CD Card Series] TEDP-11 • 1990
This is a 3" CD single in a specially made 'sleeve' which you can fold out. Nice colour drawing of a Berry-walking Chuck in a Santa Claus outfit.

CD Albums

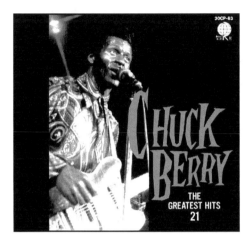

THE GREATEST HITS 21
Overseas 30CP-83 • 1986
Maybellene / Sweet Little Sixteen / School Day / Rock And Roll Music / Johnny B. Goode / Carol / Reelin' And Rockin' / Memphis, Tennessee / Bring Another Drink+ / Good Lookin' Woman / Roll Over Beethoven / Back In The USA / Sweet Little Rock And Roller / Oh Baby Doll / C.C. Rider+ *(live)* / Thirty Days / Goodnight, Well It's Time To Go [It's Time To Go] / Back To Memphis / Check Me Out / My Heart Will Always Belong To You+ / I Do Really Love You

Mercury recordings. All songs credited to Berry except 'C.C. Rider'. The LP contains a four-page inlay and the cover carries the legend: *'Golden Juke Box Hit Series - 21 Timeless Treasures'.* If the Mercury versions qualify as timeless treasures, I'll rest my case! Also issued on LP [Overseas UXP-763-V].

JOHNNY B. GOODE: CHUCK BERRY BEST HIT 25
Overseas 25CP-40 • 1989
25 classic Chess tracks, the best of the best, so to say – even if 'My Ding-A-Ling' is included – plus the single version of 'Merry Christmas Baby'.

GOLDEN HITS
Phonogram PPD-3113 • 1989
Same as the 1989 US CD reissue of the 1967 (stereo) LP [Mercury SR-61103].

CHUCK BERRY IN MEMPHIS
Phonogram PPD-3114 • 1989
Same as the 1989 US CD reissue of the 1967 (stereo) LP [Mercury SR-61123].

LIVE AT THE FILLMORE AUDITORIUM, SAN FRANCISCO
Phonogram PPD-3115 • 1989
Same as the 1989 US CD reissue of the 1967 (stereo) LP [Mercury SR-61138].

FROM ST. LOUIE TO FRISCO
Phonogram PPD-3116 • 1989
Same as the 1989 US CD reissue of the 1968 (stereo) LP [Mercury SR-61176].

CONCERTO IN B GOODE
Phonogram PPD-3117 • 1989
Same as the 1989 US CD reissue of the 1969 (stereo) LP [Mercury SR-61223].

The following six CDs were issued with original covers and liner notes and in beautiful straight-ahead mono! All had obi strips on the left side with information in Japanese, and proclaiming *'Chuck Berry Collection on Chess'*, with a small black silhouette of Chuck doing Berry-walk. The interesting thing is that the TWIST album is included, as it is the only time this particular LP has been reissued on CD. We also get the lyrics to all the songs, even on NEW JUKE BOX HITS. I also know for sure that albums like THE GREAT 28 (also reissued in 1993 as BEST ONE [MCA MVCM-25027]), ROCK'N'ROLL RARITIES and MORE ROCK'N'ROLL RARITIES came out on CD in Japan, but have no more information.

AFTER SCHOOL SESSION
Chess WMC5-301 ● 1991
Same tracks and cover as the 1957 US LP [Chess LP-1426].

BERRY IS ON TOP
Chess WMC5-302 ● 1991
Same tracks and cover as the 1959 US LP [Chess LP-1435].

ROCKIN' AT THE HOPS
Chess WMC5-303 ● 1991
Same tracks and cover as the 1960 US LP [Chess LP-1448].

NEW JUKE BOX HITS
Chess WMC5-304 ● 1991
Same tracks and cover as the 1961 US LP [Chess LP-1456].

CHUCK BERRY TWIST
Chess WMC5-305 ● 1991
Same tracks and cover as the 1962 US LP [Chess LP-1465].

ST. LOUIS TO LIVERPOOL
Chess WMC5-306 ● 1991
Same tracks and cover as the 1964 US LP [Chess LP-1488].

MORE HITS 30
Overseas TECX-25193 • 1992
Around And Around / You Can't Catch Me / Beautiful Delilah / Come On / Bye Bye Johnny / Anthony Boy / Guitar Boogie *(instr)* / You Two / Brenda Lee / Route 66+ / Little Marie *(stereo)* / Let's Boogie / Havana Moon / Liverpool Drive *(instr)* / I Will Not Let You Go / La Jaunda / Ingo *(instr)* / Rockin' On The Railroad (Let It Rock) / Surfin' Steel *(instr)* / I Still Got The Blues / I Just Want To Make Love To You+ / The Man And The Donkey / Night Beat *(instr)* / I Love You / Jaguar And The Thunderbird / It Don't Take But A Few Minutes / How You've Changed / Our Little Rendezvous / Go, Bobby Soxer *(stereo)* / Blue Feeling *(instr)*

30 tracks, including six instrumentals. Not so many hits here, but rather a selection of 'B' sides and obscure album cuts. Includes lyrics to 25 rare Berry tracks. The tracks from 'Rocking On The Railroad' to 'The Man And The Donkey' are taken from the ON STAGE album with the overdubbed audience. Overall the sound on this CD is not wonderful.

SINGLES COLLECTION (VOLUME 1)
Overseas TECX-25502 • May 1993
Maybellene / Thirty Days / Too Much Monkey Business / Brown Eyed Handsome Man / No Money Down / Johnny B. Goode / Around And Around / Anthony Boy / Oh Baby Doll / La Jaunda / Carol / Little Marie / Go, Bobby Soxer / Sweet Little Rock And Roller / Back In The USA / Memphis, Tennessee / Beautiful Delilah / Almost Grown / Little Queenie / Nadine / Jaguar And The Thunderbird / Our Little Rendezvous

SINGLES COLLECTION (VOLUME 2)
Overseas TECX-25503 • May 1993
Roll Over Beethoven / You Can't Catch Me / Havana Moon / School Day / Rock And Roll Music / Blue Feeling *(instr)* / Sweet Little Sixteen / Reelin' And Rockin' / Come On / Go, Go, Go / Let It Rock / Bye Bye Johnny / No Particular Place To Go / You Two / Promised Land / You Never Can Tell / Brenda Lee / Merry Christmas Baby+ / Run Rudolph Run+ / Let's Boogie / My Ding-A-Ling *(live, single edit)*

I don't know if there was a VOLUME 3 in this series, but anyway, there are a lot of 'B' sides missing.

BEST ONE
MCA MVCM-25027 • October 1993
Same tracks and almost the same cover as the 1982 US 2-LP, THE GREAT 28 [Chess CH-8201]. Plus you get the lyrics to 28 classic Berry songs! Goode value.

THE CHESS BOX [3-CD]
MCA MVCM-48001/3 ● September 1995

This is the same as the 1988 US 3-CD [Chess CHD3-80.001]. It was released as part of a *'40th Anniversary of Rock'n'Roll'* promotion (in Japan only).

JOHNNY B. GOODE – CHUCK BERRY'S GOLDEN HITS
Mercury PHCA-6130 ● 1995

Same tracks as the 1989 US CD reissue [Mercury 826-256-2], but a different cover.

AFTER SCHOOL SESSION
MCA MVCM-22102 ● 1997

Same tracks and cover as the 1957 US LP [Chess LP-1426] plus four bonus cuts: 'Sweet Little Sixteen' *(alt. version),* 'Beautiful Delilah' *(alt. version)*, 'County Line' and 'Reelin' And Rockin' ' *(demo).*

ONE DOZEN BERRYS
MCA MVCM-22103 ● 1997

Same tracks and cover as the 1957 US LP [Chess LP-1426] plus four bonus cuts: 'Johnny B. Goode' *(alt. take)*, 'Little Queenie' *(alt. take)*, 'Nadine' *(stereo remix)* and 'You Never Can Tell' *(stereo remix).* In addition, the CD booklet has a picture of Berry from 1965 which I haven't seen before.

BERRY IS ON TOP
MCA MVCM-22104 ● 1997

Same tracks and cover as the 1959 US LP [Chess LP-1435] plus eight bonus cuts: 'Down The Road A Piece', 'No Money Down', 'Down Bound Train', 'Jaguar And The Thunderbird', 'Things I Used To Do' *(stereo),* 'No Particular Place To Go', 'Fraulein' *(stereo)* and 'Nadine'. Previously released in Germany and France in 1993 [MCA MCD-30487] and in the UK in 1994 [Chess CHLD-19250].

THE LONDON CHUCK BERRY SESSIONS
MCA MVCM-22105 ● 1997

Same tracks and cover as the 1972 US LP [Chess CH-60020].

HAIL! HAIL! ROCK'N'ROLL
MCA MVCM-22106 ● 1997

Original soundtrack. Same tracks and cover as the 1987 US LP [MCA MCA-6217].

Various Artists LPs

AMERICAN GRAFFITI [2-LP]
MCA MCA-9254/55 ● 1973
Almost Grown / Johnny B. Goode

Same tracks and cover as the 1973 US 2-LP [MCA MCA2-8001].

Chuck Berry – Sam Moore – RC Succession
THE DAY OF R&B
East World WTP-72403 ●1982
Bio *(live)* / Johnny B. Goode *(live)*

Recorded live at Yokohama Stadium on 7 August 1982 with Rei Atsumi on keyboards, Ginji Shiokawa on bass and Tsutomu Maki on drums. Also on the album are live recordings by Sam Moore And His Sam & Dave Revue, and RC Succession, a popular Japanese R&B band. This is not as good as Berry's 1981 TOKYO SESSION album [East World WTP-90072] – maybe he missed Jim Marsala's bass lines. The sound is not as crisp either. Anyway, like TOKYO SESSION, this is also a rare album as it was only issued in Japan. It also appeared on the dark green London [Barca] label L28N-1005 in 1982. Don't ask me why! Reissued on CD in 2005 [Toshiba EMI 1004071665].

Various Artists CD Albums

Chuck Berry – Little Richard
HITS 20 – CHUCK BERRY VS. LITTLE RICHARD
Teichiku TECP-25502 ● 1990
Johnny B. Goode / Roll Over Beethoven / Carol / Sweet Little Sixteen / Rock And Roll Music / Maybellene / Little Queenie / My Ding-A-Ling *(live, single edit)* / Memphis, Tennessee / School Day

Chess cuts. Great cover! Also 10 tracks by Little Richard.

Chuck Berry – Little Richard
BEST
T.F. T-1952 ● 1993
Roll Over Beethoven / Rock And Roll Music / Sweet Little Sixteen / Maybellene / Memphis, Tennessee / Johnny B. Goode / Too Much Monkey Business / Around And Around

Chess recordings, plus eight tracks by Richard. Pictures of both artists on the front cover.

ALAN FREED'S ROCK AND ROLL DANCE PARTY
Go Cat Go TECX-20943 • 1995
Maybellene *(live, 1956 Alan Freed radio show)* / Roll Over Beethoven *(live, 1956 Alan Freed radio show)*

All the songs on this CD are live recordings from Alan Freed radio shows (see the 1978 Various Artists bootleg LP, ROCK'N'ROLL RADIO [Radiola MR-1087] for more information). This has the same tracks as the 1991 UK CD [Magnum Force CDMF-075]. However, it has a great cover that is worth the price alone. The sound is also a little better.

Chuck Berry – Sam Moore – RC Succession
THE DAY OF R&B
Toshiba EMI 1004071665 • 2005
Reissue of the 1982 LP [East World WTP-72403].

MEXICO

Central America and South America have always been difficult when it comes to finding Berry issues released in the various countries. Twenty years ago I had two albums from Mexico in my collection. Since then, several albums and three EPs have found their way to Drøbak. The EPs have very good and unusual picture covers and were probably released around 1965. The first LP I have dates from around 1970.

EPs

Gamma GX-07.151   Gamma GX-07.152

CHUCK BERRY (VOLUME 1)
Gamma GX-07.151 • 1965?
Memphis, Tennessee / Johnny B. Goode / Treinta Dias [Thirty Days] / Oh, Muñequita [Oh Baby Doll]

Chess recordings, some retitled in Spanish. Liner notes in Spanish. Great picture on the cover!

CHUCK BERRY (VOLUME 2)
Gamma GX-07.152 • 1965?
Maybellene / Dulces Dieciseis [Sweet Little Sixteen] / Dias De Escuela [School Day] / Demasiadas Tonterias [Too Much Monkey Business]

Chess recordings. Another great picture of Berry on the cover. The same liner notes as VOLUME 1.

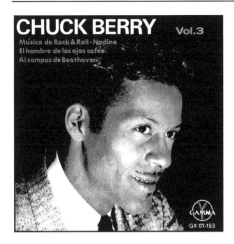 

CHUCK BERRY (VOLUME 3)
Gamma GX-07.153 • 1965?
Música de Rock & Roll [Rock And Roll Music] / Nadine / Al Compas de Beethoven [Roll Over Beethoven] / El Hombre de los Ojos Cafés [Brown Eyed Handsome Man]

Chess recordings. Again a *great* cover! The same liner notes as VOLUMES 1 and 2.

LPs

BACK HOME
Gamma GX-01.414 • 1970
Same tracks and front cover as the 1970 US LP [Chess LPS-1550].

LO MEJOR DE CHUCK BERRY
Mercury 6338 026 • 1970
Memphis, Tennessee / Roll Over Beethoven / Rock And Roll Music / School Day / Johnny B. Goode / Carol / Maybellene / Sweet Little Sixteen / Back In The USA / Thirty Days / C.C. Rider+ *(live)*

Gatefold cover with inside slot (you have to open the cover to get the record out).

THE LONDON CHUCK BERRY SESSIONS
Importa/Som 310.1008 • 1972
Same tracks and gatefold cover as the 1972 US LP [Chess CH-60020]. However, the interesting thing here is that there is a notice in red and white on the inside cover: *'For better results, this record must be played at highest volume possible.'* There are also labels on the front and on the inside advising listeners to *'Play Loud'*. This is the first time I have seen something like this printed on a Berry album. But they are quite correct – your listening experience will be quite different if you play this classic album at high volume!

COLLECTION CHUCK BERRY (VOLUME 1)
Trebol TI-70693 ● 1983

COLLECTION CHUCK BERRY (VOLUME 2)
Trebol TI-70694 ● 1983
    Same tracks as the 1982 US 2-LP set, THE GREAT 28 [Chess CH-8201], but released as two single albums. VOLUME 1 has a yellow front cover and VOLUME 2 has a blue one, both with the same drawing of Berry as on the US album. Although the titles appear in English on the covers ('COLLECTION'), the labels use the Spanish equivalent ('COLECCIÓN'). Original liner notes in English, same on both volumes.

16 SUPER EXITOS DE CHUCK BERRY
Mediterraneo LPR-2117 ● 1984
Maybellene / Sweet Little Sixteen / School Day / Rock And Roll Music / Johnny B. Goode / Carol / Reelin' And Rockin' / Memphis, Tennessee / Roll Over Beethoven / Back In The USA / Sweet Little Rock And Roller / Oh Baby Doll / C.C. Rider+ *(live)* / Thirty Days / Goodnight, Well It's Time To Go [It's Time To Go] / Back To Memphis

    Mercury tracks. Same front cover as the 1974 US LP, WILD BERRYS [Pickwick SPC-3392].

HAIL! HAIL! ROCK'N'ROLL
MCA LCA-6694 ● 1987
    Original soundtrack. Same tracks and cover as the 1987 US LP [MCA MCA-6217].

30 AÑOS DE MUSICA ROCK – SALVAT / GOLDEN HITS
Mercury 822-286-1 ● Late 1980s
    Same tracks as the 1967 US LP, GOLDEN HITS [Mercury SR-61103], but a different cover. Liner notes in Spanish.

GREATEST HITS
Peerless PEE-20032-9 ● 1989
Back In The USA / School Day / Rock And Roll Music / Around And Around / Memphis, Tennessee / Sweet Little Rock And Roller / Little Queenie / Nadine / Let it Rock / Sweet Little Sixteen / Beautiful Delilah / Route 66+

    Same front cover as the 1961 US LP, NEW JUKE BOX HITS [Chess LP-1456].

REELIN' AND ROCKIN'
Peerless PEE-20037-1 ● 1989
Johnny B. Goode / You Never Can Tell / Carol / Maybellene / No Particular Place To Go / Brown Eyed Handsome Man / Roll Over Beethoven / Reelin' And Rockin' / Bye Bye Johnny / Too Much Monkey Business / Promised Land / Thirty Days

    Chess recordings. Liner notes in Spanish. Same front cover as the 1984 UK LP with the same title (but different tracks) [Topline TOP-117].

NETHERLANDS

As far as I know, very few Chuck Berry singles were issued in the Netherlands during the '50s. It is only relatively recently that some '50s Berry singles from the Netherlands have turned up. The Dutch London labels were blue-grey. There is no complete list of the mysterious Fast label (black with silver print), which Malte Koch and I first came across in the late '90s.

However, all that changed in 1963, when Artone (who also distributed to the Benelux countries, West Germany and Austria) started releasing singles, EPs and LPs, many of them with attractive pictures on the cover. The earliest of these came out on the Funckler label, which was originally black, but then changed to orange. After the launch of the Chess International label, the label colour stayed orange. You can find many of the singles with all three label variations. The latest one I have which was issued with both the orange Funckler and Chess International labels is AR-45.133. Unfortunately, none of these records has the release year printed on the cover or label. However, 1963-66 would be a reasonable guess.

As regards the singles, they often had different picture sleeves too. You can also find Funckler sleeves with a Chess International record tucked inside. Not only that, some picture sleeves had different colours on the front. One particular single, AR-45.082, I have in five different variations.

EPs saw some equally confusing combinations of Funckler and Chess International packaging, however I have never seen any with the black Funckler label (see the singles listing for more info). There are also slight differences on the backs of the covers in the information relating to other releases on the Funckler and Chess International labels.

Nine albums were issued on Funckler and Chess International between 1964-68, again with some confusing combinations. To make things even more disorderly, the catalogue number was changed on some issues.

At least some of Berry's original US LPs were re-issued in the Netherlands in 1973-74, with original covers, starting with AFTER SCHOOL SESSION [Chess CQ-20.081]. Unfortunately I don't have all the information needed for a complete survey on these reissues.

Singles

Sweet Little Sixteen / Reelin' And Rockin'
London FL-1726 • 1958

Johnny B. Goode / Around And Around
London FL-1748 • 1958

Beautiful Delilah / Vacation Time
London FL-1786 • 1958

Carol / Hey Pedro
London FL-1796 • 1958

Too Pooped To Pop / Let It Rock
Fast 1056 • 1960

London sleeve, late '50s

London FL-1796

Fast 1068

Funckler AR-45.012

Funckler AR-45.082

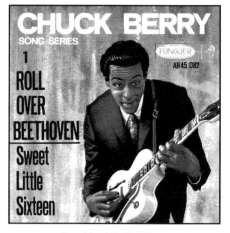

Funckler AR-45.082

394

Funckler AR-45.088

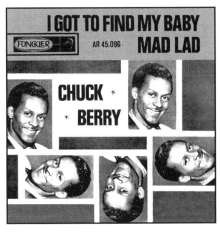

Funckler AR-45.096

Funckler AR-45.097

Funckler AR-45.097 (black label)

Funckler AR-45.098 (black label)

Funckler AR-45.098 (orange label)

Chess AR-45.098 (orange label)

Funckler AR-45.098

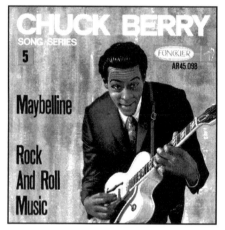

Funckler AR-45.098

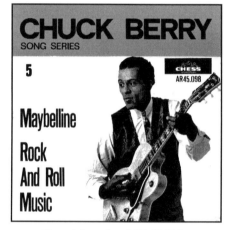

Chess International AR-45.098

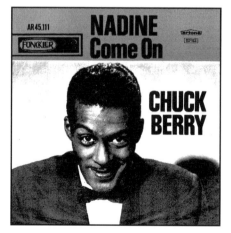

Funckler AR-45.111

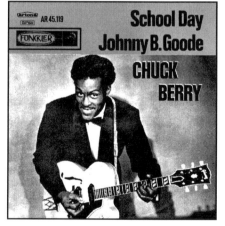

Funckler AR-45.119

Funckler AR-45.120

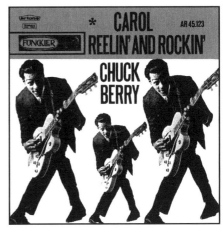

Funckler AR-45.123

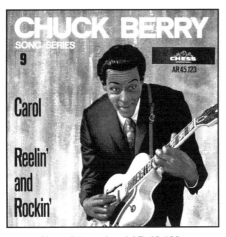

Chess International AR-45.123

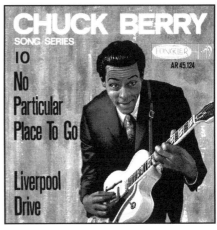

Funckler AR-45.124

Funckler AR-45.1126

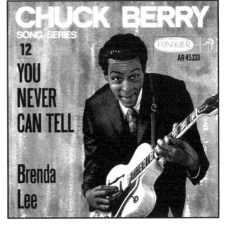

Funckler AR-45.133

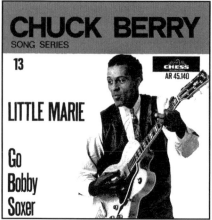

Chess International AR-45.140

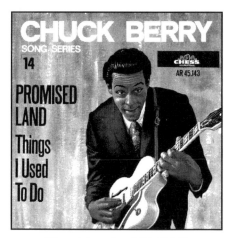

Chess International AR-45.143

Chess International AR-45.161

Chess International AR-45.179

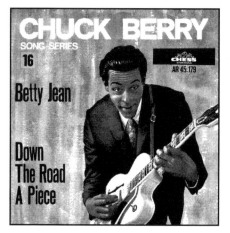

Chess International AR-45.179

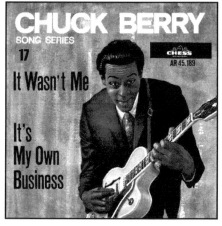

Chess International AR-45.189

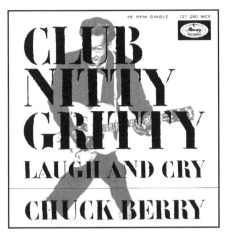

Mercury 127-260-MCF

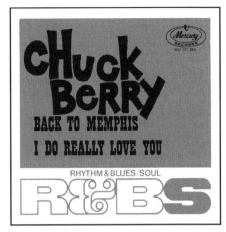

Mercury 127-295-MCF

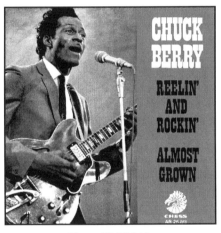

Chess AR-25.811

Chess CH-2131

Chess CH-2160

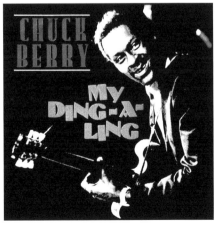

Friends 190.056

Bye Bye Johnny / Worried Life Blues+
Fast 1068 • 1960
'B' side is credited to Berry.

Almost Grown / Johnny B. Goode
Fast 1081 • 1960

Jaguar And The Thunderbird / Our Little Rendezvous
Funckler [Artone] AR-45.012 • 1963
This has the same picture sleeve as AR-45.097, but a lower number and a silver/grey label with 'Funckler' in blue.

Roll Over Beethoven / Sweet Little Sixteen *(overdubbed audience)*
Funckler/Chess International [Artone] AR-45.082 • October 1963
This first came out on the black Funckler label with a black and white picture of Berry and a bust of Beethoven rolling over (geddit?). The picture sleeve had an orange band across the top with the titles in black, and also came with a purple top. The record then came out on the orange Funckler label with an orange top on the picture sleeve. Both sides of the sleeve were the same.

Later on, it came out as No. 1 of a *'Chuck Berry Song Series'*, with a colour drawing of Berry on the sleeve. The other side of the sleeve listed the first ten volumes. All had the same artwork on the front. However, they also came out with an alternative sleeve design with a black and white picture of Berry and an orange top with *'Chuck Berry Song Series'* printed in black. Both sides were the same. To complicate things further, the *Song Series* was issued both on the orange Funckler label and the Chess International label .

The *'Chuck Berry Song Series'* itself ran to 17 issues. The earliest releases did not carry the series title on the sleeve, though this appeared on later ones. At least the first 12 singles were issued on Funckler (with black and orange labels) and then on Chess International (orange label). From AR-45.143 they only used the *'Song Series'* design. At least, I have only seen the last four issues with the 'colour drawing of Berry' sleeve.

There are some confusing combinations of Funckler sleeves and Chess International labels. Be that as it may, all are interesting collector's items.

Memphis, Tennessee *(with overdubbed audience)* / **Go, Go, Go**
Funckler/Chess International [Artone] AR-45.088 • March 1964
Picture sleeve. Later issued as No. 2 of a *'Chuck Berry Song Series'* with the same catalogue number but a different sleeve (see AR-45.082 above for more information).

I Got To Find My Baby+ / Mad Lad+ *(instr)*
Funckler/Chess International [Artone] AR-45.096 • March 1964
Picture sleeve. Later issued as No. 3 of a *'Chuck Berry Song Series'* with the same catalogue number but a different sleeve (see AR-45.082 above for more information).

Jaguar And The Thunderbird / Our Little Rendezvous
Funckler/Chess International [Artone] AR-45.097 • March 1964
Black Funckler label. Great picture sleeve with four pictures of Berry from the movie, *Go Johnny Go.* (NB This single was previously issued in 1963 as AR-45012 with a silver/grey label and 'Funckler' in blue.) Later issued as No. 4 of a *'Chuck Berry Song Series'* with the same catalogue number but a different sleeve (see AR-45.082 above for more information).

Maybellene / Rock And Roll Music
Funckler/Chess International [Artone] AR-45.098 • March 1964
Picture sleeve. Later issued as No. 5 of a *'Chuck Berry Song Series'* with the same catalogue number but a different sleeve (see AR-45.082 above for more information).

Nadine / Come On
Funckler/Chess International [Artone] AR-45.111 • April 1964
Picture sleeve. Later issued as No. 6 of a *'Chuck Berry Song Series'* with the same catalogue number but a different sleeve (see AR-45.082 above for more information).

School Day / Johnny B. Goode
Funckler/Chess International [Artone] AR-45.119 • April 1964
Picture sleeve. Later issued as No. 7 of a *'Chuck Berry Song Series'* with the same catalogue number but a different sleeve (see AR-45.082 above for more information).

Let It Rock / Too Much Monkey Business
Funckler/Chess International [Artone] AR-45.120 • April 1964
Picture sleeve. Later issued as No. 8 of a *'Chuck Berry Song Series'* with the same catalogue number but a different sleeve (see AR-45.082 above for more information).

Carol / Reelin' And Rockin'
Funckler/Chess International [Artone] AR-45.123 • April 1964
Picture sleeve. Later issued as No. 9 of a *'Chuck Berry Song Series'* with the same catalogue number but a different sleeve (see AR-45.082 above for more information).

No Particular Place To Go / Liverpool Drive *(instr)*
Funckler/Chess International [Artone] AR-45.124 • May 1964
Picture sleeve. Later issued as No. 10 of a 'Chuck Berry Song Series' with the same catalogue number but a different sleeve (see AR-45.082 above for more information).

Fraulein+ / Lonely All The Time [Crazy Arms]+
Funckler/Chess International [Artone] AR-45.125 • May 1964
This is a rare single coupling. The Netherlands is the only country to have released these two Berry recordings together on a single. The composer credits on the 'A' side read 'Traditional – arranged by Chuck Berry'. The 'B' side is credited to Berry. Picture sleeve. Later issued as No. 11 of a 'Chuck Berry Song Series' with the same catalogue number but a different sleeve (see AR-45.082 above for more information).

You Never Can Tell / Brenda Lee
Funckler/Chess International [Artone] AR-45.133 • May 1964
Picture sleeve. This was probably the last single to be released both on Funckler and Chess International. Later issued as No. 12 of a 'Chuck Berry Song Series' with the same catalogue number but a different sleeve (see AR-45.082 above for more information).

Little Marie / Go, Bobby Soxer
Chess International [Artone] AR-45.140 • November 1964
Picture sleeve. Later issued as No. 13 of a 'Chuck Berry Song Series' with the same catalogue number but a different sleeve (see AR-45.082 above for more information).

Promised Land / The Things I Used To Do+
Chess International [Artone] AR-45.143 • February 1965
Picture sleeve. Issued as No. 14 of a 'Chuck Berry Song Series' with the 'colour drawing of Berry' sleeve (see AR-45.082 above for more information).

Lonely School Days *(slow version)* / **Dear Dad**
Chess International [Artone] AR-45.161 • 1965
Picture sleeve. Issued as No. 15 of a 'Chuck Berry Song Series' with the 'colour drawing of Berry' sleeve (see AR-45.082 above for more information).

Betty Jean / Down The Road A Piece+
Chess International [Artone] AR-45.179 • 1965
Picture sleeve. Issued as No. 16 of a 'Chuck Berry Song Series' with the 'colour drawing of Berry' sleeve (see AR-45.082 above for more information).

It Wasn't Me / It's My Own Business
Chess International [Artone] AR-45.189 • 1965
Picture sleeve. Issued as No. 17 of a 'Chuck Berry Song Series' with the 'colour drawing of Berry' sleeve (see AR-45.082 above for more information).

Club Nitty Gritty / Laugh And Cry
Mercury 127-260-MCF • 1966
Blue label. Picture sleeve.

Back To Memphis / I Do Really Love You
Mercury 127-295-MCF • 1967
Art sleeve.

Johnny B. Goode / Sweet Little Sixteen
Chess [Artone] AR-25.802 • 1968
Great picture sleeve with five small pictures of Berry in a circle.

Reelin' And Rockin' / Almost Grown
Chess [Artone] AR-25.811 • 1968
Great picture sleeve! There is a reference on the label to the 1964 LP, RHYTHM & BLUES RENDEZ-VOUS [Chess International PAR-107].

My Ding-A-Ling *(live, single edit)* / **Johnny B. Goode**
Chess CH-2131 • 1972
The 'B' side is the original 1958 Chess cut, but the matrix number listed is for the 1972 live cut from England. Picture sleeve.

Memphis, Tennessee / Johnny B. Goode
Chess CH-2149 • 1972
Picture sleeve.

Reelin' And Rockin' *(live, single edit)* / **Let's Boogie**
Chess CH-2160 • 1973
Art sleeve.

My Ding-A-Ling *(live, single edit)* / **Carol**
Friends [CNR] 190.056 • 1988
This was a plug single for the 1988 2-LP, HAIL! HAIL! ROCK'N'ROLL [Friends 690.014], also released as two separate CDs on the Injection Disco Dance Label [100.181 and 100.182]. Picture sleeve. See also the 1988 CD plug single [Injection Disco Dance Label 100.179]. All these records were also released in Belgium and Norway.

EPs

RHYTHM & BLUES WITH CHUCK BERRY
London RE-1053 • 1957?
Maybellene / Wee Wee Hours / Thirty Days / Together (We Will Always Be)

This is mentioned on the back of the London EP below. The number is the same as the 1956 UK issue, except for the prefix, which is 'RE-' instead of 'RE-U-'. No more info available.

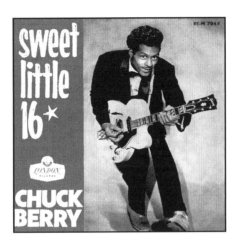

SWEET LITTLE 16
London RE-M-7043 • 1958
Sweet Little Sixteen / Around And Around / Beautiful Delilah / Carol

I have been collecting Berry records since 1963 and I had never ever heard of this EP before. It came up for auction on eBay in November 2006 and went for around £350.

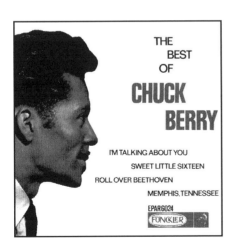

THE BEST OF CHUCK BERRY
Funckler/Chess International [Artone] EPAR-6024 • 1964
Memphis, Tennessee / Roll Over Beethoven / I'm Talking About You / Sweet Little Sixteen

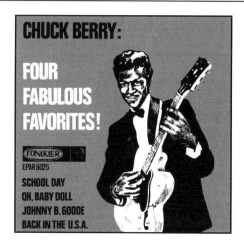

FOUR FABULOUS FAVORITES!
Funckler/Chess International [Artone] EPAR-6025 • 1964
Johnny B. Goode / Oh Baby Doll / School Day / Back In The USA

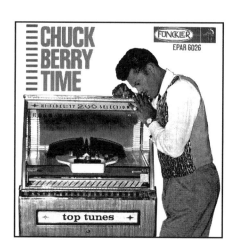 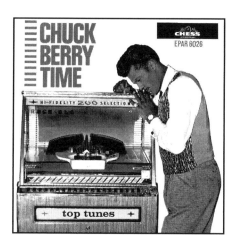

CHUCK BERRY TIME
Funckler/Chess International [Artone] EPAR-6026 • 1964
Bye Bye Johnny / Rock And Roll Music / You Can't Catch Me / No Money Down

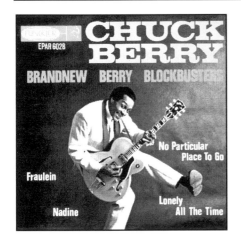

BRANDNEW BERRY BLOCKBUSTERS
Funckler/Chess International [Artone] EPAR-6028 • 1964
No Particular Place To Go / Fraulein+ / Nadine / Lonely All The Time [Crazy Arms]+

An interesting coupling of tracks and, although I like the title of this EP, the two ballads won't go down in history as Berry blockbusters.

FOUR MORE FAVORITES
Funckler/Chess International [Artone] EPAR-6030 • 1965
You Never Can Tell / Brenda Lee / Promised Land / The Things I Used To Do+

The front cover has a great picture of Berry!

LPs

Funckler MGCH-9218   Chess International PAR-106

CHUCK BERRY ON STAGE
Funckler MGCH-9218 / Chess International MGCH-9218 / Chess International PAR-106 [Artone] • March 1964

Same tracks as the 1963 US LP [Chess LP-1480], but a different cover. 'How High The Moon' is referred to as an 'Instrumental Sign-Off'. The label states that the album was recorded live. This LP was originally issued on Funckler MGCH-9218 with a black label and same number, then with an orange label. It was subsequently released on Chess International with the same number, and later with the number PAR-106. The latter release came in a folded cover (3 sides open) inside a clear plastic sleeve ('CHUCK BERRY ON STAGE' was printed in red on the back of the cover), and also in a standard flip-over cover without the plastic sleeve (with 'CHUCK BERRY ON STAGE' in black on the back cover). Just to set the record straight, all the other versions had 'CHUCK BERRY ON STAGE' printed in red on the back cover. However, on MGCH-9218, 'Surfin' Steel' ['Crying Steel'] was shown as 'Surfin' USA'. On PAR-106 it was shown as 'Surfin' Steel'. In total, you would need five copies of this album to have all the permutations.

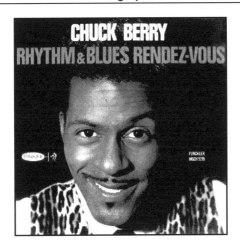

RHYTHM & BLUES RENDEZ-VOUS
Funckler MGCH-9219 / Chess International PAR-107 [Artone] • April 1964
Same tracks as the 1962 US LP, CHUCK BERRY TWIST and 1963's MORE CHUCK BERRY [Chess LP-1465], but a different cover. On the back there's a reference to the ON STAGE album: *'For another Chuck Berry session listen to Funckler MGCH-9218, 'Chuck Berry On Stage'. Recorded live in the Tivoli Theatre, Chicago, Chuck creates tremendous excitement and audience response thru' such classics as 'Memphis, Tennessee', 'Jaguar And The Thunderbird', 'Go, Go, Go', 'Brown Eyed Handsome Man' and ten more dynamic Berry-composed ditties!'* No wonder people here in Northern Europe thought it was a live album!

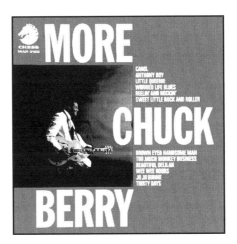

MORE CHUCK BERRY
Chess International PAR-104 / MAR-3123 [Artone] • 1964
Same tracks as the 1963 UK LP [Pye International NPL-28028], but a different cover. Since this album also has the number PAR-104, it means it probably came out before the reissues of the two above, possibly in February 1964.

JUKE BOX SPECIAL
Chess International PAR-119 [Artone] ● 1964
Same tracks as the 1961 US LP, NEW JUKE-BOX HITS [Chess LP-1456], but a different cover.

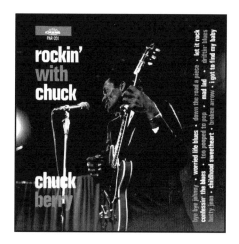

ROCKIN' WITH CHUCK
Chess International PAR-031 [Artone] ● 1964
Same as the 1960 US LP, ROCKIN' AT THE HOPS [Chess LP-1448], but a different cover – great picture!

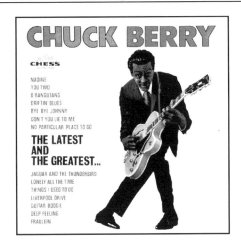

THE LATEST AND THE GREATEST
Chess International MGAR-9223 [Artone] ● 1964
  Same tracks as the 1964 UK LP [Pye International NPL-28031], but a different cover.

ST. LOUIS TO LIVERPOOL
Chess International MGAR-9224 [Artone] *(mono)* **● 1965**
  Same tracks and cover as the 1964 US LP [Chess LP-1488]. Reissued in stereo in 1973 [Chess CQ-20.062].

CHUCK BERRY IN LONDON
Chess International MGAR-9225 [Artone] *(mono)* **● 1965**
  Same tracks as the 1965 UK LP [Chess CRL-4005], but a different cover – great picture!

FRESH BERRY'S
Chess International MGAR-9227 [Artone] • 1966
    Same tracks and cover as the 1965 UK LP [Chess CRL-4506].

GOLDEN HITS
Fontana International 858 002-FPY • 1967
    Same tracks as the 1967 US LP [Mercury SR-61103], but a different cover –
probably the worst ever on a European Berry album. No picture of Berry in sight, but a
young girl on the front cover with braids and – unlike most females adorning album
covers at the time – fully dressed. The cover states *'New Recordings'*.

CHUCK BERRY IN MEMPHIS
Fontana International 858 027-FPY • 1967
    Same tracks as the 1967 US LP [Mercury SR-61123]. Same front cover and liner
notes on the back cover. However, if you're a fanatical Berry collector, you need to
note that there are different LP covers from other artists on the back (I have two
variations).

LIVE AT THE FILLMORE AUDITORIUM, SAN FRANCISCO
Fontana International 858 047-FPY ● 1967
Same tracks and cover as the 1967 US LP [Mercury SR-61138].

FROM ST. LOUIE TO FRISCO
Fontana International 134 082-MCY ● 1968
Same tracks and cover as the 1968 US LP [Mercury SR-61176].

CONCERTO IN B GOODE
Fontana International 134 222-MCY ● 1969
Same tracks and cover as the 1969 US LP [Mercury SR-61223].

THE LONDON CHUCK BERRY SESSIONS
Chess CH-60020 ● 1972
Same tracks and cover as the 1972 US LP [Chess CH-60020].

SAN FRANCISCO DUES
Chess CH-50008 ● 1972
Same tracks and cover as the 1971 US LP [Chess CH-50008].

CHUCK BERRY'S GREATEST HITS
Chess HJC-171 ● 1972
Same tracks as the 1964 US LP [Chess LP-1485], but a different cover. Reissued in the late '70s [Chess SPLO-122].

ROCK HITS
Fontana International 6430 022 ● 1972
Same tracks as the 1967 US LP, GOLDEN HITS [Mercury SR-61103], but a different cover. This reissue appeared in many European countries with substantially the same cover but different titles. It was released in 1972 in the Netherlands as ROCK HITS [Fontana International 6430 022], in West Germany as ATTENTION! [Fontana 6430 022], in Norway and Spain as ROCK AND ROLL MUSIC [Fontana Special 6430 022 and Fontana 6430 022 respectively]. (However, the record label inside the Spanish issue actually says GOLDEN HITS.) In 1973 it was released in Italy as ROCK HITS [Fontana Special 6430 022], in France as ROCK AND ROLL MUSIC [Fontana 6430 022] and in the UK – with a different catalogue number from all the other variations – as BACK IN THE USA [Philips 6336 216].

BIO
Chess CH-50043 ● 1973
Same tracks and cover as the 1973 US LP [Chess CH-50043].

ST. LOUIS TO LIVERPOOL
Chess CQ-20.062 ● 1973
Same tracks and cover as the 1964 US LP [LPS-1488]. Also issued in Italy in 1972 [Cadet CQ-20.062].

AFTER SCHOOL SESSION
Chess CQ-20.081 • 1974
Same tracks and cover as the 1957 US LP [Chess LP-1426].

SPOTLIGHT ON CHUCK BERRY
Chess SPLO-3 • 1975
My Ding-A-Ling *(live, single edit)* / No Particular Place To Go / You Never Can Tell / No Money Down / Roly Poly *(instr)* / Let's Boogie / Go, Go, Go / Reelin' And Rockin' *(live, single edit)* / Carol / Run Rudolph Run+ / Around And Around / Bye Bye Johnny / Wee Wee Hours / Berry Pickin' *(instr)*

MYSTERY LP

UNKNOWN TITLE
Unknown label, 9198 198 • Netherlands(?), 1977(?)
Roll Over Beethoven / School Day / Around And Around / Reelin' And Rockin' / Johnny B. Goode / Down The Road A Piece+ / Jaguar And The Thunderbird / I Got To Find My Baby / Go, Go, Go / Go, Bobby Soxer / No Particular Place To Go / Nadine / You Never Can Tell / St. Louis Blues+

I recently bought a white label pressing of what appears to be yet another collection of Chuck Berry's Chess cuts. There is no information on it at all, other than the number "9198 198" scratched in the run-off groove on both sides. I have been unable to track down any more information about this album, so it is possible it was never released.

ROCKIN' WITH CHUCK BERRY
Philips Success Series 9279 540 • 1977
Sweet Little Sixteen / Memphis, Tennessee / Roll Over Beethoven / Thirty Days / Carol / Nadine / Johnny B. Goode / Rock And Roll Music / School Day / Maybellene / Back In The USA / No Particular Place To Go

Chess recordings. Same tracks, title and cover as the 1977 UK LP [Philips SUC-114].

PORTRAIT OF CHUCK BERRY
Chess Success Series 9279 541 • 1977
My Ding-A-Ling *(live, single edit)* / Little Queenie / Let It Rock / Too Pooped To Pop+ / Bye Bye Johnny / Oh Baby Doll / Reelin' And Rockin' / Sweet Little Rock And Roller / Jo Jo Gunne / Run Rudolph Run+ / Almost Grown / Thirty Days

'Too Pooped To Pop' is credited to Berry. 'Let It Rock' is the version without Berry's lead guitar.

CHUCK BERRY'S GREATEST HITS
Chess 9283 004 • 1977
Maybellene / Oh Baby Doll / Too Pooped To Pop+ / Sweet Little Sixteen / Rock And Roll Music / Back In The USA / School Day / Johnny B. Goode / Wee Wee Hours / Roll Over Beethoven / Thirty Days / Memphis, Tennessee

'Too Pooped To Pop' is credited to Berry.

MOTORVATIN'
Chess 9283 020 • 1977
Same tracks and cover as the 1977 UK LP [Chess 9286 690].

GREATEST HITS
Chess SPLO-122 • 1979
Same tracks as the 1972 LP [Chess HJC-171], with slightly different front cover and different back cover.

ROCK LIONS – CHUCK BERRY
Philips 6337 151 • 1981
Same tracks as the 1967 US LP, GOLDEN HITS [Mercury SR-61103], but a different cover. On the back cover are US and UK chart positions for each song, would you believe (except 'Club Nitty Gritty', of course). There is a notice in small print that the songs on the album are re-recordings. The fanciful liner notes state that Berry was born in 1931, and that 'Roll Over Beethoven' was a hit in 1965!

GREATEST HITS (VOLUME 1)
Rainbow 6063 • 1981
Sweet Little Rock And Roller / Goodnight, Well It's Time To Go [It's Time To Go] / Oh Baby Doll / Thirty Days / Reelin' And Rockin' / Back In The USA / I Do Really Love You / My Heart Will Always Belong To You+ / Good Lookin' Woman / Back To Memphis

GREATEST HITS (VOLUME 2)
Rainbow 6064 • 1981
Roll Over Beethoven / Memphis, Tennessee / Sweet Little Sixteen / Maybellene / Carol / C.C. Rider+ *(live)* / Johnny B. Goode / Ramblin' Rose+ / School Day / Rock And Roll Music

Once again we get the Mercury recordings under the strange title of GREATEST HITS, and in two volumes! Same tracks as the 1976 US LP, GREATEST HITS [Everest FS-321], but not in the same order. On VOLUME 2, 'C.C. Rider' is faded out on Side 1 and comes in again on Side 2. (Help!) Identical and very dull covers. The two Rainbow albums were also issued in Belgium on Surprise Records as part of a three-LP box set. See also Belgian discography.

20 GREATEST HITS
Masters MA-0016983 • 1982
Roll Over Beethoven / Back In The USA / Johnny B. Goode / Good Lovin' Woman [Good Lookin' Woman] / School Day / Sweet Little Rock And Roller / Maybellene / Oh Baby Doll / Rock And Roll Music / Thirty Days / Ramblin' Rose+ / Goodnight, Well It's Time To Go [It's Time To Go] / Carol / Back To Memphis / C.C. Rider+ *(live)* / My Heart Will Always Belong To You+ / Sweet Little Sixteen / Reelin' And Rockin' / Memphis, Tennessee / I Do really Love You

20 Mercury tracks with *very* bad sound quality. You don't really want to know what songs are on this, but I listed them anyway. These kind of albums are so poor that you can probably find them at cheap sales for next to nothing. Reissued in 1985 on two CDs [Masters SPEC-85004 and M Music MM-85004].

20 GREATEST HITS
Black Tulip BT.555017 • 1983
Mercury recordings and the usual poor sound quality. The tracks are very similar to the one above on Masters.

ROCK! ROCK! ROCK'N'ROLL!
Mercury 6463 044 • 1983
Same tracks and cover as the 1980 German LP with the same number.

HAIL! HAIL! ROCK'N'ROLL [2-LP]
Friends [CNR] 690.014/15 • 1988
Not the movie soundtrack. Same tracks as the 1988 UK 2-LP [Chess DETD-207], but different gatefold cover. Also released as separate CDs [Injection Disco Dance Label 100.181 and 100.182]. There was also a plug single [Friends 690.014 (7" vinyl) and Injection Disco Dance Label 100.179 (CD)]. All these records were also released in Belgium and Norway.

20 GREATEST HITS
Black Tulip 2636801 • 1988
Sweet Little Sixteen / School Day / Maybellene / Rock And Roll Music / Johnny B. Goode / No Particular Place To Go / Carol / Let It Rock / Thirty Days / Beautiful Delilah / Roll Over Beethoven / Around And Around / Memphis, Tennessee / Little Queenie / Back In The USA / Reelin' And Rockin' / Too Much Monkey Business / You Can't Catch Me / Sweet Little Rock And Roller / Brown Eyed Handsome Man

Chess recordings. Good picture of Berry on the front cover. The label and cover say '*Made in W. Germany*', but the cover was designed in the Netherlands. As far as I know this album emanates from the Netherlands. Also issued on CD [Black Tulip 2636802].

ROCK & ROLL MUSIC (VOLUME 1)
Roots RTS-113008 • 1990
Maybellene / Wee Wee Hours / Thirty Days / Together (We Will Always Be) / Berry Pickin' *(instr)* / Down Bound Train / No Money Down / Roly Poly *(instr)* / You Can't Catch Me / Too Much Monkey Business / Brown Eyed Handsome Man / Roll Over Beethoven / Drifting Heart / Havana Moon / School Day / Blue Feeling *(instr)* / Oh Baby Doll / Rock And Roll Music / I've Changed / Reelin' And Rockin'

Interesting and good selection of digitally remastered Chess tracks. The authoritative liner notes by Herman van der Horst get this author's approval – well done! Also issued on CD [Roots RTS-33008].

MY DING-A-LING / THE LONDON CHUCK BERRY SESSIONS
Roots RTS-113019 • 1990
Same tracks as the 1972 US LP [Chess CH-60020], digitally remastered, plus four bonus cuts: 'Tulane', 'Have Mercy Judge', 'My Dream' and 'Bio'. Be sure to get the LP to fully appreciate the great front cover! Also issued on CD [Roots RTS-33019]. The LP cover says '*Made in Belgium*', but the CD says '*Made in the Netherlands*'. However, this only indicates where the records were pressed or the album covers printed; it does not indicate where they were actually released.

SWEET LITTLE SIXTEEN
Roots RTS-113032 • 1990
Deep Feeling *(instr)* / Low Feeling *(instr)* / La Jaunda / How You've Changed / Thirteen Question Method / Sweet Little Sixteen *(original speed)* / Rock At The Philharmonic *(instr)* / Guitar Boogie *(instr)* / Surfin' USA [Sweet Little Sixteen *(with overdubbed audience)*] / Night Beat *(instr)* / Ingo

(instr) / It Don't Take But A Few Minutes / Johnny B. Goode / Around And Around / Surfin' Steel [Crying Steel *(instr, overdubbed audience)*] / Blues For Hawaiians *(instr)* / Carol / Hey Pedro / Beautiful Delilah / House Of Blue Lights+ / Time Was+ [1958] / Oh Yeah / Vacation Time

A very strange but interesting selection of songs. I don't think there ever was an album by Berry with so many instrumentals (8) assembled together on one issue. However, to include 'Sweet Little Sixteen' twice is just plain stupid. The second one is taken from the ON STAGE album with the overdubbed live audience. The same goes for 'Crying Steel' (or 'Surfin' Steel' as it was titled on the ON STAGE album), which of course is very similar to 'Blues For Hawaiians'. For some strange reason, in the Netherlands they have fallen in love with 'Low Feeling', which is incomprehensible, as 'Blue Feeling' is so much better. Also issued on CD [Roots RTS-33032].

CD Singles

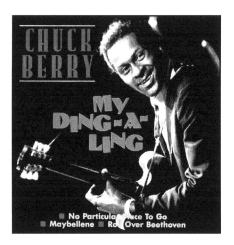

MY DING-A-LING
Injection Disco Dance Label [CNR] 100.179 • 1988
My Ding-A-Ling *(live, single edit)* / No Particular Place To Go / Maybellene / Roll Over Beethoven

This was a plug single for the 1988 2-LP, HAIL! HAIL! ROCK'N'ROLL [Friends 690.014], also released as two separate CDs [Injection Disco Dance Label 100.181 and 100.182]. Same front cover picture. See also 1988 7" plug single [Friends 190.056]. All these records were also released in Belgium and Norway.

CD Albums

20 GREATEST HITS
Spectrum SPEC-85004 • 1985
Same tracks and cover as the 1982 LP [Masters MA-0016983]. Also issued on CD [M Music MM-85004], same cover. Both were probably also issued as LPs but I have no other information. Cover says *'Printed in France'*.

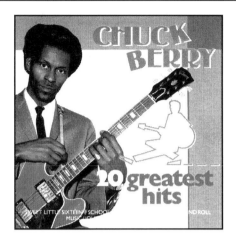

20 GREATEST HITS
Black Tulip 2636802 ● 1988
Sweet Little Sixteen / School Day / Maybellene / Rock And Roll Music / Johnny B. Goode / No Particular Place To Go / Carol / Let It Rock / Thirty Days / Beautiful Delilah / Roll Over Beethoven / Around And Around / Memphis, Tennessee / Little Queenie / Back In The USA / Reelin' And Rockin' / Too Much Monkey Business / You Can't Catch Me / Sweet Little Rock And Roller / Brown Eyed Handsome Man

Chess recordings. Good picture of Berry on the front cover. Also issued on LP [Black Tulip 2636801]. The LP cover says *'Made in Belgium'*, but the CD says *'Made in the Netherlands'*. However, this only indicates where the records were pressed or the album covers printed; it does not indicate where they were actually released. The same comments also apply to the two following CDs.

GREATEST HITS
Black Tulip Special 2640772 ● 1988

SUPER HITS
Black Tulip Special 2640782 ● 1988
These two contain almost the same Chess tracks (ten each) as the 20 GREATEST HITS set above, but have different covers. I have never seen LP issues of these two, but I reckon they also came out on vinyl.

HAIL! HAIL! ROCK'N'ROLL (1955-58)
Injection Disco Dance Label [CNR] 100.181 ● 1988

HAIL! HAIL! ROCK'N'ROLL (1959-72)
Injection Disco Dance Label [CNR] 100.182 ● 1988
Not the movie soundtrack. This is the 1988 2-LP, HAIL! HAIL! ROCK'N'ROLL [Friends 690.014/15] released as two separate CDs, both with the same cover. There was also a plug single [Friends 690.014 (7" vinyl) and Injection Disco Dance Label 100.179 (CD)]. All these records were also released in Belgium and Norway.

You wouldn't believe how many Chuck Berry CDs have been released in the Netherlands on various independent labels. In the late '80s to the mid-'90s I bought everything I could get hold of. Many of these CDs were not collectable items and never will be! So, at the end of the decade, I stopped being a fool. I have listed below only the albums that are of particular interest to Berry collectors.

HEROES OF ROCK'N'ROLL – CHUCK BERRY
Heroes of Rock'n'Roll HR-002 • 1989
Johnny B. Goode / Roll Over Beethoven / Carol / Rock And Roll Music / Thirty Days / No Particular Place To Go / Sweet Little Sixteen / Maybellene / School Day / Brown Eyed Handsome Man / Too Much Monkey Business / Almost Grown

Chess tracks in okay sound quality.

HEROES OF ROCK'N'ROLL – CHUCK BERRY (VOLUME 2)
Heroes of Rock'n'Roll HR-006 • 1990
My Ding-A-Ling *(live, single edit)* / Let It Rock / Sweet Little Rock And Roller* / Nadine / Back In The USA* / Bring Another Drink+* / You Never Can Tell *(stereo)* / Little Queenie / Promised Land *(stereo)* / Good Lookin' Woman* / Merry Christmas Baby+ *(single version)* / Goodnight, Well It's Time To Go [It's Time To Go]*

Mainly Chess tracks, except those marked *, which are Mercury.

HEROES OF ROCK'N'ROLL – CHUCK BERRY (VOLUME 3)
Heroes of Rock'n'Roll HR-007 • 1990
Memphis, Tennessee* / Reelin' And Rockin'* / You Can't Catch Me / My Heart Will Always Belong To You+* / Oh Baby Doll* / Run Rudolph Run+ / Around And Around / I Do Really Love You* / Check Me Out* / Beautiful Delilah / C.C. Rider+* *(live)* / Back To Memphis*

Mainly Chess tracks, except those marked *, which are Mercury. 'Run Rudolph Run' is credited to Berry.

In 1990 the above three CDs came out as a box set titled HEROES OF ROCK'N'ROLL – CHUCK BERRY [Heroes of Rock'n'Roll HR-301].

ROCK & ROLL MUSIC (VOLUME 1)
Roots RTS-33008 • 1990
Maybellene / Wee Wee Hours / Thirty Days / Together (We Will Always Be) / Berry Pickin' *(instr)* / Down Bound Train / No Money Down / Roly Poly *(instr)* / You Can't Catch Me / Too Much Monkey Business / Brown Eyed Handsome Man / Roll Over Beethoven / Drifting Heart / Havana Moon / School Day / Blue Feeling *(instr)* / Oh Baby Doll / Rock And Roll Music / I've Changed / Reelin' And Rockin'

Interesting and good selection of digitally remastered Chess tracks. The authoritative liner notes by Herman van der Horst get this author's approval – well done! Also issued on LP [Roots RTS-113008].

MY DING-A-LING / THE LONDON CHUCK BERRY SESSIONS
Roots RTS-33019 • 1990
Same tracks as the 1972 US LP [Chess CH-60020], digitally remastered, plus four bonus cuts: 'Tulane', 'Have Mercy Judge', 'My Dream' and 'Bio'. Also issued on LP [Roots RTS-113019]. The LP cover says *'Made in Belgium'*, but the CD says *'Made in the Netherlands'*. However, this only indicates where the records were pressed or the album covers printed; it does not indicate where they were actually released.

SWEET LITTLE SIXTEEN
Roots RTS-33032 • 1990

Deep Feeling *(instr)* / Low Feeling *(instr)* / La Jaunda / How You've Changed / Thirteen Question Method / Sweet Little Sixteen *(original speed)* / Rock At The Philharmonic *(instr)* / Guitar Boogie *(instr)* / Surfin' USA [Sweet Little Sixteen *(with overdubbed audience)*] / Night Beat *(instr)* / Ingo *(instr)* / It Don't Take But A Few Minutes / Johnny B. Goode / Around And Around / Crying Steel *(instr)* [Surfin' Steel] / Blues For Hawaiians *(instr)* / Carol / Hey Pedro / Beautiful Delilah / House Of Blue Lights+ / Time Was+ [1958] / Oh Yeah / Vacation Time

A very strange but interesting selection of songs. I don't think there ever was an album by Berry with so many instrumentals (8) assembled together on one issue. However, to include 'Sweet Little Sixteen' twice is just plain stupid. The second one is taken from the ON STAGE album with the overdubbed live audience. The same goes for 'Crying Steel' (or 'Surfin' Steel' as it was titled on the ON STAGE album) which of course is very similar to 'Blues For Hawaiians'. For some strange reason, in the Netherlands they have fallen in love with 'Low Feeling', which is incomprehensible, as 'Blue Feeling' is so much better. Also issued on LP [Roots RTS-113032].

GOLDEN HITS
Mercury 826-256-2 • 1990

Same tracks and cover as the 1989 US CD reissue with four bonus cuts [Mercury 826-256-2]. This CD was also sold in Germany.

CHUCK BERRY IN MEMPHIS
Mercury 836 071-2 • 1990

Same tracks and cover as the 1989 US CD reissue with one bonus cut [Mercury 836-071-2]. This CD was also sold in Germany.

LIVE AT FILLMORE AUDITORIUM
Mercury 836 072-2 • 1990

Same tracks and cover as the 1989 US CD reissue with five bonus cuts [Mercury 836 072-2]. This CD was also sold in Germany.

FROM ST. LOUIE TO FRISCO
Mercury 836 073-2 • 1990

Same tracks and cover as the 1989 US CD reissue with four bonus cuts [Mercury 836 073-2]. This CD was also sold in Germany.

CONCERTO IN B GOODE
Mercury 836 074-2 • 1990

Same tracks and cover as the 1989 US CD reissue [Mercury 836 074-2]. This CD was also sold in Germany.

20 ROCK & ROLL HITS
Point 2642162 • 1990

Sweet Little Sixteen / School Day / Maybellene / Rock And Roll Music / Johnny B. Goode / No Particular Place To Go / Carol / Let It Rock / Thirty Days / Beautiful Delilah / Roll Over Beethoven / Around And Around / Memphis, Tennessee / Little Queenie / Back In The USA / Reelin' And Rockin' / Too Much Monkey Business / You Can't Catch Me / Sweet Little Rock And Roller / Brown- Eyed Handsome Man

Exactly what it says on the tin: 20 rock'n'roll classics without the 'Ding-A-Ling' – they're all here! Good Berry-walk picture on the cover.

ROCKIN' THE HITS
Special Music SPCD-342 • 1990
Sweet Little Sixteen / Rock And Roll Music / Almost Grown / Back In The USA / You Never Can Tell / You Can't Catch Me / Oh Baby Doll / Roll Over Beethoven / No Particular Place To Go / Too Pooped To Pop+ / Memphis, Tennessee / Around And Around / Too Much Monkey Business / Promised Land *(stereo)*

14 Chess tracks with okay sound quality, but 'Promised Land' has exceptionally good sound. 'Too Pooped To Pop' is credited to Berry.

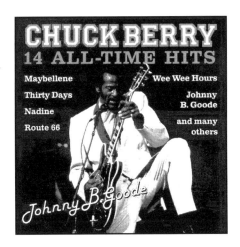

14 ALL-TIME HITS
Special Music SPCD-343 • 1990
Maybellene / Thirty Days / No Money Down / Sweet Little Rock And Roller / Nadine / Little Queenie / Brown Eyed Handsome Man / School Day / Carol / Route 66+ / Reelin' And Rockin' / Little Marie *(stereo, with count-in)* / Wee Wee Hours / Johnny B. Goode

Again 14 Chess tracks with okay sound quality, but 'Route 66' is in dreadful electronic stereo and is even credited to Berry, which is just too much! This CD was also issued in 1990 [Woodford Music WMCD-5547] with the same cover and title.

CHUCK BERRY
Signal 50650 • 1990
Irritating combination of 16 Chess and Mercury tracks. Forget it.

20 GOLDEN HITS
Happy Days 2605422 • 1990
Golden hits, my foot! 19 Mercury tracks plus one from the 1969 *Toronto Rock & Roll Revival.* You don't need to know any more.

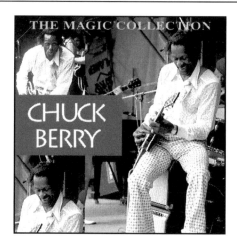

THE MAGIC COLLECTION – CHUCK BERRY
Arc MEC-949141 • 1991
School Day *(live)* / Wee Wee Hours *(live)* / *Medley:* Johnny B. Goode – Carol – Promised Land *(live)* / Hoochie Coochie Man+ *(live)* / Sweet Little Sixteen *(live)* / Rock And Roll Music *(Chess)* / My Ding-A-Ling *(live, single edit, Chess)* / Maybellene *(Chess)* / Too Much Monkey Business *(live)* / Nadine *(live)* / Reelin' And Rockin' *(live)* / Johnny B. Goode *(live, faded)* / Bonsoir Chéri [Hoochie Coochie Man+] *(live)*

Live cuts from the 1969 *Toronto Rock & Roll Revival*. This starts off very well with the first six songs from the show in very good sound quality and no fading in between. Then we get three original Chess tracks, after which we're back again in Toronto with bad sound quality and faded songs. As you can see they have even included 'Hoochie Coochie Man' again, calling it 'Bonsoir Chéri' (credited to *'Berry-Hudson'* !).

THE LONDON SESSIONS
Zillion 2610422 • 1991
Same tracks as the 1972 US LP, THE LONDON CHUCK BERRY SESSIONS [Chess CH-60020], but a different cover with a Berry picture I have never seen before. Also issued as part of a 4-CD box set, together with similar albums by Bo Diddley, Howlin' Wolf and Muddy Waters, titled THE LONDON SESSIONS [Zillion 2698102].

CHUCK BERRY ON STAGE
On Stage OS-007 • 1991
Warning! Apart from the live Chess recording of 'My Ding-A-Ling' (the edited single version), this contains 15 Mercury tracks in pretty bad sound quality that are certainly not live, on stage, in concert, or anything else. The front cover picture is good, though.

MY DINGALING
Royal Collection RC-83148 • 1991
My Ding-A-Ling / School Day / Sweet Little Sixteen / Rock And Roll Music / Wee Wee Hours / Reelin' And Rockin' / Johnny B. Goode... / Maybellene *(live, 1956 Alan Freed radio show)* / Memphis, Tennessee / Too Much Monkey Business

This is bad, very bad! All bar one are from the 1969 *Toronto Rock & Roll Revival*. 'Ding-A-Ling' is edited down to 5:21. 'Johnny B. Goode' is actually the medley version, but stops after the first verse of Carol. 'Maybellene' is a live recording from a 1956 Alan Freed radio show (see the 1978 Various Artists bootleg LP, ROCK'N'ROLL RADIO [Radiola MR-1087] for more information).

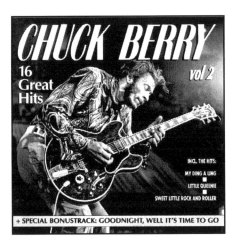

CHUCK BERRY (VOLUME 2) – 16 GREAT HITS
Rock 16 CD-10013 • 1991
The front cover is good. However, this is another irritating combination of (17) Chess and Mercury tracks. Why, oh why? Great hits? Six of the tracks have never seen the light of day on any chart in the world! 'Goodnight, Well It's Time To Go' ['It's Time To Go'] is included as a bonus cut. Give me a break! I haven't seen VOLUME 1 – but who cares? A similarly-titled CD on the same label was issued in France in 1988, but this contained the original Chess tracks.

REELIN' AND ROCKIN'
Arc TOPCD-117 • 1991
Rock And Roll Music / Nadine / School Day / Sweet Little Sixteen / Johnny B. Goode / Maybellene / Memphis, Tennessee / Too Much Monkey Business / My Ding-A-Ling

The 1969 *Toronto Rock & Roll Revival* again. Every song is faded. 'Johnny B. Goode' is the song Berry ended the show with, not the medley version.

CHARTBREAKERS
Point 2620772 • 1992

    20 Chess tracks. Apart from 'Reelin' And Rockin' ', all are featured on the 3-CD box set below.

BROWN EYED HANDSOME MAN [3-CD]
Point 2698262 • 1992

❶ *Come On* [Point 2620892]: Come On / You Can't Catch Me / Roll Over Beethoven / Betty Jean / Thirty Days / How You've Changed / Beautiful Delilah / Run Rudolph Run+ / No Particular Place To Go *(stereo)* / Trick Or Treat *(with overdubbed audience)* / Down Bound Train / Too Much Monkey Business / Run Around / Liverpool Drive *(instr, stereo)* / Away From You / Worried Life Blues+ / The Things I Used To Do+ *(stereo)* / My Ding-A-Ling *(live, album version)* / Still Got The Blues *(with overdubbed audience)* / Bye Bye Johnny

❷ *Go, Go, Go* [Point 2620902]: Go, Go, Go *(stereo, long version)* / Brown Eyed Handsome Man / Down The Road A Piece+ *(stereo, long version)* / Too Pooped To Pop+ / Nadine *(stereo, longer fade)* / Memphis, Tennessee / Sweet Little Rock And Roller *(alt. version)* / Johnny B. Goode / Wee Wee Hours / Guitar Boogie *(instr)* / Around And Around / Jo Jo Gunne / Rip It Up+ / Drifting Heart / Viva, Viva Rock & Roll / Promised Land / Let It Rock / Little Queenie / Havana Moon / Confessin' The Blues+

❸ *Oh Yeah* [Point 2620912]: Oh Yeah / Sweet Little Sixteen *(alt. version)* / Low Feeling *(instr)* / Route 66+ *(stereo, alt. version)* / Driftin' Blues+ / School Day / All Aboard *(with overdubbed audience)* / Maybellene / You Never Can Tell *(stereo)* / Almost Grown / I Got To Find My Baby+ / Carol / St. Louis Blues+ / Oh Baby Doll / Little Marie *(stereo, with count-in)* / Back In The USA / Blues For Hawaiians *(instr)* / Brenda Lee / Stop And Listen / Rock And Roll Music *(demo)*

    A good Berry set with well-known classics, alternate takes and more obscure songs. The sound is mostly good, apart from the tracks with overdubbed audience from the 1963 ON STAGE LP [Chess LP-1480]. The three CDs were also sold separately, but it is the set that is interesting and quite collectable.

THE WORLD OF CHUCK BERRY [3-CD]
Trace 0490022 • 1992

❶ *Let It Rock* [Trace 0400672]: Let It Rock / Brown Eyed Handsome Man / Down The Road A Piece+ *(longer stereo version)* / Go, Go, Go *(longer stereo version)* / Nadine *(longer stereo version)* / Memphis, Tennessee / Sweet Little Rock And Roller *(alt. version)* / Johnny B. Goode / Wee Wee Hours / Guitar Boogie *(instr)* / Around And Around / Jo Jo Gunne / Rip It Up+ / Little Queenie / Havana Moon / Confessin' The Blues+

❷ **Rock & Roll Music [Trace 0400682]:** Rock And Roll Music *(demo)* / Sweet Little Sixteen *(alt. version)* / Low Feeling *(instr)* / Route 66+ *(alt. stereo version)* / Driftin' Blues+ / School Day / All Aboard *(with overdubbed audience)* / Maybellene / You Never Can Tell *(stereo)* / Almost Grown / I Got To Find My Baby+ / Carol / St. Louis Blues+ *(mono)* / Oh Baby Doll / Little Marie *(stereo)* / Back In The USA

❸ **Reelin' And Rockin' [Trace 0400692]:** Reelin' And Rockin' / You Can't Catch Me / Roll Over Beethoven / Betty Jean / Thirty Days / How You've Changed / Beautiful Delilah / Run Rudolph Run+ / No Particular Place To Go / Trick Or Treat *(with overdubbed audience)* / Come On / Too Much Monkey Business / Drifting Heart / My Ding-A-Ling *(live, album version)* / Still Got The Blues *(with overdubbed audience)* / Bye Bye Johnny

Very goode sound quality here, apart from the tracks with overdubbed audience from the 1963 ON STAGE LP [Chess LP-1480]. But who in his right mind can actually say that 'Low Feeling' is a worthwhile track? This set is almost the same as the one above, however, there are only 16 songs on each CD, which makes 48 tracks altogether, in contrast to the above Point box set which has 60. The three CDs were also sold separately. I find it somewhat odd that two box sets with almost the same tracks were issued the same year, and on top of that that all the CDs were also sold separately in addition to the Point CHARTBREAKERS CD. Seven CDs issued the same year containing many of the same tracks. You certainly couldn't forget about Chuck Berry in the Netherlands in the '90s!

THE BEST OF CHUCK BERRY – LEGENDARY HITS
Blues Legends 90.156-2 • 1992
18 common Chess tracks with bad sound quality, including the single edit version of 'My Ding-A-Ling'. *Blues* legends? Only the track 'Wee Wee Hours' qualifies; the rest are solid rock'n'roll.

CHUCK BERRY COLLECTION – 25 SONGS
The Collection COL-002 • 1993
I don't want to list all the songs here, because it's yet another combination of Chess and Mercury tracks in rather poor sound quality. Nothing new, and nothing to brag about. Actually nothing worth having!

CHUCK BERRY – GOLD
Gold GOLD-003 • 1993
Roll Over Beethoven / Maybellene / Rock And Roll Music / Sweet Little Sixteen / Carol *(Mercury)* / Johnny B. Goode / School day / No Particular Place To Go / Memphis, Tennessee *(Mercury)* / Let It Rock / Nadine / Reelin' And Rockin' / You Never Can Tell / My Ding-A-Ling *(live, single edit)*

Chess tracks, except for 'Carol' and 'Memphis' which are Mercury. Bad sound quality overall.

28 GREAT ROCK & ROLL SONGS [2-CD]
Unknown label, BXCL-256 • 1993
No booklet, no liner notes and no label! Again, an irritating combination of Chess and Mercury tracks with bad sound quality. What's the point? 'Bring Another Drink' and 'Goodnight, Well It's Time To Go' ['It's Time To Go'] are both credited to Berry. This is the baddest of the bad. You sure don't need this. In fact, no one does.

LET IT ROCK
Sm'art Art WZ-98006 • 1994

Rock And Roll Music / Johnny B. Goode / Maybellene / Reelin' And Rockin' / You Never Can Tell / Sweet Little Sixteen / Let It Rock / Roll Over Beethoven / Back In The USA / Little Queenie / No Particular Place To Go / No Money Down / Memphis, Tennessee / Nadine / I Got To Find My Baby+ / School Day / Wee Wee Hours / Too Much Monkey Business

This comes in a metal box, but was also available in a normal CD jewel case. However, it is the metal box that makes the issue collectable. Nice picture of Berry which I haven't seen before. Believe it or not, 'Rock And Roll Music' is actually credited to *'H. Williams'*! Jambalaya!

CHUCK BERRY - ROCK & ROLL HERO
WWG RR-003 • 2001

Johnny B. Goode / My Ding-A-Ling / Maybellene / Rock And Roll Music / Reelin' And Rockin' / School Day / Too Much Monkey Business / Memphis, Tennessee / Nadine

The 1969 *Toronto Rock & Roll Revival* yet again. The only reason for including this particular issue is that the music is in better sound quality than most of the other Toronto CDs.

Various Artists Singles

HIT SINGLE
Roll Over Beethoven
Van Gilse 84801 • 1984

Van Gilse is a Dutch company which makes all kinds of sweets, sugar and syrup. The single was a promotional item for a drawing competition for their syrup. The 'A' side of the single featured the two songs (the other is 'Feeling All Right' by Joe Cocker), and the 'B' side contains a long description of the competition and its rules. However, it starts with the announcer singing *'Roll Over Beethoven'* several times! Art sleeve. A real curiosity.

Various Artists LPs

Chuck Berry – Bo Diddley – Jerry Lee Lewis – Carl Perkins
ROCK SMUK
Sun/Chess NQCS-1 • 1973
    This unusual release with a Sun label on one side and a Chess label on the other is of dubious legality and is therefore listed in *Section 4 (Bootlegs)*. See also the 1974 LP, 4 ROCK GIANTS – TALKS & HITS [Bellaphon BI-15119] in the (West) German discography.

AMERICAN HOT WAX [2-LP]
A&M AMLM-66500 • 1978
    Original soundtrack. Same tracks and gatefold cover as the 1977 US LP [A&M SP-6500].

GOLDEN GREATS OF THE '50s AND '60s [8-LP]
Reader's Digest N82001-ND • 1981
Maybellene / School Day / Rock And Roll Music / You Never Can Tell / Let It Rock / Memphis, Tennessee / No Particular Place To Go / My Ding-A-Ling *(live, single edit)*

    A good compilation at the time featuring 16 artists, all of whom get one side each, with good pictures and liner notes. Unfortunately too many of the tracks are in electronic stereo, and 'Johnny B. Goode' is unaccountably omitted from Berry's selections. Also includes 8 songs each by Bill Haley, Fats Domino, Sam Cooke, the Platters, Pat Boone, Eddie Cochran, the Everly Brothers, Lonnie Donegan, Buddy Holly, Jerry Lee Lewis, Connie Francis, Duane Eddy, Brenda Lee, Bobby Vee and Roy Orbison... but where is Gene Vincent? Manufactured in the Netherlands, probably for distribution in Northern Europe.

LA BAMBA (VOLUME 2)
London 828 097-1 • 1988
Betty Jean

    Original soundtrack. Chess recording. Also released on CD [London 828 097-2].

BABY LOVE (LEMON POPSICLE 5) – ORIGINAL SOUNDTRACK
Arcade ADEH-211 • 1986
Maybellene / Sweet Little Sixteen

    32 great rockin' tracks including five that do not appear in the film. Artists include Eddie Cochran, Little Richard, the Platters, Bobby Darin, Sam Cooke, the Crests, the Tremeloes, etc.

Various Artists CD Albums

LA BAMBA (VOLUME 2)
London 828 097-2 • 1988
Betty Jean

    Original soundtrack. Chess recording. Also released on LP [London 828 097-1].

ROCK, ROCK, ROCK
Chess CD-1016 • 1989
    Reissue of the 1957 LP [Chess LP-1425]. Same tracks and cover (with 1965 shot of Berry) as the 1986 LP [Chess CH-9254] and 1988 CD [Chess CHD-31270].

Deventer, Lochem, Netherlands – 19 May 1977.

THE SAMPLER – SOUNDS NICE (VOLUME 1) [promo only]
Point 2601992 • 1992
Reelin' And Rockin' *(live, album version)*

A 16 track promo CD featuring various artists (no pictures) released by the Point label (no pictures). The Berry track here is the full-length from the 1972 LONDON SESSIONS LP [Chess CH-60020]. Other artists include Dr. John, Bob Marley, Santana, the Flying Pickets, Desmond Dekker, Howlin' Wolf and Muddy Waters. The booklet is a catalogue containing details of 16 CDs including the LONDON SESSIONS albums by Berry, Muddy and Wolf. This label put out several good compilation albums by Berry.

THE ROCK & ROLL BOX (VOLUME 2) [2-CD]
R&R Box BXCL-223 • 1993
You Never Can Tell / Roll Over Beethoven

40 tracks featuring various rock'n'roll artists and groups. The two Berry tracks are Chess recordings. The interesting thing about this issue is that Berry is the only artist depicted on the cover.

In the Netherlands, as in all other countries, Berry's music has also appeared on many other compilations, but I'll stop here.

NEW ZEALAND

Only a small country, but some interesting releases. I have never seen any New Zealand singles with picture sleeves. Some of the albums that were issued in New Zealand were also available in Australia and vice versa.

Singles

London NZL-323   Chess CH-2136

Roll Over Beethoven / Drifting Heart
London NZL-110 ● 1956
Black label with gold lettering. I have only seen this as a 78 rpm release.

Sweet Little Sixteen / Reelin' And Rockin'
London NZL-323 ● 1958
Black label with silver lettering.

You Never Can Tell / Brenda Lee
Chess [Viking] C-1013 ● 1964
Blue label with vertical silver Chess, small centre hole. Viking Record Co. sleeve.

Chuck Berry & Bo Diddley
Chuck's Beat *(single edit)* / **Bo's Beat** *(single edit)*
Chess [Viking] C-1015 ● 1964
Blue label with vertical silver Chess, small centre hole. Viking Record Co. sleeve.

My Ding-A-Ling *(live, single edit)* / Johnny B. Goode *(live)*
Chess [Polygram] CH-2131 ● 1972
Black label.

Reelin' And Rockin' *(live, single edit)* **/ Let's Boogie**
Chess [Polygram] CH-2136 • 1972
   Black label.

EPs

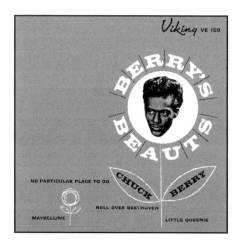

BERRY'S BEAUTS
Viking VE-159 • 1965
Roll Over Beethoven / Little Queenie / No Particular Place To Go / Maybellene

   Orange label.

MORE BERRY'S BEAUTS
Viking VE-160 • 1965
Memphis, Tennessee / Johnny B. Goode / You Never Can Tell / Nadine

   Orange label. On the back cover it says *'The Beatles' favourite artist'* !

LPs

JUKE BOX HITS
Chess [Viking] LP-1485 • 1964

Same tracks as the 1964 US LP, CHUCK BERRY'S GREATEST HITS [Chess LP-1485], except 'No Particular Place To Go' replaces 'Oh Baby Doll'. Same front-cover as the 1962 UK LP, JUKE BOX HITS [Pye International NPL-28019]. No liner notes on back cover. Blue label with silver lettering and vertical 'Chess' logo.

Chuck Berry & Bo Diddley
TWO GREAT GUITARS
Chess [Viking] LP-2991 • 1964

Same tracks and cover as the 1964 US LP [Checker LP-2991]. Same label as the JUKE BOX HITS LP above.

CHUCK BERRY'S GREATEST HITS
Chess CHLS-215 • 1972

Same tracks as the 1964 US LP [Chess LP-1485]. The front cover is purple (instead of blue) and there are liner notes on back cover. Also, no song titles are printed on front cover. Black label with silver lettering and Chess logo on top.

CHUCK BERRY'S GOLDEN DECADE [2-LP]
Chess CH-21514 • 1972

Same tracks and gatefold cover as the second pressing of the 1972 US 2-LP reissue [Chess 2CH-1514] (pink radio). Black label.

THE LONDON CHUCK BERRY SESSIONS
Chess CH-60020 • 1972

Same tracks as the 1972 US LP [Chess CH-60020]. No gatefold cover. Black label.

CHUCK BERRY'S GOLDEN DECADE (VOLUME 2) [2-LP]
Chess CH-60023 • 1972

Same tracks and gatefold cover as the 1972 US 2-LP [Chess 2CH-60023]. Black label.

MOTORVATIN'
Chess 9124 204 • 1977

Same tracks as the 1977 UK LP [Chess 9286 690]. Black label with silver lettering and 'Chess' across the top.

ROCKIN' WITH CHUCK BERRY
Philips SS-001 • 1977

Chess recordings. Same tracks and cover as the 1977 Dutch LP, PORTRAIT OF CHUCK BERRY [Philips Success Series 9279 541].

MY DING-A-LING
Lucky LUC-047 • 1984

Same tracks (nine songs from 1969 *Toronto Rock & Roll Revival*) and cover as the 1983 UK LP, THE GREATEST HITS – CHUCK BERRY LIVE [Spot SPR-8512].

NORWAY

Compared to Sweden, not much Berry material was released in Norway. However, most Swedish issues were also available in this country. The few singles on Sonet that were released in Norway in 1964 are extremely rare.

The Norwegian Sonet label was red with a round push-out centre. The first three Sonet singles all have the same picture sleeve that is exclusive to Norway. Finding a nice copy is almost impossible. T-7605 has a different front sleeve and is one that might turn up if you're lucky. The 'Nadine' single sold in Norway [Sonet T-7591] was a Swedish pressing.

In the mid-60s, various Dutch releases were also available in Norway.

Singles

School Day / Deep Feeling *(instr)*
Columbia DB-3951 • May 1957
This is the only Berry 78 issued in Norway, and also the only Berry record released during the '50s. Same green label as the UK, but says *'Made in Norway'* and has the NCB (Nordic Copyright Bureau) logo in a square. This was also issued as a promo ('prøveplate') with a white label, and is the rarest Norwegian pressing of all (see overleaf).

Let It Rock / Memphis, Tennessee
Pye 7N.25218 • 1963
This has the same record number as the 1963 UK Pye International issue, but the label is reddish-brown. 'Let It Rock' was actually the 'A' side. It was also issued in Sweden with a picture sleeve.

Roll Over Beethoven / Sweet Little Sixteen
Sonet T-7594 • 1964
'B' side has overdubbed live audience. Picture sleeve.

Maybellene / Rock And Roll Music
Sonet T-7596 • 1964
Picture sleeve.

No Particular Place To Go / Liverpool Drive *(instr)*
Sonet T-7597 • 1964
Picture sleeve.

You Never Can Tell / Brenda Lee
Sonet T-7605 • 1964
Picture sleeve.

Club Nitty Gritty / Laugh And Cry
Mercury 127. 260 MCF • 1967
Probably not released with a picture sleeve. As a matter of fact this turned up as recently as March 2006. Prior to that, nobody knew that this single had been pressed in Norway for the Scandinavian market.

Columbia DB-3951 (promo)

Sonet T-7596

Sonet T-7597

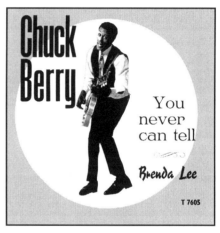

Sonet T-7605

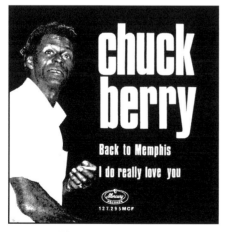

Mercury 127.295 MCF

Mercury 127.295 MCF

Back To Memphis / I Do Really Love You
Mercury 127.295 MCF • 1968

I have never seen the picture used on the front sleeve before or since. Very rare indeed!

My Ding-A-Ling *(live, single edit)* / **Carol**
Friends [CNR] 190.056 • 1988

This was a plug single for the 1988 2-LP, HAIL! HAIL! ROCK'N'ROLL [Friends 690.014], also released as two separate CDs on the Injection Disco Dance Label [100.181 and 100.182]. Picture sleeve. See also the 1988 CD plug single [Injection Disco Dance Label 100.179]. All these records were also released in Belgium and the Netherlands.

LPs

GOLDEN HITS
Fontana International 858 002-FBY • 1967

Same tracks as the 1967 US (stereo) LP [Mercury SR-61103]. The cover is the same as the dreadful one used in the Netherlands.

LIVE AT THE FILLMORE AUDITORIUM, SAN FRANCISCO
Fontana International 858 047-FPY • 1968

Same tracks as the 1967 US (stereo) LP [Mercury SR-61138]. The cover was made in the Netherlands.

ROCK AND ROLL MUSIC
Fontana Special 6430 022 • 1972

Same tracks as the 1967 US LP, GOLDEN HITS [Mercury SR-61103], but a different cover. This reissue appeared in many European countries with substantially the same cover but different titles. It was released in 1972 in the Netherlands as ROCK HITS [Fontana International 6430 022], in West Germany as ATTENTION! [Fontana 6430 022], in Norway and Spain as ROCK AND ROLL MUSIC [Fontana Special 6430 022 and Fontana 6430 022 respectively]. (However, the record label inside the Spanish issue actually says GOLDEN HITS.) In 1973 it was released in Italy as ROCK HITS [Fontana Special 6430 022], in France as ROCK AND ROLL MUSIC [Fontana 6430 022] and in the UK – with a different catalogue number from all the other variations – as BACK IN THE USA [Philips 6336 216].

Around 1981 some of the original US albums were pressed in Norway. The label was light blue and carried the NCB logo. The covers were near-duplicates of the French reissues which came out a that time and followed the same numerical series.

BERRY IS ON TOP
Chess 9124 214 • 1981

Same tracks and cover as the 1959 US LP [Chess LP-1435].

AFTER SCHOOL SESSION
Chess 9124 215 • 1981

Same tracks and cover as the 1957 US LP [Chess LP-1426].

ROCKIN' AT THE HOPS
Chess 9124 218 • 1981
Same tracks and cover as the 1960 US LP [Chess LP-1448].

NEW JUKE BOX HITS
Chess 9124 220 • 1981
Same tracks and cover as the 1961 US LP [Chess LP-1456].

HAIL! HAIL! ROCK'N'ROLL [2-LP]
Friends [CNR] 690.014/15 • 1988
Not the movie soundtrack. Same tracks as the 1988 UK 2-LP [Chess DETD-207], but different gatefold cover. Also released as separate CDs [Injection Disco Dance Label 100.181 and 100.182]. There was also a plug single [Friends 690.014 (7" vinyl) and Injection Disco Dance Label 100.179 (CD)]. All these records were also released in Belgium and the Netherlands.

CD Singles

MY DING-A-LING
Injection Disco Dance Label [CNR] 100.179 • 1988
My Ding-A-Ling *(live, single edit)* / No Particular Place To Go / Maybellene / Roll Over Beethoven

This was a plug single for the 1988 2-LP, HAIL! HAIL! ROCK'N'ROLL [Friends 690.014], also released as two separate CDs [Injection Disco Dance Label 100.181 and 100.182]. Same front cover picture. See also 1988 7" plug single [Friends 190.056]. All these records were also released in Belgium and the Netherlands.

CD Albums

HAIL! HAIL! ROCK'N'ROLL (1955-58)
Injection Disco Dance Label [CNR] 100.181 • 1988

HAIL! HAIL! ROCK'N'ROLL (1959-72)
Injection Disco Dance Label [CNR] 100.182 • 1988
Not the movie soundtrack. This is the 1988 2-LP, HAIL! HAIL! ROCK'N'ROLL [Friends 690.014/15] released as two separate CDs, both with the same cover. There was also a plug single [Friends 690.014 (7" vinyl) and Injection Disco Dance Label 100.179 (CD)]. All these records were also released in Belgium and the Netherlands.

Various Artists LPs

SUPERHITS OF THE '50s
Philips 6641 947 • 1980
Sweet Little Sixteen

This album is only mentioned because it has a huge picture of Berry on the inside of the gatefold cover (the same one as on the front of the JUKE BOX HITS album), plus two more pictures of Berry on the front cover. Sadly, the Berry track is the awful

Mercury cut, and several other artists' recordings are not the originals either. Also featured are Frankie Laine, Patti Page, the Royal Hawaiian Guitars, Georgia Gibbs, Louis Jordan, the Crew Cuts, Fats Domino (2, both live), the Platters (2), George Jones, Bill Justis (2), Jerry Lee Lewis (Mercury cuts), the Merry Miller Singers, Shirley Bassey (2), David Carroll And His Orchestra, Dinah Washington, Frankie Vaughn, Sarah Vaughan, Pete Drake and Leroy Van Dyke.

Various Artists CD Albums

THE BEST AIR GUITAR ALBUM IN THE WORLD... EVER! [2-CD]
Virgin-EMI 7243 8 12822-2 • 2002
Johnny B. Goode

Chess track. This is listed in the UK discography with more information; however, it is also mentioned here because, when it was released in the summer of 2002, it actually sold over 25,000 copies, which qualifies for gold certification in Norway.

96% ROCK'N'ROLL
Universal 068923 2 • 2003
Maybellene / Rock And Roll Music / No Particular Place To Go

27 rockin' tracks by Bill Haley (3), Buddy Holly (2), Danny & The Juniors (2), Lloyd Price (2), the Kalin Twins, Eddie Fontaine, Tommy Roe, the Monotones, Arthur Alexander, Jerry Keller, Brenda Lee, Tab Hunter, the Surfaris, Billy Williams, Brian Hyland, Dale Hawkins, the Del Vikings, the Crickets and... Jive Bunny! Berry's selections are all Chess recordings, and many of the tracks are in true stereo. Liner notes by Colin Escott. Picture of Berry inside the booklet.

THE BEST AIR GUITAR ALBUM IN THE WORLD... EVER! (VOLUME 2) [2-CD]
Virgin-EMI 7243 5 93989-2 • 2003
Carol *(Chess)*

This didn't do as well as the first one (see UK discography for more information).

DET GLADE 60-TALL 1960-63 [2-CD]
Sony COL-516160-2 • July 2004
No Particular Place To Go *(Chess)*

In English the album title means 'THE HAPPY '60s'. This sold 50,000 copies and was certificated for a Platinum Award in Norway. To be quite honest, the Berry track didn't chart until 1964, so the title proclaiming 1960-63 is of course incorrect. The inner sleeve has info on the highest positions for each track on the US and UK charts.

DET GLADE 50-TALL 1955-59 [2-CD]
SONY COL-519161-2 • November 2004
Sweet Little Sixteen *(Chess)*

In English the album title means 'THE HAPPY '50s'. Other than the notable absence of Elvis Presley, the set contains 24 tracks per CD featuring one song each by the likes of Berry, Bill Haley, Jerry Lee Lewis, Fats Domino, Gene Vincent, Eddie Cochran, Buddy Holly, Carl Perkins and the Everly Brothers, plus a bunch of other great '50s classics. Not bad at all! No pictures of any artists unfortunately, but the hit positions in the US and UK are listed for each track.

DET GLADE 60-TALL (VOLUME 2) 1964-69 [2-CD]
Sony COL-519286-2 • December 2004
You Never Can Tell *(Chess)*

Berry in goode company. Again 24 tracks on each CD. Good value for money, with one song each by US and UK artists like Alma Cogan, Roy Orbison, the Archies, the Animals, the Drifters, Tom Jones, Stevie Wonder, Dusty Springfield, Tim Hardin, Marvin Gaye, the Swinging Blue Jeans and a bunch of others. All well-known hits and classics from the period. Again hit positions in the US and UK are given for each track. This CD and the two above were first released in Sweden in 2003.

PERU

LPs

HAIL! HAIL! ROCK'N'ROLL
MCA 255 182-1 • 1987
   Original soundtrack. Same tracks and cover as the 1987 US LP [MCA MCA-6217].

PHILIPPINES

Singles

In recent years, several strange and unique 78s have turned up, starting with 'Sweet Little Sixteen' from 1958. So, I think it is safe to assume that others – like 'Johnny B. Goode' – will surface in due course.

Empire 41-EA

Custom Audio T-007

Custom Audio T-007

Chess ARI-1012

Sweet Little Sixteen / Reelin' And Rockin'
Empire 41-EA • 1958
78 rpm on an obscure maroon label. This rarity is currently on display at the Rock'n'Roll & Blues Heritage Museum in Clarksdale, Mississippi.

437

Beautiful Delilah
Ace AB-1001 • 1958
78 rpm released by the (Philippines) Ace label, light tan colour, again an obscure issue. The other side – 'Stardust' by Billy Ward – was actually the 'A' side.

Sweet Little Rock And Roller / Joe Joe Gunne
Sun, unknown number • 1959
Another 78, this time issued by the (Philippines) Sun Record Company. Red label. No more information.

That's My Desire+ / Too Much Monkey Business
Custom Audio T-007 • 1959
Interesting coupling. Green labels with silver lettering. 'A' side described as *'Off Beat Cha-Cha'*.

Rock And Roll Music / Johnny B. Goode
Chess ARI-1012 • Mid-1960s
This has the multicoloured Chess label and a small centre hole. There are references to Chess LP-1485, GREATEST HITS, which suggests that this single probably came out around 1964. My copy says *'Made in Philippines'*, however, Malte Koch has the same record without any references as to where it was manufactured.

Reelin' And Rockin' *(live, single edit)* **/ Let's Boogie**
Chess CS-45-722 • 1973
Blueish label. *'JET-2163'* is printed in small letters on the label, which is the Japanese Chess single number for this release. Don't ask me why.

LPs

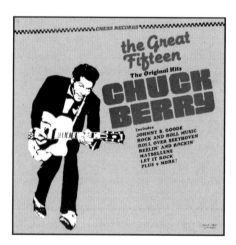

THE GREAT FIFTEEN
Sugarhill SHLP-12502 • 1980s
Johnny B. Goode / Roll Over Beethoven / Sweet Little Rock And Roller / Carol / Back In The USA / Maybellene / Memphis, Tennessee / I'm Talking About You / Rock And Roll Music / Reelin' And Rockin' / Let It Rock / Sweet Little Sixteen / Around And Around / Little Queenie / Nadine

This has the same front cover as the 1982 US 2-LP, THE GREAT 28 [Chess CH-8201]. The back cover has session details for each song.

POLAND

Singles

 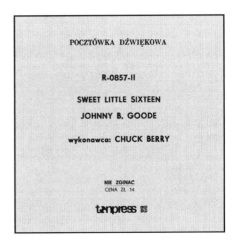

Sweet Little Sixteen / Johnny B. Goode [postcard]
Tonpress R-0857-II • 1960s
This is a transparent flexi disc pressed onto a square postcard of a landscape. It comes in an orange paper bag (45 rpm size) with a few bits of Polish writing on it – nothing too exciting: *'Sound postcard'*, *'Do not bend'*, *'Price 14 złotys'* plus the titles).

LPs

GREATEST HITS
Tonpress SX-T-128 • 1987
Maybellene / Brown Eyed Handsome Man / Roll Over Beethoven / Too Much Monkey Business / School Day / Rock And Roll Music / Sweet Little Sixteen / Reelin' And Rockin' / Johnny B. Goode / Around And Around / Carol / Memphis, Tennessee / Sweet Little Rock And Roller / Little Queenie / Back In The USA / Let it Rock / Nadine / You Never Can Tell / Promised Land / No Particular Place To Go / Bye Bye Johnny

20 greatest hits from the Chess files from 'Maybellene' to 'Promised Land' – but no 'Ding-A-Ling'! Great picture on front cover. This has the same front cover, title and tracks as the 1986 UK CD [Chess CD-21], except that 'Thirty Days' and 'Beautiful Delilah' are omitted. Liner notes in Polish and English.

CHUCK BERRY LIVE
Wifon LP-122 • 1988
　　The 1969 *Toronto Rock & Roll Revival* again. Same tracks and title as the 1981 US LP, CHUCK BERRY LIVE (VOLUME 1) [SSS International SSS-36]. Similar front cover.

Various Artists LPs

FLASHBACK
Poljazz K-PSJ-022 • 1970s
Rock And Roll Music *(live)*

　　Berry's track is from the 1969 *Toronto Rock & Roll Revival*. A few original versions, mostly re-recordings from the artists including Solomon Burke, Little Richard (2), Gene Vincent, the Drifters (2), Lee Dorsey, Herman's Hermits, the Beach Boys, Bill Haley, the Archies (2), Ray Charles and Gary 'US' Bonds. No pictures of any artists.

PORTUGAL

Singles

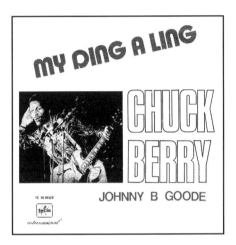

My Ding-A-Ling *(live, single edit)* **/ Johnny B. Goode** *(live)*
Tecla International TE-30.003/S • 1973
    Picture sleeve. Copies of the *NME*, *Billboard* and other charts on the back of the sleeve.

LPs

CHUCK BERRY'S GREATEST HITS
Dargil FS-321 • 1976
    Same tracks, cover and catalogue number as the 1976 US LP [Everest FS-321]. Liner notes in Portugese on the back cover.

THE BEST OF CHUCK BERRY
MVM MV-08.3.040 • Late 1980s
Nadine / School Day / Wee Wee Hours / *Medley:* Johnny B. Goode – Carol – Promised Land / Hoochie Coochie Man+ / Sweet Little Sixteen / Too Much Monkey Business / Reelin' And Rockin' / My Ding-A-Ling / Johnny B. Goode / Maybellene / Rock And Roll Music

    The 1969 *Toronto Rock & Roll Revival* again. Exceedingly dull cover. Liner notes in Portugese.

RUSSIA

CD Albums

KINGS OF WORLD MUSIC – CHUCK BERRY
Восток *(Vostok)* **VK193-01 • 2000**

Rock And Roll Music / Roll Over Beethoven / Johnny B. Goode / You Never Can Tell *(stereo)* / Maybellene / Too Much Monkey Business / Havana Moon / Reelin' And Rockin' *(live single edit)* / Sweet Little Sixteen / Brown Eyed Handsome Man / School Day / Wee Wee Hours / Beautiful Delilah / Memphis, Tennessee / Sweet Little Rock And Roller / Confessin' The Blues+ / Nadine *(stereo)* / Promised Land *(stereo)* / I Want To Be Your Driver *(stereo)* / No Money Down / Tulane *(stereo)* / Do You Love Me *(alt. version)* / My Ding-A-Ling *(live single edit)* / Bye Bye Johnny / Come On / Back In The USA

Chess recordings. Berry CDs from Russia don't come around all that often. The sound is quite good, the cover is okay and the liner notes are in Russian, which makes it even more of a collector's item. The two live songs are from the 1972 *London Sessions* album.

CHUCK BERRY
Landy Star Series 68 • 2002

Reelin' And Rockin' / Johnny B. Goode / Nadine *(stereo)* / Don't You Lie To Me+ / Around And Around / No Particular Place To Go *(stereo)* / Childhood Sweetheart / My Little Love-Light / Maybellene / I'm Talking About You / Roll Over Beethoven / Sweet Little Sixteen *(original speed)* / You Can't Catch Me / Memphis, Tennessee / I Got A Booking / You Never Can Tell *(stereo)* / The Things I Used To Do+ *(stereo)* / Jamaica Farewell+ / Thirty Days / Oh Baby Doll / School Day / Bye Bye Johnny / Back In The USA / Rock And Roll Music

All Chess tracks. 'Jamaica Farewell' is the UK mono version. Another interesting concept and good sound, despite the fact that more tracks should have been in stereo. Liner notes in Russian and four pictures inside the booklet, two I haven't seen before. This is a 'red' CD in the right sense of the word – the cover, the CD itself and the booklet are all in red!

Various Artists Singles

School Day – Deep Feeling *(instr)* / **Too Much Monkey Business** [flexi, 33⅓ rpm]
Мэлодия *(Melodiya)* **10 (11-12)** • **October 1988**

This blue flexi disc was given away with the monthly Soviet arts magazine, *Кругозор ('Horizon')*. 'School Day' is faded out when the guitar solo starts and 'Deep Feeling' is faded in half-way through. 'Monkey Business' is faded out just before the end. The magazine also has a picture of Berry inside (from the ROCKING AT THE HOPS album cover) and a brief article introducing Berry to Russian readers. For the record, the other side features extracts from the opera *Dzhordano* by L. Kvint sung by Valerji Leontyev. Other discs in this series feature an intriguing mixture of Russian folk songs, humour, poetry, readings from Chekhov and... Kim Wilde! Strange concept.

Various Artists EPs

Chuck Berry – Jerry Lee Lewis – Bill Haley – Unknown artist
ШКОЛА ПОПУЛЯРНОЙ МУЗЫКИ **3-4** [flexi, 33⅓ rpm]
Журнал: Клуб и Художэственная Самодеятельность **19** • **1979**
Memphis, Tennessee

This blue flexidisc appears to be one of a set issued by a state magazine for the edification of Soviet youth. Its title translates as 'SCHOOL OF POPULAR MUSIC 3-4'. The label states 'Magazine: Club & Amateur Activities 19'. Berry's cut is the Mercury re-recording. Also features one track each by Jerry Lee Lewis and Bill Haley. The flip side features the songs of one A. Mazhukov performed by an unidentified Russian female singer which are of no rock'n'roll interest whatsoever.

SAUDI ARABIA

I have never seen any vinyl albums or singles from this country, but I did come across some information on audio tapes:

Cassette Tapes

THE LONDON CHUCK BERRY SESSIONS
Austa, unknown number • 1972
No other information.

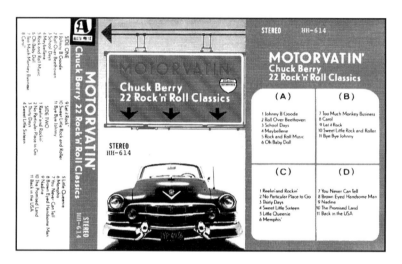

MOTORVATIN'
Austa HH-614 • 1978
Same tracks and similar front cover to the 1977 UK LP [Chess 9286 690].

ROCKIT
Imd IMD-7577 • 1979
Same tracks and front cover to the 1979 US LP [Atco SD-38.118].

SOUTH AFRICA

I would love to know more about the Berry releases from this country. These are the ones I know about up to press (August 2007):

Singles

Teal sleeve, mid-60's

Teal TSP-41

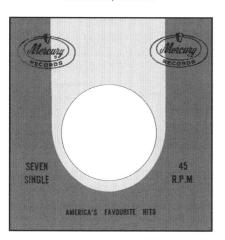

Mercury sleeve, mid-60's

Mercury MRC-1101

Sweet Little Sixteen / School Day
Teal TSP-40 ● 1964
   Chess recordings.

Nadine / No Particular Place To Go
Teal TSP-41 • 1964
> Chess recordings. Light green label, company sleeve.

Back To Memphis / I Do Really Love You
Mercury MRC-1101 • June 1967
> Black label, company sleeve.

My Ding-A-Ling *(live, single edit)* / **Johnny B. Goode** *(live)*
Chess, unknown number • 1972

LPs

CHUCK BERRY'S GREATEST HITS
Teal TL-1093 • 1965
> Same tracks as the 1964 US LP [Chess LP-1485]. Slightly different cover. Bears the legend *'The Gold Disc Selection'.* No picture of Berry.

YOU NEVER CAN TELL
Teal, unknown number • 1965
> Probably same tracks as the 1964 UK LP [Pye International NPL-28039].

CHUCK BERRY'S GREATEST HITS
Chess CSC-4014 • 1968
> Reissue in electronic stereo like the US 1964 reissue [Chess LP-1485]. Black label with the Chess knight logo in silver on top.

MORE CHUCK BERRY
Chess CSC-4015 • 1968
> Same tracks and cover as the 1964 US LP [Chess LP-1465]. Black label with the Chess knight logo in silver on top.

THE CHUCK BERRY LEGEND
Mercury 6336 371 • 1975
Sweet Little Sixteen / Memphis, Tennessee / School Day / Maybellene / Back In The USA / Johnny B. Goode / Rock And Roll Music / Roll Over Beethoven / Carol / C.C. Rider+ *(live)* / Forty Days [Thirty Days] / Club Nitty Gritty / So Long+ / Wee Baby Blues+ *(live)* / Hoochie Coochie Man+ *(live)* / Goodnight, Well It's Time To Go [It's Time To Go]

> Not much of an album actually. No picture of Berry either, just a white cover with the printing in green. Blue Mercury label with silver printings.

ROCKIN' WITH CHUCK BERRY
Philips Success Series SUC-114 • 1978
> Same cover and tracks as the 1977 UK LP [Philips Success Series SUC-114].

THE GREAT TWENTY-EIGHT [2-LP]
Plum Records TRN-3013 • 1982
> Same gatefold cover and tracks as the 1982 US LP [Chess CH-8201]. Purple label.

SOUTH KOREA

LPs

TOKYO SESSION
Oasis [EMI] OLE-406 ● 1982
   Same as the 1981 Japanese LP [East World WTP-90072] – even the same label. Different inlay card, but with English lyrics to all songs.

SPAIN

The history of Berry releases in Spain began in 1965, with the appearance of three EPs. The first single I know of came out in 1968, and the first LP was released in 1972. It is therefore something of a problem to present a complete survey of Berry's Spanish releases. These are the ones I know about up to press (August 2007):

Singles

Mercury 127 396-MCF

Mercury 127 396-MCF

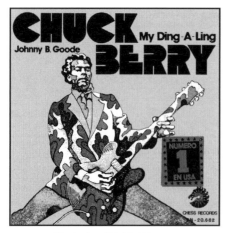

Movieplay SN-20.682

Movieplay SN-20.682

St. Louie To Frisco / Ma Dear
Mercury 127 396-MCF ● 1968
    Picture sleeve.

My Ding-A-Ling *(live, single edit)* **/ Johnny B. Goode** *(live)*
Movieplay SN-20.682 ● 1972
    Chess recordings. Picture sleeve with sticker saying '*Numero 1 en USA'*.

EPs

    The EPs below all featured Chess recordings:

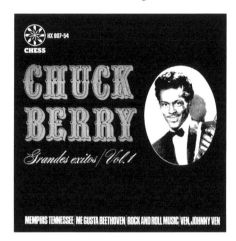

CHUCK BERRY – GRANDES EXITOS (VOLUME 1)
Hispa Vox HX-007.54 ● 1965
Memphis, Tennessee / Roll Over Beethoven / Rock And Roll Music / Johnny B. Goode

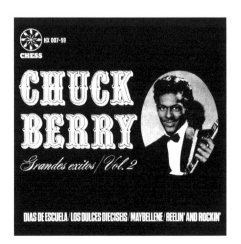

CHUCK BERRY – GRANDES EXITOS (VOLUME 2)
Hispa Vox HX-007.59 ● 1965
School Day / Sweet Little Sixteen / Maybellene / Reelin' And Rockin'

Berry back home in St. Louis, August 1983.

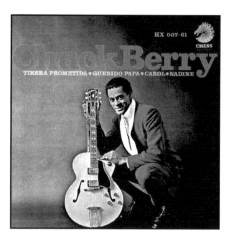

CHUCK BERRY
Hispa Vox HX-007.61 • 1965
Promised Land / Dear Dad / Carol / Nadine

Great picture of Berry on the cover! It's interesting that they included 'Dear Dad' instead of 'No Particular Place To Go' or 'You Never Can Tell'. 'Dear Dad' is one of Berry's best and most under-rated rockers, especially when you consider it was recorded in 1965 – ten years after 'Maybellene'. Great '50s picture of Berry on the front. Liner notes in Spanish on the back.

LPs

CHUCK BERRY – EXITOS
Movieplay S-26.103 • 1972
Johnny B. Goode / Memphis, Tennessee / Sweet Little Sixteen / Thirty Days / Brown Eyed Handsome Man / Too Much Monkey Business / School Day / Rock And Roll Music / Maybellene / Roll Over Beethoven / Oh Baby Doll / Nadine

Chess recordings. Same front cover as the 1971 US LP, SAN FRANCISCO DUES [Chess CH-50008].

LOUISIANA
Movieplay S-26.130 • 1972
Chess recordings. Same tracks as the as the 1971 US LP, SAN FRANCISCO DUES [Chess CH-50008]. Same cover as the 1970 US LP, BACK HOME [Chess LPS-1550], but different colours. Red label.

THE LONDON CHUCK BERRY SESSIONS
Movieplay S-26.151 • 1972
Same tracks and cover as the 1972 US LP [Chess CH-60020] and all the other pressings around the world.

ROCK AND ROLL MUSIC
Fontana 6430 022 • 1972
Same tracks as the 1967 US LP, GOLDEN HITS [Mercury SR-61103], but a different cover. This reissue appeared in many European countries with substantially the same cover but different titles. It was released in 1972 in the Netherlands as ROCK HITS [Fontana International 6430 022], in West Germany as ATTENTION! [Fontana 6430 022], in Norway and Spain as ROCK AND ROLL MUSIC [Fontana Special 6430 022 and Fontana 6430 022 respectively]. (However, the record label inside the Spanish issue actually says GOLDEN HITS.) In 1973 it was released in Italy as ROCK HITS [Fontana Special 6430 022], in France as ROCK AND ROLL MUSIC [Fontana 6430 022] and in the UK – with a different catalogue number from all the other variations – as BACK IN THE USA [Philips 6336 216].

BIO
Movieplay S-26.211 • 1974
Same tracks and gatefold cover as the 1973 US LP [Chess CH-50043]. Green eight-square label with a white border. The title on the label reads: CHUCK BERRY: BIOGRAFIA.

MOTORVATIN' [2-LP]
Philips 66 41 660 • 1977
Same tracks as the 1977 UK LP, MOTORVATIN' [Chess 9286 690]. In Spain, however, it was issued as a 2-LP set with a gatefold cover, with five or six tracks per side, 22 in all. The two records are numbered 91 99 078 and 91 99 079.

GIGANTES DEL POP (VOLUME 51) – CHUCK BERRY
Mercury 92 79 140 • 1981
Same tracks as the US LP, GOLDEN HITS [Mercury SR-61103], but a different cover. Blue label. Reissued in 1988.

HISTORIA DE LA MUSICA ROCK – 20
Mercury 68 41 151 • 1982
Same tracks as the US LP, GOLDEN HITS [Mercury SR-61103], but a different cover.

HAIL! HAIL! ROCK'N'ROLL
MCA 255182-1 • 1987
Original soundtrack. Same tracks and cover as the 1987 US LP [MCA MCA-6217].

CHUCK BERRY COLLECTION
Celebration CELP-04 • 1988
Down Bound Train / Drifting Heart / Beautiful Delilah / Hey Pedro / Roly Poly *(instr)* / *Johnny B. Goode / House Of Blue Lights+ / *Roll Over Beethoven / My Little Love Light / Time Was+ / *Oh Baby Doll / Ingo *(instr)* / *Sweet Little Sixteen / Oh Yeah / Childhood Sweetheart / *Maybellene

Dull cover, but interesting and unusual tracks for a Berry album: the obscure tracks are from Chess, but the others (*) are actually Mercury tracks. How do they come up with such a mess? The compiler must have decided that the Mercury versions are somewhat better recordings than the originals. Perhaps the person responsible should have chosen another profession.

GIGANTES DEL POP – CHUCK BERRY
Mercury 92 79 140 • 1988
Reissue of the LP originally released in Spain in 1981. Same cover and same title, except that 'VOLUME 51' is erased. Black label.

HAIL! HAIL! ROCK'N'ROLL [2-LP]
Zafiro [Charly] 313 12240 • 1988
Not the movie soundtrack. Same tracks and cover as the 1988 UK 2-LP [Chess DETD-207].

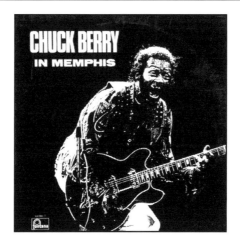

CHUCK BERRY IN MEMPHIS
Fontana 424 589-1 • 1989
    Same tracks as the 1967 US LP [Mercury SR-61123]. However, the cover is different and in black and white, and nothing is written on the back side except the title and tracks. A typical cheapo, I would think.

ROLL OVER BEETHOVEN
Rock Melody 303.1055-1 • 1989
Roll Over Beethoven / You Never Can Tell / No Particular Place To Go / Sweet Little Sixteen / Wee Wee Hours / Maybellene / Nadine / Johnny B. Goode / Promised Land / School Day / Back In The USA / Oh Baby Doll / Reelin' And Rockin' / Rock And Roll Music

    Chess recordings. The album was distributed by Serenade SA, 08014 Barcelona, Spain; however it was made in Italy. Also issued on CD [Rock Melody 303.1055-2], made in Austria.

CHUCK BERRY – ESTO ES ROCK'N'ROLL (VOLUME 6)
Perfil ACC-78386 • 1991
Rock And Roll Music / Johnny B. Goode / Roll Over Beethoven / Maybellene / School Day / Sweet Little Sixteen / My Ding-A-Ling *(live, single edit)* / Memphis, Tennessee / Carol / Too Much Monkey Business / Hoochie Coochie Man+* *(live)* / Wee Wee Hours* *(live)* / Nadine / No Particular Place To Go

    12 Chess tracks plus two from the 1969 *Toronto Rock & Roll Revival* (marked *). Also issued on CD [Perfil CD-5429].

CD Singles

GRANDES MITOS II – CHUCK BERRY
Grandes Mitos AD-06366 • 2000
Reelin' And Rockin' / Johnny B. Goode / Memphis, Tennessee / Sweet Little Sixteen / Too Much Monkey Business

    Chess recordings.

CD Albums

ROLL OVER BEETHOVEN
Rock Melody 303.1055-2 • 1989
Roll Over Beethoven / You Never Can Tell / No Particular Place To Go / Sweet Little Sixteen / Wee Wee Hours / Maybellene / Nadine / Johnny B. Goode / Promised Land / School Day / Back In The USA / Oh Baby Doll / Reelin' And Rockin' / Rock And Roll Music

Chess recordings. The CD was distributed by Serenade SA, 08014 Barcelona, Spain, however it was made in Austria. Also issued on LP [Rock Melody 303.1055-1], made in Italy.

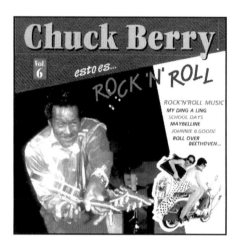

CHUCK BERRY – ESTO ES ROCK'N'ROLL (VOLUME 6)
Perfil CD-5429 • 1991
Rock And Roll Music / Johnny B. Goode / Roll Over Beethoven / Maybellene / School Day / Sweet Little Sixteen / My Ding-A-Ling *(live, single edit)* / Memphis, Tennessee / Carol / Too Much Monkey Business / Hoochie Coochie Man+* *(live)* / Wee Wee Hours* *(live)* / Nadine / No Particular Place To Go

12 Chess tracks plus two from the 1969 *Toronto Rock & Roll Revival* (marked *). Also issued on LP [Perfil ACC-78386].

CHUCK BERRY – GREATEST
Goldies [Movieplay] GLD-63035 • 1992
16 rockin' and rollin' Chess tracks from 'Maybellene' to 'Bye Bye Johnny'.

THE GREAT CHUCK BERRY
Goldies [Movieplay] GLD-63126 • 1993
Roll Over Beethoven / School Day / Sweet Little Sixteen *(original speed)* / Johnny B. Goode / Carol / Memphis, Tennessee / Let It Rock / Nadine / No Particular Place To Go / You Never Can Tell / Little Marie / Promised Land / Dear Dad / Reelin' And Rockin' *(live, album version)*

14 Chess tracks. Good compilation with original stereo tracks from 'Nadine' onwards. Both the above CDs were made in Portugal and distributed from Spain to the European market. I bought them in Norway.

Various Artists EPs

Bo Diddley – Johnny Cash – Shangri-Las – Chuck Berry
GO CHARLY WITH...
Charly [Zafiro] EP-101 • 1988
Promised Land

Also includes Bo Diddley's 'Spanish Guitar' (naturally), Johnny Cash's 'Rock Island Line' and the Shangri-Las' 'Leader Of The Pack'. Great picture of Diddley on the front sleeve.

SWEDEN

In the '50s, only EPs were released in Sweden. The three London EPs issued in Sweden in 1958 are very hard to find – especially the first and third, which are sought after because they contained different tracks than the US ones, even though they used the US EP covers. These EPs all had a red label with silver print. In 1964, Pye issued no fewer than seven EPs (reddish-brown label), which were followed by three on Sonet (red label with round push-out centre) and two on Chess International (black label, round push-out centre).

The first Swedish Berry single was issued on Pye in 1963, and was followed by three on Sonet in 1964 and seven on Chess International between 1964 and 1972. The singles has the same label colours and round push-out centres as the EPs.

Apart from the three London EPs, the three Sonet singles and the two Pye EPs, all the other releases were also sold in Norway and Denmark, with the notable exception of 'Vaya Con Dios' [Chess International AR-50.003]. All the Swedish singles had different and often very attractive picture sleeves, and some of them are now rather rare and expensive. They also came in various coloured vinyls, as did the Chess International EPs. Promo singles had white labels, but it is uncertain whether any were issued for singles after Chess AR-50.004. See also the Danish and Norwegian discographies.

(For those who are interested, issue 58 (from 1999) of the Norwegian collectors' magazine *Goldies* contains a complete listing of all Chuck Berry single and EPs releases in Scandinavia plus photos of all the covers and labels, even of cover versions. Write to *Goldies*, Nordveien 2, N-1440 Drøbak, Norway or email **bluka@online.no**.)

Singles

Let It Rock / Memphis, Tennessee
Pye 7N.25218 • 1963
This is the rarest Swedish Berry single (valued around £65). It was actually pressed and released in Norway (see Norwegian discography for more information), but was also issued in Sweden with a picture sleeve (in Norway it was only available in a company sleeve). According to the sleeve, 'Memphis' was the 'A' side in Sweden, but the Norwegian pressing had 'Let It Rock' as the 'A' side.

Nadine / O'Rangutang *(instr)*
Sonet T-7591 • March 1964
Issued on red and blue vinyl. Picture sleeve. Coloured band across top of sleeve was orange or green.

No Particular Place To Go / Liverpool Drive *(instr)*
Sonet T-7597 • May 1964
Issued on red, green and black vinyl. Picture sleeve. Coloured band across top of sleeve was orange, yellow or dark blue.

You Never Can Tell / Brenda Lee
Sonet T-7605 • 1964
Issued on green, red and black vinyl. Picture sleeve. Coloured band across top of sleeve was violet, green, red or dark blue. This was reissued in 1965 (on black vinyl only) with a new-style Sonet label, half orange and half red.

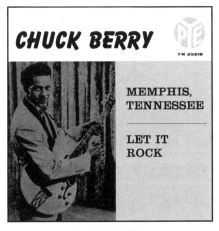

Pye 7N.25218

Pye 7N.25218

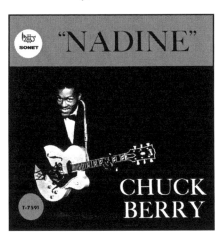

Sonet T-7591

Sonet T-7591

Sonet T-7597

Sonet T-7597 (promo)

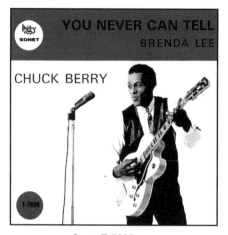

Sonet T-7605

Sonet T-7605

Chess International AR-45.140

Chess International AR-45.143

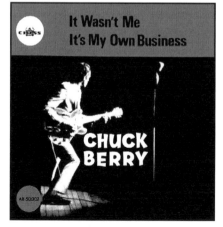

Chess International AR-50.002

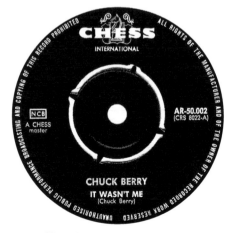

Chess International AR-50.002

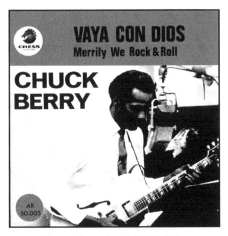

Chess International AR-50.003

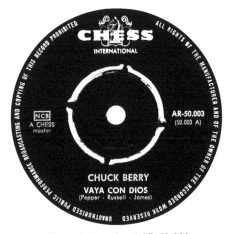

Chess International AR-50.003

Chess International AR-50.004

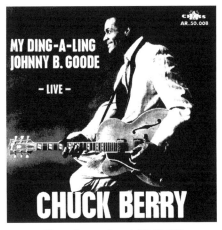

Chess International AR-50.008

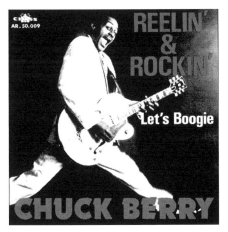

Chess International AR-50.009

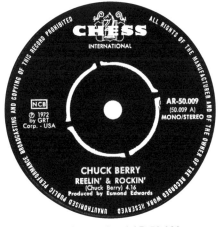

Chess International AR-50.009

Little Marie / Go, Bobby Soxer
Chess International AR-45.140 • November 1964
Issued on red vinyl. Picture sleeve. Coloured band across top sleeve was violet.

Promised Land / Things I Used To Do
Chess International AR-45.143 • February 1965
Issued on red and black vinyl. Picture sleeve. Coloured band across top of sleeve was either orange or blue.

It Wasn't Me / It's My Own Business
Chess International AR-50.002 • 1965
Issued on red and black vinyl. Picture sleeve. Coloured band across top of sleeve was dark blue. Great picture of Berry!

Vaya Con Dios+ / Merrily We Rock And Roll
Chess International AR-50.003 • 1965
This is exclusive to Sweden, as the songs here have never been released on a single anywhere else in the world. Great picture sleeve too! Coloured band across top of sleeve was red. If you can find it you will have to pay at least £40 for a mint copy. Add another £15 for a white promo label. I have only ever seen this on black vinyl.

Ramona Say Yes / Lonely School Days *(fast version)*
Chess International AR-50.004 • 1966
As far as I know this was issued only in black vinyl. Picture sleeve. Coloured band across top of sleeve was light blue.

My Ding-A-Ling *(live, single edit)* **/ Johnny B. Goode** *(live)*
Chess International AR-50.008 • 1972
Black and white picture on sleeve. Nice action pic, but unfortunately it's back-to-front.

Reelin' And Rockin' *(live, single edit)* **/ Let's Boogie**
Chess International AR-50.009 • 1972
Black and white picture on sleeve.

EPs

ROCK AND ROLL MUSIC
London RE-5010 • April 1958
Roll Over Beethoven / Drifting Heart / Rock And Roll Music / Blue Feeling *(instr)*

This has the same title and front cover as the 1957 US EP [Chess EP-5119]. The last two songs are the same, but the first two never appeared on any US EP. However, the first French EP (CHUCK BERRY NO.1 [London RE-U 10.004] 1958) is identical to this – different cover though.

SWEET LITTLE SIXTEEN
London RE-5014 • 1958
Sweet Little Sixteen / Rock At The Philharmonic *(instr)* / Reelin' And Rockin' / Guitar Boogie *(instr)*

Same tracks and front cover as the 1958 US EP [Chess EP-5121].

AFTER SCHOOL SESSION
London RE-5030 • 1958
Hey Pedro / Carol / Beautiful Delilah / Vacation Time

Same front cover as the 1957 US EP [Chess EP-5118], but same tracks as the 1958 US EP, PICKIN' BERRIES [Chess EP-5124].

The following two EPs were pressed in Norway for the Swedish market (they were not sold in Norway). Both have the same picture on the front cover.

JUKE BOX HITS (VOLUME 1)
Pye NEP-5023 • 1964
Go, Go, Go / School Day / Rock And Roll Music / Sweet Little Sixteen

EP title in red letters. On the back cover there are references to 3 UK Pye International albums with pictures of the covers and track listings. Black vinyl only.

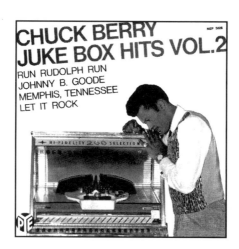

JUKE BOX HITS (VOLUME 2)
Pye NEP-5026 • 1964
Run Rudolph Run+ / Johnny B. Goode / Memphis, Tennessee / Let It Rock

EP title in green letters. On the back cover there are references to four UK Pye International albums with pictures of the covers and track listings. Black vinyl only.

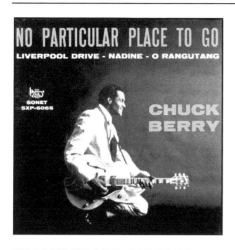

NO PARTICULAR PLACE TO GO
Sonet SXP-6065 • June 1964
No Particular Place To Go / Liverpool Drive *(instr)* / Nadine / O'Rangutang *(instr)*

Issued on both red and black vinyl. Reissued in 1965 (with same cover but in black vinyl only) with a new-style Sonet label, half orange and half red.

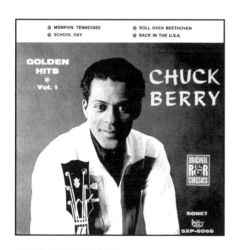

GOLDEN HITS (VOLUME 1)
Sonet SXP-6066 • September 1964
Memphis, Tennessee / Roll Over Beethoven / School Day / Back In The USA

Red, green and black vinyl. This was also reissued in 1965 with a new-style Sonet label, half orange and half red, but same cover and black vinyl only.

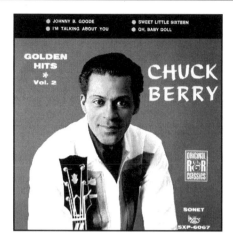

GOLDEN HITS (VOLUME 2)
Sonet SXP-6067 • September 1964
Johnny B. Goode / Oh Baby Doll / I'm Talking About You / Sweet Little Sixteen

Red, green and black vinyl. This was also reissued in 1965 with a new-style Sonet label, half orange and half red. Same cover and black vinyl only.

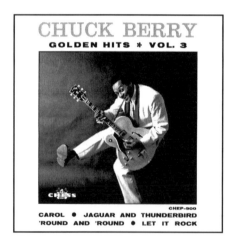

GOLDEN HITS (VOLUME 3)
Chess International CHEP-900 • May 1965
Carol / Jaguar And The Thunderbird / Around And Around / Let It Rock

Red vinyl. The back cover refers to the other EPs SXP-6065, 6066 and 6067, and the Dutch EP, *Chuck Berry Time* [Funckler/Chess International EPAR-6026]. But they reversed the picture, making Berry left-handed. Why?

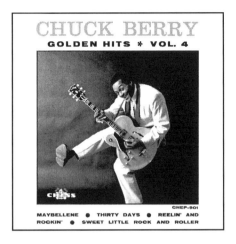

GOLDEN HITS (VOLUME 4)
Chess International CHEP-901 • 1965
Maybellene / Thirty Days / Reelin' And Rockin' / Sweet Little Rock And Roller

Red vinyl. Same cover as CHEP-900.

LPs

ST. LOUIS TO LIVERPOOL
Sonet [Grand Prix] GP-9912 *(mono)* **• 1972**
Same tracks and cover as the 1964 US LP [Chess LP-1488].

GREATEST HITS BY CHUCK BERRY [2-LP]
Sonet [Grand Prix] GPD-9967 • 1972
Same tracks as the 1967 US 2-LP, CHUCK BERRY'S GOLDEN DECADE [Chess LPS-1514D]. Same gatefold cover, but with a different front.

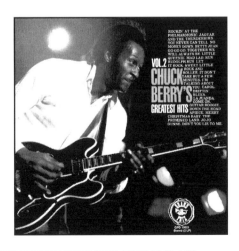

CHUCK BERRY'S GREATEST HITS (VOLUME 2) [2-LP]
Sonet [Grand Prix] GPD-10021 • 1973

Same tracks as the 1973 US 2-LP, CHUCK BERRY'S GOLDEN DECADE (VOLUME 2) [Chess 2CH-60023]. Same gatefold cover, but with a really great different front!

CHUCK BERRY'S GREATEST HITS (VOLUME 3) [2-LP]
Sonet [Grand Prix] GPD-10032 ● 1974
Same as the 1974 US 2-LP, CHUCK BERRY'S GOLDEN DECADE (VOLUME 3) [Chess 2CH-60028]. It has the same cover as the US version, but with the addition of a round white sticker with black print saying *'Chuck Berry's Greatest Hits Vol. 3' GPD-10032'*. The liner notes on the inside of the gatefold cover contain the same errors as the original US album (see US discography for details).

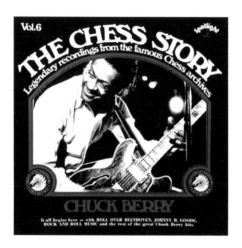

THE CHESS STORY (VOLUME 6 – CHUCK BERRY)
Chess Spotlight SPO-112 ● 1974
Same tracks as the 1964 US LP, CHUCK BERRY'S GREATEST HITS [Chess LP-1485], but a different nice cover and liner notes. This is the sixth in a series of ten volumes covering the biggest Chess artists, the others being Muddy Waters, John Lee Hooker, Little Walter, Bo Diddley, Billy Stewart, Memphis Slim, Buddy Guy, Sonny Boy Williamson and Howlin' Wolf.

20 ORIGINALE ROCK'N'ROLL HITS
Chess SP-19749 ● 1975
Maybellene / Johnny B. Goode / Roll Over Beethoven / Too Much Monkey Business / Reelin' And Rockin' / Go, Go, Go / I'm Talking About You / Little Queenie / Around And Around / You Never Can Tell *(stereo)* / My Ding-A-Ling *(live, single edit)* / Shake, Rattle And Roll+ *(stereo)* / No Particular Place To Go *(stereo)* / Memphis, Tennessee / Come On / Sweet Little Sixteen / Rock And Roll Music / Sweet Little Rock And Roller / School Day / Bye Bye Johnny

Apart from the tracks marked 'stereo', the rest are unfortunately in electronic stereo. This album was actually pressed and printed in England, but the label carries the NCB designation exclusive to Scandinavian issues.

THE GREAT 28 [2-LP]
Chess [SOS] SOSLP-074 ● 1982
Same tracks and gatefold cover as the 1982 US 2-LP [Chess CH-8201].

CD Albums

NEWPORT JAZZ FESTIVAL 1958, JULY 3RD-6TH (VOLUME 3)
Phontastic PHONT NCD-8815 • 1992
  See *Various Artists CD Albums.*

Various Artists Singles

SKIVTIPS VINTERN 1965/66
Sonet SPR-65 • 1965
It's My Own Business

  Now this is interesting: a promo single for record shops with snippets of sixteen songs from various artists and groups released on the Sonet, Gazell and Chess labels in the winter of 1965-66. The track is off the Chess International AR-50.002 single. The picture sleeve contains small images of all the singles and EPs included on the record. A real collectors' item. Also see below.

Various Artists EPs

KLINGANDE POST
Decca, no number • April 1958
Rock And Roll Music (from EP *Rock And Roll Music* [London RE-5010])

  Promotional record sent to various dealers to make them aware of what's new on the record scene. Divided into 'Part 1' and 'Part 2' (rather than Side 1 and Side 2). Just a small snippet is heard of each song. Little Richard, Larry Williams and Tommy Steele are some of the more notable artists featured. Plain sleeve, maroon label. The interesting thing is that this sort of record rarely turns up on the market, yet it's likely that most – if not all – of the Swedish Berry singles and EPs were promoted like this (*Klingande Post* means 'Musical Mail'). Also see the previous entry.

The following EPs were all club issues released from 1965-74 and had red labels. Many of these were released exclusively in Sweden, often containing covers of foreign hits by Swedish artists. However, this was not *always* the case, as you will see from the EPs that featured Chuck Berry. The sleeves always had a picture of him, alone or together with the other participants. The first four (with JSEP- prefix) are regular 45 rpm EPs with four tracks, the others (with JSLP- prefix) have six tracks and play at 33⅓ rpm.

JUKEBOX SERIES
Jukebox JSEP-5543 • 1965
Don't You Lie To Me+

'Don't You Lie To Me' is credited to Berry. Other tracks are 'Like A Rolling Stone' by Lenne & The Lee Kings, 'Satisfaction' by Ola & The Janglers and 'We've Gotta Get Out Of This Place' by the Violents.

JUKEBOX SERIES
Jukebox JSEP-5552 • 1966
Down The Road A Piece+

Other tracks are 'Very Last Day' by the Panthers, 'Sloop John B' by the Hounds and 'Lullaby Serenade' by the Sherrys.

JUKEBOX SERIES
Jukebox JSEP 5565 • 1967
Promised Land

Other tracks are 'A Whiter Shade Of Pale' by Impact, 'Carrie Anne' by Jar and 'The Wind Cries Mary' by Willie Johnson, but only Berry is depicted on the cover.

JUKEBOX SERIES
Jukebox JSEP-5611 • 1971
No Particular Place To Go

Other tracks are 'On The Banks Of The Ohio' by Joan Baez, 'Sol Och Regn' by Tommy Körberg and 'Where Is My Life' by Claes af Geijerstam.

JUKEBOX SERIES [33⅓ rpm]
Jukebox JSLP-5615 • 1971
Roll Over Beethoven

Other tracks are 'Highway To Freedom' by Jerry Williams, 'Gypsy Woman' by Muddy Waters, 'Viva l'Amour' by Tommy Körberg, 'A Flower' by Alexis Korner and 'Black Is The Colour' by Joan Baez.

JUKEBOX SERIES [33⅓ rpm]
Jukebox JSLP-5625 • 1973
Little Marie / Our Little Rendezvous

Other tracks are 'Dance Around The Clock' and 'Bony Maronie' by Bill Haley & His Comets, and 'Baby' and 'Can't Believe You Wanna Leave' by Little Richard.

JUKEBOX SERIES [33⅓ rpm]
Jukebox JSLP-5630 • 1973
Sweet Little Sixteen

The first pressing of this EP [matrix JSLP 5630 B] did not feature Berry's version, but rather a cover version by Jerry Lee Lewis. However, it was corrected on the second issue, although you can't see any difference on the cover or label. However, it says 'JSLP 5630 B2' in the dead wax on the Berry side. Other tracks are 'Hello Josephine' by Jerry Lee Lewis, 'Lucille' by Little Richard, 'Ring Dang Doo' by Burken, 'Everyday' by Jan Rohde and 'All Shook Up' by Jerry Williams.

JUKEBOX SERIES [33⅓ rpm]
Jukebox JSLP-5639 • 1974
Beautiful Delilah / Go, Bobby Soxer / I Got To Find My Baby**+**

This is almost a Chuck Berry EP in itself, with three Berry songs and only Chuck on the cover. Other tracks are 'Hey Rock And Roll' by Rod & The Buckles, 'Always Yours' by Frank Salinas and 'The 'In' Crowd' by Peter Eden Sr.

Various Artists LPs

MARABOU MIXED HITS
Mercury 6830 122 • 1970s
Roll Over Beethoven / Sweet Little Sixteen

Berry picture on sleeve. Other artists include Fats Domino (2), Jerry Lee Lewis (2), Roger Miller (1), the Platters (2) and Dave Dudley (1). This album was specially made for the Swedish candy and chocolate manufacturer Marabou by Mercury Records, USA.

Various Artists CD Albums

NEWPORT JAZZ FESTIVAL 1958, JULY 3RD-6TH
(VOLUME 3: BLUES IN THE NIGHT, NO. 1)
Phontastic PHONT NCD-8815 • 1992
Introduction – School Day / No Money Down / Sweet Little Sixteen / Johnny B. Goode

This is just GREAT! Berry's complete show from the festival recorded on 5 July 1958. It's the only time that you can actually hear Berry live in good sound quality from the '50s – the only pity is that he was backed by jazz musicians who didn't have a clue as to what rock'n'roll or rhythm & blues were all about. Berry's so-called 'blues band' consisted of Buck Clayton on trumpet, Jack Teagarden on trombone, Tony Scott on clarinet, Buddy Tate, Rudy Rutherford and George Auld on saxes, Ray Bryant on piano, Kenny Burrell on guitar (he sure didn't like rock'n'roll), Tommy Bryant on bass and Jo Jones on drums. There's also a great picture of Berry inside the booklet. In 1998, a CD called JAZZ ON A SUMMERS DAY [Charly CDGR-196] containing *'Highlights From the Original Soundtrack'* including Berry's 'Sweet Little Sixteen' was issued in Germany (see German discography for more details). In 2001, Charly released a DVD + bonus audio CD of this classic movie in the UK and Germany [Charly SDVD-001]. See UK discography for more info.

JERRY WILLIAMS VÄLJER ÅRHUNDRADETS ROCKLÅTAR [2-CD]
Stockholm 545 389-2 • 2000
You Never Can Tell / Johnny B. Goode

Swedish rock'n'roller Jerry Williams selecting the best rock songs of the last century. 42 songs altogether, and, yes, Williams knows his stuff: Little Richard, Duane Eddy, Eddie Cochran, Ronnie Self, Cliff Richard – you name it. Extensive liner notes for each song, with US and UK chart positions. No pictures of any artists, but Berry is the only one with two songs.

JERRY WILLIAMS VÄLJER ÅRHUNDRADETS ROCKLÅTAR (VOLUME 2)
Stockholm 013 065-2 • 2001
Let It Rock

Another 24 rockin' tunes selected by Sweden's own King of Rock'n'Roll. Many of the same artists as on VOLUME 1 but also features new entries like Ray Charles, Ray Smith, Bobby Comstock and Ronnie Hawkins (who performs 'Forty Days'). Extensive liner notes and chart positions, as before. It would appear that VOLUME 1 sold quite well, as a VOLUME 2 was released – a goode start to the new century.

LJUVA 50-TAL 1955-59 [2-CD]
SONY COL-511197-2 • 2003
Sweet Little Sixteen *(Chess)*

In English the album title means 'HAPPY '50s'. 24 tracks on each CD. No pictures of any artists unfortunately, but hit positions in the US, UK and the Swedish *Tio i Topp* charts are given for each track. This album was certificated for a Platinum Award in Sweden.

LJUVA 60-TAL 1960-63 [2-CD]
Sony COL-511198-2 • 2003
No Particular Place To Go *(Chess)*

In English the album title means 'HAPPY '60s'. 24 tracks on each CD. This was also certificated for a Platinum Award in Sweden. The inner sleeve contains info on the highest positions for each track in the US, UK and Swedish charts.

LJUVA 60-TAL (DEL 2) 1964-69 [2-CD]
Sony COL-513870-2 • 2003
You Never Can Tell *(Chess)*

Berry in goode company. In English the album title means 'HAPPY '60s (PART 2)'. Again 24 tracks on each CD. Also hit positions in the US, UK and Swedish charts for each track. This CD and the two above were also released in Norway in 2004.

SWITZERLAND

LPs

ROCK
Blue Vox BV/129-LP • 1983
Rock And Roll Music / Nadine / Hall, Hall, Rock And Roll [School Day] / In The Wee Wee Hours (I Think Of You) / Medley [Reelin' And Rockin'] / Johnny B. Goode / Oh Carol [Carol] / Blues Time [Hoochie Coochie Man+] / Sweet Little Sixteen [Maybellene]

The titles are printed exactly as they appear on the cover and label. The tracks are from the 1969 *Toronto Rock & Roll Revival*. According to the composer credits, both 'Hall, Hall, Rock And Roll' ['School Day'] and 'Medley' ['Reelin' And Rockin' '] are *'unbekannt'* (unknown). 'Oh Carol' ['Carol'] is credited to *'Chinn Nick'!* 'Blues Time' ['Hoochie Coochie Man'] is listed as *'Traditional'* and 'Sweet Little Sixteen' is nowhere to be found. Instead we get 'Maybellene'. This album must rank as one of the shoddiest ever! See also the dreadful 1996 French CD, CHUCK BERRY [Locomotive Int. CDLMM-81].

TAIWAN

All the albums from this country followed the Japanese issues, except that the covers are bad photocopies and thinner, more like paper sleeves. The front covers were the same as the Japanese releases, and I have assumed that they all appeared in the same year.

LPs

CHUCK BERRY TWIST
First S-FL-1022 • 1964
Same tracks as the 1962 US LP [Chess LP-1465]. Orange vinyl. The sound quality is actually as good as the US original. Some titles are misprinted ('Thirty Drys', for example). The label says '*Stereo Record*', and title and songs are printed in both English and Chinese. The back cover has pictures of other albums (not by Berry) and bears the legend, '*First Stereodisc*'.

ON STAGE
Chong Sheng CSJ-512 • 1964
Same tracks and cover design as the 1964 Japanese LP [Globe DJET-7204], except the background here is yellow instead of light blue. Issued on both orange and black vinyl. 'How High The Moon' is the version with the longer fade. Great cover like the Japanese one. The back cover includes pictures of other albums in the series.

CHUCK BERRY'S GREATEST HITS (THE BEST OF CHUCK BERRY)
Chong Sheng CSJ-513 • 1964
No Particular Place To Go / You Never Can Tell / Maybellene / Nadine / Brenda Lee / You Two / Rock And Roll Music / School Day / Sweet Little Sixteen / Brown Eyed Handsome Man / Too Much Monkey Business / Johnny B. Goode
Issued on black and red vinyl. However, this is a strange mixture of tracks. Side A has the same tracks as the 1964 Japanese LP [Globe DJET-7198], while

Side B features the tracks which should have been on the album below, CSJ-514. The front cover is a copy of the original one with the yellow sticker proclaiming *'Featuring the original hits 'Memphis', 'Maybellene', 'Johnny B. Goode' '* – even though 'Memphis' is not actually included.

ST. LOUIS TO LIVERPOOL
Chong Sheng CSJ-514 *(stereo)* • 1965
Memphis, Tennessee / Sweet Little Sixteen / Roll Over Beethoven / Rock And Roll Music / Johnny B. Goode / Brown Eyed Handsome Man / No Particular Place To Go / Little Marie / You Never Can Tell / Go, Bobby Soxer / Brenda Lee / Promised Land

Issued on both black and orange vinyl. As can be seen, this is a strange mixture of tracks (again), as several on this album are also featured on the previous one, CSJ-513. 'School Day' is printed on the front cover as being on the album, but it's not. It looks like someone made a big mistake, as the two albums were probably pressed at the same time. See also the 1964 Japanese LP, Globe DJET-7198.

SAN FRANCISCO DUES
Chong Sheng CSJ-1146 • 1971
Same tracks as the 1971 US LP [Chess LP-50008] and the 1971 Japanese LP [Chess SJET-8345]. The back cover is the same as the US one.

CHUCK BERRY'S GREATEST HITS (THE BEST OF CHUCK BERRY)
Haishan HS-295 • 1970s
They finally got it right though. Same tracks as the 1964 Japanese LP [Globe DJET-7198]. Almost the same cover, but white with blue dots. Black vinyl.

THAILAND

Various Artists EPs

Bill Withers – Hot Butter – Michael Jackson – Chuck Berry
UNTITLED
No label, MTR-600 ● 1972
My Ding-A-Ling *(live, single edit)*

Other artists include Bill Withers ('Use Me'), Hot Butter ('Popcorn') and Michael Jackson ('Ben'). No pictures of any artists, just a naked girl on the front sleeve.

Chuck Berry - Timmy Thomas - Brighter Side of Darkness - Cornelius Brothers & Sister Rose
REELIN' AND ROCKIN'
4 Star P-125 ● 1973
My Ding-A-Ling *(live, single edit)*

Picture of Berry which fills the entire front sleeve plus smaller pictures of the other artists. To be quite honest this looks like a Berry record. Other artists include Timmy Thomas ('Why Can't We Live Together'), the Brighter Side of Darkness ('Love Jones') and the Cornelius Brothers & Sister Rose ('I'm Never Gonna Be Alone Anymore').

Stevie Wonder – Ivy League – Luther Ingram – Chairmen Of The Board
UNTITLED
Cash Box KS-146 • 1973
Includes Stevie Wonder ('Superstition'), the Ivy League ('Funny How Love Can Be'), Luther Ingram ('I Can't Stop') and the Chairmen Of The Board ('I'm On My Way To A Better Place'). Why have I listed this, you wonder? Well, even though the EP has no Berry track on it, it does have a *very good colour picture of Berry* (from 1972) on the front, and also smaller pictures of T-Bone Walker, Willie Dixon and Bo Diddley. As you can see, none of these artists are featured on the record. That really is *too* much monkey business!

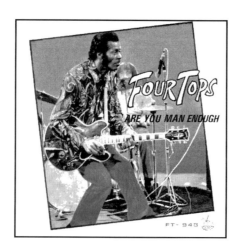

Four Tops – Foster Sylvers – Temptations – Tower of Power
ARE YOU MAN ENOUGH
4 Track FT-943 • 1973

Includes the Four Tops ('Are You Man Enough'), Foster Sylvers ('Misdemeanor'), the Temptations ('The Plastic Man') and Tower of Power ('So Very Hard To Go').

Yet another EP with a colour picture of Chuck Berry on the front, but *no* Berry tracks! The front sleeve says *'Four Tops – 'Are You Man Enough' '*, which one might ordinarily have expected to be accompanied by a picture of the Four Tops.

Chuck Berry – Coasters – Shirley & Lee – Fats Domino
LET THE GOOD TIMES ROLL – ORIGINAL MOTION PICTURE SOUNDTRACK
4 Track FT-980 • 1974
Maybellene

Although the title of this EP is technically correct, these are not live recordings but four original 1950s studio tracks which were used on the soundtrack of *Let The Good Times Roll*. 'Maybellene' (the original Chess version) plays in the background during Berry's interview while he walks through Berry Park, showing among other things the old tour bus they called 'Maybellene'. Other artists include the Coasters ('Poison Ivy'), Shirley & Lee ('Let The Good Times Roll'), Bill Haley ('Rock Around The Clock'), Little Richard ('Tutti Frutti') and Fats Domino ('Blueberry Hill'). Great colour sleeve with Berry in the middle.

LPs

NEW TOPS
Unknown label, WALP-8383 • Mid-1970s
Small picture of Chuck Berry... but there's no Berry song on the album!

TURKEY

Cassette Tapes

MOTORVATIN'
Chess MüY-7256005
Same tracks and almost the same front cover as the 1977 UK LP, MOTORVATIN'
[Chess 9286 690].

Various Artists LPs

Chuck Berry – Jerry Lee Lewis – Fats Domino
ROCK'N'ROLL – ESKI USTALAR NO. 2
S&S LP.11059 • 1978
Same as the 1969 UK LP, ROCK'N'ROLL [Fontana SFL-13120] and all the other
pressings on Fontana in other countries. Tan label.

YUGOSLAVIA

As far as I know, the following is the complete output of Berry LPs issued in this country. All albums were almost-duplicates of LPs already issued in other European countries and USA. I have no information about any singles.

There was a guy in this country who several years ago supplied me with most of these albums and told me that these were the only Berry LPs released over there. And, although he said he would get back to me with his wants list for Norwegian Cliff Richard records, he never did. Unfortunately, I have lost his name and address, so if you know who he is, please tell him I still have a box of Cliff singles for him.

LPs

20 SUPER HITS
Diskos LPL-761 • 1981
Same tracks and cover as the 1980 West German LP [Chess 6.24372-AP]. Silver-grey label.

ROCKIN' WITH CHUCK BERRY
Philips 9276 540 / RTB 2220369 • 1981
Chess recordings. Same tracks, title and cover as the 1977 Dutch LP [Philips 9279 540] and the 1977 UK LP [Philips SUC-114].

MR. ROCK'N'ROLL
RTB 221608 • 1983
Same tracks as the 1964 US LP, CHUCK BERRY'S GREATEST HITS [Chess LP-1485]. However, the cover and layout are the same as the 1981 French LP, MR. ROCK'N'ROLL [Mode 509075].

CHUCK BERRY'S GOLDEN DECADE [2-LP]
RTB 3220133 • 1983
Same tracks and gatefold cover as the second pressing of the 1972 US reissue [Chess 2CH-1514] (pink radio).

REELIN' AND ROCKIN'
ZTT Est [Jugoton] LSADIT-11105 • 1984
Same tracks (from the 1969 *Toronto Rock'n'Roll Revival*) and cover as the 1984 UK LP [Magnum Force MFM-017].

ST. LOUIS TO LIVERPOOL
RTB 2223406 • 1986
Same tracks and cover as the 1984 US reissue LP [Chess CH-9186].

ILLUSTRATIONS & PHOTO CREDITS

All from author's collection except:

Per Arvesen: Cassettes on pages 115 and 116.
Theo Dasbach/Rock'n'Roll & Blues Heritage Museum, Clarksdale: Empire 41-EA (pg 437).
Tore Jensen: Photo on page 142.
Helge Jørgensen: Photo on page 95.
Malte Koch: Argo 5353 (pg 27), London HLU-8275 demo and original pressing (pg 154), London HLM-8767 (pg 156), Philips 35121-BE (pg 251), Quality 1413 (pg 270), Down Beat 234 (pg 368), Globe SJET-270 (pg 372), Fast 1068 and London FL-1796 (pg 394), London NZL-323 (pg 427) and London VE-159 (pg 428).
Jean-Pierre Ravelli: Photos on pages 62, 81, 91, 226, 245, 247, 287, 426 and 450.
Dietmar Rudolph: Barclay 60522 (pg 291), Funckler AR-45.012 (pg 394) and Chess SHLP-12502 (pg 438).

COVER ILLUSTRATIONS

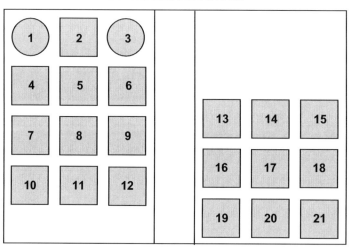

Back   Front

1 - London HLM-8629 *promo* (UK) 1958
2 - Hispa Vox HX-007.61 (Spain) 1965
3 - Chess 1610 *promo* (USA) 1955
4 - Bellaphon BLPS-19034 (West Germany) 1970
5 - Chess International AR-50.003 (Sweden) 1965
6 - Barclay 70790 (France) 1965
7 - Bellaphon BF-18316 (West Germany) 1975
8 - Grand Prix GPD-10021 (Sweden) 1973
9 - Chong Sheng CSJ-512 (Taiwan) 1964
10 - Chess SN-20.682 (Spain) 1972
11 - Chess EP-5188 (USA) 1957
12 - London RE-U-10.004 (France) 1958

13 - London RE-M-7043 (Netherlands) 1958
14 - Philips 35121.BE (Australia) 1958/59
15 - Gamma GX-07.151 (Mexico) 1965?
16 - Mercury 6463 015 (France) 1972?
17 - Sonet T-7605 (Sweden) 1964
18 - Mercury SM-1061 (Japan) 1968
19 - Mercury 6052 257 (West Germany) 1972
20 - Chess JET-2146 (Japan) 1972
21 - London RE-U-1053 (UK) 1956

OTHER TITLES FROM MUSIC MENTOR BOOKS

American Rock'n'Roll: The UK Tours 1956-72
Ian Wallis
ISBN-13: 978-0-9519888-6-2 *(pbk, 424 pages)* £19.99

The first-ever detailed overview of every visit to these shores by American (and Canadian!) rock'n'rollers. It's all here: over 400 pages of tour itineraries, support acts, show reports, TV appearances and other items of interest. Illustrated with dozens of original tour programmes, ads, ticket stubs and great live shots, many rare or previously unpublished.

Back On The Road Again
Dave Nicolson
ISBN-13: 978-0-9547068-2-1 *(pbk, 216 pages)* £12.99

A third book of interviews by Dave Nicolson in the popular *On The Road* series, this time with more of a Sixties flavour: Solomon Burke, Gene Chandler, Bruce Channel, Lowell Fulson, Jet Harris, Gene McDaniels, Scott McKenzie, Gary S. Paxton, Bobby 'Boris' Pickett, Martha Reeves & The Vandellas, Jimmie Rodgers, Gary Troxel (Fleetwoods), Leroy Van Dyke and Junior Walker.

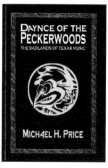

Daynce of the Peckerwoods: The Badlands of Texas Music
Michael H. Price
ISBN-13: 978-0-9547068-5-2 *(pbk, 350 pages)* £18.99

From a childhood spent among such key roots-music figures as Bob Wills and Big Joe Turner, and an extended dual career as a musician and journalist, Michael H. Price has forged this frenzied chronicle of life among the denizens of the vanishing borderlands of Texas' indigenous music scene over the past half-century. Contains essays on Billy Briggs, Ornette Coleman, the Light Crust Doughboys, Big Bill Lister, Rudy Ray Moore, Eck Robertson, Ray Sharpe, Robert Shaw, Major Bill Smith, Stevie Ray Vaughan and many more.

Elvis: A Musical Inventory 1939-55
Richard Boussiron
ISBN-13: 978-0-9519888-7-9 *(pbk, 264 pages)* £17.99

This 'musical inventory' is the product of over 30 years' original research including interviews with Elvis' teacher, church ministers, work colleagues and fellow musicians. Presented like a discography, it is an extraordinarily detailed listing of the King's earliest musical influences, with full historical details shown for each song. The book also includes — for the first time anywhere — complete details of all the legendary Sun sessions, taken directly from the personal files of Marion Keisker. Quite simply a 'must have' for anyone with an interest in early Elvis.

Elvis & Buddy – Linked Lives
Alan Mann
ISBN-13: 978-0-9519888-5-5 *(pbk, 160 pages)* £9.99

The achievements of Elvis Presley and Buddy Holly have been extensively documented, but until now little if anything has been known about the many ways in which their lives were interconnected. The author examines each artist's early years, comparing their backgrounds and influences, chronicling all their meetings and examining the many amazing parallels in their lives, careers and tragic deaths. Over 50 photographs, including many rare/previously unpublished.

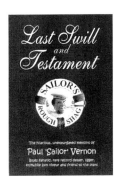

Last Swill and Testament
– The hilarious, unexpurgated memoirs of
Paul 'Sailor' Vernon
ISBN-13: 978-0-9547068-4-5 *(pbk, 228 pages)* £12.99

Born in London shortly after the end of World War II, Paul 'Sailor' Vernon came into his own during the 1960s when spotty teenage herberts with bad haircuts began discovering The Blues. For the Sailor it became a lifelong obsession that led him into a whirlwind of activity as a rare record dealer, magazine proprietor/editor, video bootlegger and record company director.
It's all here in this one-of-a-kind life history that will leave you reaching for an enamel bucket and a fresh bottle of disinfectant!

Let The Good Times Rock!
– A Fan's Notes On Post-War American Roots Music
Bill Millar
ISBN-13: 978-0-9519888-8-6 *(pbk, 362 pages)* £18.99

For almost four decades, the name 'Bill Millar' has been synonymous with the very best in British music writing. This fabulous new book collects together 49 of his best pieces — some previously unpublished — in a thematic compilation covering hillbilly, rockabilly, R&B, rock'n'roll, doo-wop, swamp pop and soul. Includes essays on acappella, doo-wop and blue-eyed soul, as well as detailed profiles of some of the most fascinating and influential personalities of each era.

On The Road
Dave Nicolson
ISBN-13: 978-0-9519888-4-8 *(pbk, 256 pages)* £14.99

Gary 'US' Bonds, Pat Boone, Freddy Cannon, Crickets Jerry Allison, Sonny Curtis and Joe B. Mauldin, Bo Diddley, Dion, Fats Domino, Duane Eddy, Frankie Ford, Charlie Gracie, Brian Hyland, Marv Johnson, Ben E. King, Brenda Lee, Little Eva, Chris Montez, Johnny Moore (Drifters), Gene Pitney, Johnny Preston, Tommy Roe, Del Shannon, Edwin Starr, Johnny Tillotson and Bobby Vee tell their own fascinating stories. Over 150 illustrations including vintage ads, record sleeves, label shots, sheet music covers, etc.

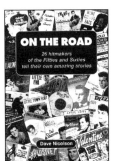

On The Road Again
Dave Nicolson
ISBN-13: 978-0-9519888-9-3 *(pbk, 206 pages)* **£12.99**

In this second book of interviews with the stars of pop and rock'n'roll, Dave Nicolson delves deeper into the dazzling and often treacherous world of the music industry, with more revealing and highly personal first-hand accounts from 15 pioneering performers who were at the forefront of the Fifties' music revolution: Freddie Bell, Martin Denny, Johnny Farina (Santo & Johnny), the Kalin Twins, Robin Luke, Chas McDevitt, Phil Phillips, Marvin Rainwater, Herb Reed (Platters), Tommy Sands, Joe Terranova (Danny & The Juniors), Mitchell Torok, Marty Wilde and the 'Cool Ghoul' himself, John Zacherle.

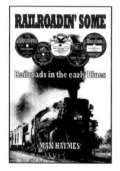

Railroadin' Some: Railroads In The Early Blues
Max Haymes
ISBN-13: 978-0-9547068-3-8 *(pbk, 390 pages)* **£18.99**

This groundbreaking book, written by one of the foremost blues historians in the UK, is based on over 30 years research, exploration and absolute passion for early blues music. It is the first ever comprehensive study of the enormous impact of the railroads on 19th and early 20th Century African American society and the many and varied references to this new phenomenon in early blues lyrics. Includes ballin' the jack, smokestack lightning, hot shots, the bottoms, chain gangs, barrelhouses, hobo jungles and much, much more. 118 illustrations.

**Music Mentor books
are available from all good bookshops
or by mail order from:**

**Music Mentor Books
69 Station Road
Upper Poppleton
YORK YO26 6PZ
England**

Telephone/Fax: **01904 330308**
International Telephone/Fax: **+44 1904 330308**
Email: **music.mentor@lineone.net**
Website: **http://musicmentor0.tripod.com**